𝕿𝖍𝖊 𝕽𝖚𝖗𝖆𝖑 𝕾𝖈𝖎𝖊𝖓𝖈𝖊 𝕾𝖊𝖗𝖎𝖊𝖘

EDITED BY L. H. BAILEY

PLANT–BREEDING

The Rural Science Series

PLANT-BREEDING

BY

L. H. BAILEY

NEW EDITION REVISED BY

ARTHUR W. GILBERT, Ph.D.

PROFESSOR OF PLANT-BREEDING IN THE NEW YORK
STATE COLLEGE OF AGRICULTURE AT
CORNELL UNIVERSITY

New York
THE MACMILLAN COMPANY
1917

Norwood Press
J. S. Cushing Co. — Berwick & Smith Co.
Norwood, Mass., U.S.A.

HISTORY

This book had its beginning in a lecture that I gave twenty-three years ago (December 1, 1891) before the Massachusetts State Board of Agriculture, in Boston, on "Cross-Breeding and Hybridizing"; and this lecture, in turn, was the outgrowth of one given in 1885 and soon afterwards published. Under the same title, but with a bibliography added, the Boston lecture was published as a pamphlet in 1892, and placed on sale, by the Rural Publishing Company of New York, as one of the Rural Library Series. It comprised forty-four pages, and sold for 40 cents. In the summer of 1895, I gave two addresses on variation and the origination of domestic varieties of plants under the auspices of the American Society for the Extension of University Teaching at the University of Pennsylvania. In the meantime, I had been teaching the subject to my classes in horticulture in Cornell University. In the latter part of 1895, I put together these materials in book form, and having no short descriptive title I used the word or compound "Plant-Breeding." Of this work, the Massachusetts lecture comprised Chapter II, and the Philadelphia lectures Chapters I and III. The bibliography was not included. Chapter IV comprised "Borrowed opinions" from the writings of Verlot, Carrière, and Focke. Carrière's work on "Production et Fixation des Variétés dans les Vegetaux" had been translated, with a view to publication, as early as 1886. The book, "Plant-Breeding," was translated into the French by J. M. and E. Harraca, and published in Paris in 1901 as " La Production des Plantes."

Having been twice reprinted, the second edition was issued in 1902, although, through an inadvertence, it was not so marked on the title-page. Few text-changes were made, but the bibliography was included.

Early in 1904 the third edition was issued. The bibliography was extended, and some changes were made in the text; but the principal departure was a new Chapter IV, from which the old "Borrowed opinions" were omitted, and "Recent opinions" were substituted, comprising a discussion of the work of de Vries, Mendel, and others, and a statement of the current tendencies of American plant-breeding practice. "In the eight years since this book was sent to the printer," it was stated in the preface to the third edition, "there have been great changes in our attitude toward most of the fundamental questions that are discussed in its pages. In fact, these years may be said to have marked a transition between two habits of thought in respect to the means of the evolution of plants,—from the points of view held by Darwin and the older writers to those arising from definite experimental studies in species and varieties. We have not given up the old nor wholly accepted the new, but it is certain that our outlook is shifting. So far as practical plant-breeding is involved, the changing attitude is concerned chiefly with discussions of the nature of varieties and the nature of hybridization." It was declared that "the time cannot be far distant when the subject of plant-breeding will be rewritten from a new point of view."

In 1906, the fourth edition appeared, with a new chapter on "Current plant-breeding practice"; and the book had grown from the 293 pages of the original edition to 483 pages. This edition was translated into the Japanese by D. Karashima, and published in 1907.

We now come to the present edition. The book has been made over by Dr. Gilbert, who has rewritten some of it and who has added all the new material, and in whose hands I have been glad to place it. My work in this edition has been only editorial. A considerable part of the old work has been preserved, whether wisely or not will be the occasion for different opinions. It has seemed to be desirable to retain something of a former point of view while at the same time expressing the applications of the work in the method and the language of the day. Considerable use has been made of the work of others, as is apparent in the pages. The Open Court Publishing Company has loaned illustrations from the important work of de Vries, and pictures have been taken from the Yearbooks of the United States Department of Agriculture. All these aids we are glad to acknowledge.

These new investigations have taken us far from the point of view of Darwin, in which the original editions of the book were founded. I doubt whether the students receiving their instruction to-day, with all their abounding facilities and opportunities, have any such feeling for a master-spirit as we had in those days when the studies of Darwin had given a new meaning to nature, when there were still a few naturalists left, and when the glow of his writings was warm in every person's work. To one coming out of a plant-growing relationship, the masterful works of Darwin had introduced order, and the forms of cultivated plants had been made worthy of serious study. This interest was further stimulated by the writings of Wallace and others.   All these writings were fascinating to read.   How to produce new forms of vegetation seized some of us with irresistible power.   The literature has now become complex and difficult, with considerable gain, no doubt, in a closer acquaintance with the subject, and a nearer approach to the ultimate truth; but the charm of the simple literature is largely buried, and I fear that much of our interest is now expressed in the discussion of methods and in disputing about the reasons.   Yet we are accumulating knowledge, and after a time we shall come back to clarity and to a simplicity that the layman can use.

L. H. BAILEY.

Ithaca, N. Y.,
      December 1, 1914.

TABLE OF CONTENTS

CHAPTER I

CHAPTER II

CHAPTER III

CHAPTER VII

LIST OF ILLUSTRATIONS

The Rural Science Series

EDITED BY L. H. BAILEY

PLANT–BREEDING

PLANT–BREEDING

CHAPTER I

THE FACT AND PHILOSOPHY OF VARIATION

THERE is no one fact connected with agriculture that more greatly interests all persons than the existence of numerous varieties of plants that seem to satisfy every need of the gardener. Whence came all this multitude of forms? What are the methods employed in securing them? Are they merely isolated facts or phenomena of gardening, or have they some relation to the broader phases of the evolution of the forms of life? These are some of the questions that occur to every reflective mind when it contemplates an attractive garden, but they are questions that seem never to be answered. Whatever attempt the gardener may make at answering them is either obscured by an effort to define what a variety is, or else it consists in simply reciting how a few given varieties came to be known. But there must be some method of arriving at a conception of the ways whereby the varieties of fruits and flowers and other culti-vated plants have originated. If there is no such method, then the origination of these varieties must follow no law, and the discussion of the whole subject is fruitless. But we have every confidence in the consecutive uniform-

ity of the operations of nature, and it were strange if
some underlying principle of the unfolding or progression
of plant-life does not dominate the origin of the varied
and innumerable varieties which, from time unknown,
have responded to the touch of the cultivator. Let us
first, therefore, make a broad survey of the subject in
a philosophical spirit, and later, discuss the more specific
instances of the origination of varieties.

The fact of individuality. — There is universal difference
in nature. No two living things are counterparts, for no
two are born alike or into exactly the same conditions and
experiences. Every living object has individuality; that
is, there is something about it that enables the acute
observer to distinguish it from all other objects, even of
the same class or species. Every plant in a row of lettuce
is different from every other plant, and the gardener,
when transplanting them, selects out, almost uncon-
sciously, some plants that please him and others that do
not. Every apple tree in an orchard of a thousand
Baldwins is unlike every other one, perhaps in size or
shape, or possibly in the vigor of growth or the kind of
fruit it bears. Persons who buy apples for export know
that fruit from certain regions stands the shipments better
than the same variety from other regions; and if one were
to go into the orchards where these apples are grown, he
would find the owner still further refining the problem by
talking about the merits of individual trees in his orchard.
If one were to make the effort, he would find that it is
possible to distinguish differences between every two
spears of grass in a meadow, or every two heads of wheat
in a grain-field.

In timothy, one of the commonest of our grasses, a casual observer may find differences in the length, shape, and color of heads; tendency of some plants to produce asexual leaves in the head; form of base of the head;

Fig. 1. — Variation in heads of timothy.

length, width, and color of leaves; erect or drooping character of the leaves; susceptibility of the leaves and stems to rust; period of blooming; habit of growth of ·plant, — erect or decumbent; few or many culms to the plant; ability to recover after cutting; quantity of seed

Fig. 2. — Two seedling timothy plants, growing side by side, shewing a common kind and degree of difference.

Fig. 3. — A productive timothy plant.

produced, and others (Figs. 1–5). Similar differences may be found in any group of plants if the group is sufficiently studied.

Fig. 4. — A timothy plant that runs much to seed.

Variation and adaptation. — All this is equivalent to saying that plants are infinitely variable. The ultimate

causes of all this variation are beyond the purposes of the
present discussion, but it must be evident, to the reflective
mind, that these differences are a means of adapting
the innumerable individuals to every little difference or

Fig. 5. — A timothy plant that runs almost wholly to leaf.

advantage in the environment in which they live. And
if the result of variation is better adaption to the physical
conditions of life, then the same forces must have been
present in the circumstances which determined the birth
of the individual. This change in environment may be

the cause of much of the variation in plants, since differences in plants were positively injurious if it were possible for the conditions of environment to be the same.

Species-formation. — If no two plants are anywhere alike, then it is not strange if now and then some departure, more marked than common, is named and becomes a garden variety. We have been taught to feel that plants are essentially stable and inelastic, and that any departure from the type is an exception and calls for immediate explanation. The fact is, however, that plants are essentially unstable and plastic, and that variation between the individuals must everywhere be expected. This erroneous notion of the stability of organisms comes of our habit of studying what we call species. We set for ourselves a type of plant or animal, and group about it all those individuals that are more like this type than they are like any other, and this group we name a species.

Nowadays, the species is regarded as nothing more than a convenient and arbitrary expression for classifying our knowledge of the forms of life, but the older naturalists conceived that the species is the real entity or unit in nature, and we have not yet wholly outgrown the habit of mind which was born of that fallacy. Nature knows little about species; she is concerned with the individual, the ultimate complete and working unit. This individual she molds and fits into the opportunities of environment, and each individual tends to become the more unlike its birthmates the more the environments of the various individuals are unlike.

We must consider, therefore, as a fundamental conception to the discussion of the general subject before us, the importance of the individual plant, rather than the importance of the species; for thereby we put ourselves as nearly as possible in sympathetic attitude with nature, and, resting upon the ultimate object of her concern, we are able to understand what may be conceived to be her motive in working out the problem of life. Recall the fact that the whole tendency of contemporary civilization, in sociology and religion, is to deal with the individual person and not with the mass. The present-day method of studying the evolution of plants and animals is essentially analytical. As the chemist attempts to discover the smallest units from which the substances of nature have been built up, so the student of biology and evolution is seeking for the smallest heritable units of which plants and animals are composed. This is only an unconscious feeling after natural methods of solving the most complex of problems, for it is exactly the means to which every organic thing has been subjected from the beginning.

Conception of unit-characters.— The student of evolution now conceives animals and plants to be composed of what he terms "unit-characters," analogous, roughly, to the atoms of the chemist. These are the smallest heritable units that a plant or animal may possess. Any distinct entity that can be traced from one generation to another, such as the presence or absence of pubescence on the leaves or stems, the height of the plant, whether dwarf or tall, the color of the flower or fruits, and very many others are now known as unit-characters. The more any group of plants is studied, the more definite and distinct these unit-characters become. The time may come when the gardener, from long experience, shall become acquainted with these qualities, so that he may synthetically put many units together by crossing and produce new varieties almost at will.

Differences between plants and animals with regard to general association of parts and their methods of reproduction. — Unit-characters are nature's blocks, which she uses to build up plants and animals into various shapes for different purposes. These combinations of units when added together in proper extent and proportion constitute the plant and animal as we know it, the ultimate living and working organism, with power of growth and reproduction.

In looking for the ultimate working unit, individuality or personality in nature, we must make a broad distinction between the animal and the plant. Every higher animal is itself a working unit; it is one. It has a more or less definite span of life, and every part and organ contributes a certain indispensable part to the life and personality of the organism. No part is capable of propagating itself independently of the sex-organs of the animal, nor is it capable of developing sex-organs of its own. If any part is removed, the animal is maimed and perhaps it dies. The plant, on the contrary, has no definite or distinct autonomy. Most plants live an indefinite existence, dependent very closely upon the immediate conditions in which they grow. Every part or branch of the plant lives largely for itself, it is capable of propagating and multiplying itself when removed from the parent or the colony of branches of which it is a member, and it develops sex-organs and other individual features of its own. If any branch is removed, the tree or plant does not necessarily suffer; in fact, the remaining branches usually profit by the removal, a fact which shows that there is a competition, or struggle for existence, between the different branches or elements of the plant. The whole theory and practice of pruning rests upon the fact of the individual unlikenesses of the branches; and the unlikenesses are of the same kind and often of the same degree as those that exist between different plants grown from seeds.

Bud-variation and bud-varieties. — The branches of a Crawford peach tree, for example, differ amongst themselves in size, shape, vigor, productiveness, and season of maturity, much the same as any two or more separate Crawford trees, or any number of trees of other varieties, differ the one from the others. If any one of these branches or buds is removed and is grown into an independent tree, a person could not tell — if he were ignorant of its history — whether this tree were derived from a branch or a seed. This proves that there is no essential unlikeness between branches and independent plants, except the mere accident that one grows upon another branch or plant whilst the other grows in the ground. But the branch may be severed and grown in the ground, and the seedling may be pulled up and grafted on the tree, and no one can distinguish the different origins of the two. And then, as a matter of fact, a very large proportion of our cultivated plants are not distinct plants at all, in the sense of being different creations from seeds, but are simply the result of the division of branches of one original plant or branch. All the fruit trees of any one variety are obtained from the dividing up and multiplication of the branches of the first or original tree.

The reader is curious to know how this original tree came to be, and this we may find out before we are done; but for the present, let it be said that it is equally possible for it to have come from a seed, or to have sprung from a branch which some person had noticed to be very different from the associated branches in the tree-top. In other words, the ultimate unit or individual of variation is the bud and the bit of wood or tissue to which it is attached; for every bud, like every seed, produces an offspring that can be distinguished from every other offspring whatsoever.

CHAPTER II

THE CAUSES OF INDIVIDUAL DIFFERENCES

WE have now gone back to the starting-point, to that unit with which nature begins to make her initial differences or individualities; that is, to the point where variations arise. This point is the bud and the seed, — one sexless, or the offspring of one parent; the other sexual, or the offspring of two parents. Now, inasmuch as the horticultural variety is only a well-marked variation which the gardener has chanced to notice and to propagate, it follows that the only logical method of determining how garden varieties originate is to discover the means by which plants in general vary or differ one from another.

There is probably no one fact of organic nature concerning the origin of which modern philosophers are so much divided as the causes or reasons for the beginnings of variations or differences. It seems to be an inscrutable problem, and it would be useless, therefore, for us to attempt to discover these ultimate forces in the present book. Still, we must give them sufficient thought to enable us to satisfy our minds as to how far these variations may be produced by man; and, in doing this, we must discover at least the underlying philosophy of plant variation. It is the nature of organisms to be unlike their parents and their birthmates. Why?

13

Fortuitous variation. — It will probably never be possible to refer every variation to a distinct cause, for it is probable that some of them have no antecedent. If we conceive of the forms of life as having been created with characters exactly uniform from generation to generation, then we should be led to look for a distinct occasion or cause for every departure from the type; but we know, as has already been pointed out, that heredity by its very nature is not so exact as to carry over every attribute, and no other, of the parent to the offspring. Plasticity is a part of the essential constitution of all organic beings. There is perhaps no inherent tendency in organisms towards any ultimate or predetermined completion of forms, as the older naturalists supposed, but simply a laxity or indefiniteness of constitution which is expressed in numberless minor differences in individuals.

That is, some variation may be simply fortuitous, an inevitable result of the inherent plasticity of organisms, and it may have no immediate inciting cause.

Action of natural selection on variation. — If we were to assume that every minor difference is the result of some immediate cause, then we should expect every individual plant or animal to fill some niche, to satisfy some need, to produce the definite effect for which the cause stands. But it is apparent to one who contemplates the operations of nature that very many — certainly more than half — of the organisms which are born are not useful to the perpetuity of the species and very soon perish. From these fortuitous variations nature selects, to be sure, many individuals to be the parents of other generations because they chance to be fitted to live, but this does not affect the methods or reasons of their origin. It is possible that, whilst many of these mere individual differences have no direct and immediate cause, they may still be the result of a devious line of antecedent causes long since so much diffused and modified that they will remain forever unrecognizable; but even so, the fact still remains that these present differences or variations may be purposeless, and it is quite as well to say that they exist because it is a part of the organic constitution of living things that unlike produces unlike.

Sex as a factor in the variation of plants. — All plants have the faculty, either potential or expressed, of propagating themselves by means of buds, or asexual parts. This is obviously the cheapest and most direct possible method of propagation for many-membered plants, since it requires no special reproductive organization and energy, and, as only one parent is concerned in it, there is none of the risk of failure that obtains in any mode of propagation in which two parents must find each other and form a union. There must be some reason, therefore, for the existence of such a costly mechanism as sex aside from its use as a mere means of propagation.

It may be said that sex exists because it is a means of more rapid multiplication than bud-propagation, but such is not necessarily the fact. Many plants produce buds as freely as they produce seeds; and then, if mere multiplication were the only destiny of the plant, bud-production would no doubt have greatly increased to have met the demand for new generations. The chief reason for the existence of sex in the vegetable world seems to be the need for a constant rejuvenation and modification of the offspring by uniting the features of two individuals into one. There thus arises from every sexual union a number of new or different forms from which nature may select the best, — that is, those best fitted to live in the conditions in which they chance to be placed. But whilst sex is undoubtedly one of the most potent sources of present unlikenesses, it is not necessarily an original cause of individual differences, since the two parties to any sexual contract must be unlike before they can produce unlike. When once the initial unlikenesses were established, every new sexual union must produce new combinations, so that now, when every new form, from whatever source it appears, comes into existence, there are other intimately related forms with which it may cross. This state of things has existed to a greater or less degree from the moment sex first appeared, so that the organic world is now endlessly varied as the result of a most complex ancestry.

Physical environment and variation. — Every phase and condition of physical circumstances, which are not absolutely prohibitive of plant life, have plants which thrive in them. Every soil and climate, every degree of humidity, hills, swamps, and ponds, — every place is filled with plants. Even the trunks and branches of trees support other plants, as epiphytes and parasites. That is, plants have adapted themselves to every physical environment; or, to turn the proposition around, every physical environment produces adaptive changes in plants. There are those, like Weismann and his adherents, who contend, from purely speculative reasons, that these changes do not become hereditary or permanent until they have in-

fluenced a certain physiological substance which is assumed
to reside in the reproductive regions of the organisms,
and that all those changes which have not yet reached
this germ-plasm are, therefore, lost, or die with the organisms.

*Do external influences produce permanent effects in
plants?* — It is not necessary to discuss here the intricate arguments in the time-honored controversy of the
permanent inheritance of external modifications. Such
violent modifications as traumatic injury do not affect its
germ cells and are not inherited. But it is the common
experience of gardeners that the modifications of the environment of plants, such as changing food supply or changing
seed from one environment to another, produce changes
which eventually become hereditary. Whether these
changes of environment act directly upon the germ-plasm
to produce the change or whether they stimulate a germinal change which was otherwise latent, is a question
which long and patient experimentation must decide.
Certain it is, that plants have gone through a profound
modification and it is easy to believe that environment has
played no little part in these changes.

Weismann teaches that "acquired characters," or those
variations which first appear in the life-time of the individual because of the influences of environment, are lost,
because they have not yet affected the reproductive substances; but if these characters are induced by the effect
of impinging environment during two or more generations,
they may come to be so persistent that the plant cannot
throw them off, and they become, thereby, a part of the
hereditary and non-negotiable property of the species.

c

Now, it is apparent that in one or another of the generations which are thus acted upon by the environment, there must be a beginning towards the fixing or hereditable permanency of the new forms, and we might as well assume that this beginning takes place in the first generation as in the last, since there can be no proof that it does not take place in either one. The tendency towards fixity, if it exists at all, undoubtedly originates at the very time that the variation itself originates, and it is only sophistry to assume that the form appears at one time and the tendency towards permanency at another time. Since plants fit themselves into their circumstances by means of adaptive variations, we must conclude that all adaptive variations have the power of persisting, upon occasion.

All these remarks, whilst somewhat abstruse, have a most important bearing on the philosophy of the origin of garden varieties, because they show, first that changes in the conditions in which plants grow introduce modifications in the plants themselves, and second, that wherever any modification occurs it is probable that it may be fixed and perpetuated.

Natal and post-natal variations. — It is necessary at this point that we distinguish between natal and post-natal variations,—that is, between those variations which are born with plants, and those which appear, as a result of environment, after the plant has begun to grow. It is commonly assumed that the form and general characters of the plant are already determined in the seed, but a moment's reflection will show that this is far from the truth. One may sow a hundred selected peas, for example, all of which may be alike in every discernible character. If these are planted in a space of a foot apart, it will be found, after two or three weeks, that some individuals are outstripping the others, although all of them came up equally well and were at first practically indistinguishable. This means that, because of a little advantage in food or moisture, or other circumstances, some plants have obtained the mastery and are crowding out the less fortunate ones. The theory and practice of agriculture rests on the fact that plants can be modified greatly by the conditions in which they grow, after they have become thoroughly established in the soil. Plants may start equal, but differ widely at the harvest; and this difference may be controlled to a nicety by the cultivator. Every farmer is confident, also, that the best results for the succeeding year are to be got only when he selects seeds from the best that he has been able to produce this year. So, given uniformity or equality at the start, the operator molds the individual plants largely at his will.

Conception of biotypes. — Most varieties are not as uniform as would at first appear. A careful study of plants, when growing, indicates that they are not only modified in different degrees by environment but the plants themselves are not the same. They have different potentialities to begin with. Environment causes direct modifications to appear; it also allows expression in different degrees of the inherent variability present. Most varieties of plants are polytypic, being composed of many distinct types, or "biotypes" as they have been called by Johannsen. All this is a matter of the commonest observation with the gardener, who is so accustomed to seeing great differences arise in batches of plants, all of which start apparently equal and with an equal chance, that he never thinks to comment upon the occurrence.

Having noticed that physical environments may modify plants, we are now ready to consider just what changes in these circumstances of plant life are most fruitful in the production of new forms.

Variation in food supply. — The greater part of the changes in the physical conditions of life hinge upon the relative supply of food. Climbing plants assume their form because, by virtue of the divergence of character, they are enabled to fit themselves into places that other plants cannot occupy. They rear their foliage into the air, where food and sunlight are unappropriated. The lower branches of tree-tops die, and the others thereby appropriate the more food and grow the faster. The entire practice of agriculture is built upon the augmentation of the food supply. For this purpose, we set the plants in isolated positions, we till the ground, keep down other plants or weeds, add plant-food to the soil, and prune the tree and thin the fruit.

Thomas Andrew Knight, the chief of horticultural philosophers, appears to have been the first clearly to enunciate the law that excess of food supply is the most prolific cause of the variations of plants. Darwin subscribes to it without reserve: "Of all the causes which induce variability, excess of food, whether or not changed in nature, is probably the most powerful." Alexander Braun, an earlier philosophical writer on natural history, said that "it appears rather, on the whole, as if the unusual conditions favorable to a luxuriant state of development, afforded by cultivation, awakened in the plant the inward impulse to the display of all those variations possible within the more or less narrowly circumscribed limits of the species." It is generally agreed by those who have given the matter much thought, that an excess of food above the amount normally or habitually received is one of the very chief, if not the most dominant, causes of individual differences in plants. Certainly every farmer or gardener knows that the richer the soil in available plant-food, the stronger and the more abnormal and unusual his product will be.

If, then, excess of food supply is a strong factor in the modification of plants, and the one fundamental aim of agriculture is to supply food in excess of natural conditions, it must naturally follow that cultivated plants should be, of all others, the most variable. This is notably true. Now, the first variation that usually comes of this liberal food supply is increase in mere bulk. Probably every plant which has ever been cultivated has increased its stature or the size of some or all of its parts. Moreover, this is generally the direct object of cultivation, — to secure larger herbage, fruits, seeds, or flowers. Incidentally, we find here an indubitable proof of the truth of the hypothesis of evolution, for if it were impossible for plants to vary or to assume new characters, there would be no cultivation and no agriculture; for there would be little object in cultivating a product if it grew equally well in the wild.

This variation into mere bigness is more important than it may seem at first. All thoughtful horticulturists agree in thinking that the first thing to be done in ameliorating any plant is to "break the type," that is, to cause it to vary. The particular direction of variation is not so important, at first; for all experience has shown that if once the seedlings of a plant begin to depart from the parental type, other and various modifications will soon follow. If a plant is once strongly modified in size, variations in shape, color, flavor, or other attributes are forthcoming. This apparent accumulation of variation seems at first to be incapable of scientific explanation, but the reasons for it are not difficult to understand when once they are presented.

We now ask ourselves why these many variations appear when once the type begins to modify itself. Consider the fact that the world is now full of plants. In untamed nature, but one more plant can grow unless another plant dies. All plants, therefore, are held down to narrow limits of numbers, and since there are so few individuals, — in comparison with the seeds and buds which each plant produces for the chance of multiplying itself, — there must be, also, few kinds and degrees of individual differences. The farther and more freely a plant distributes itself, the greater must be the differences between various individuals, because they must adapt themselves to a wider range of conditions. All plants are held in equilibrium, so to speak; but the plant organism is plastic by nature and quickly responds to every touch of environment; so, as soon as the pressure is removed in any direction, the plant at once springs into the breach. Recall the monotonous vegetation of the deep forest, where the battle of centuries has subdued all but the strongest. Clear away the forest, and then observe the fierce scramble

for place and life amongst a multitude of forms which
spring in for an opportunity to better their conditions.
In a few years more, the tender low herbs have gone.
The briers and underbrush have usurped the land. As
time goes on, one species after another perishes, and when
the place is again reforested, two or three species hold un-
disputed sway over the land. The poplars that followed
the pines have long since perished and pines again dominate
the forest. Or, if the area were turned to pasture a few
years after the woods were removed, the herbs and bushes
die with the browsing, and in time the June-grass covers
the whole landscape with the mantle of conquest. So
plants may be said to be always ready to fill new places
in the polity of nature by adapting themselves to the new
circumstances as they grow into them. The appearance
of any one marked variation, therefore, is indication that
the plant may have found a new condition, that pressure is
somewhat lifted, and that the whole plastic organization
may soon respond to the new environment. It is apparent, then, how the simplest and rudest cultivation has
been able, through the centuries, so profoundly to modify
our domestic plants that we are often unable to recognize
the forms from which they have sprung.

Food supply of different branches. — We must not forget
to notice, at this point, that the food supply differs amongst
the various branches of the same plant. Some branches,
by reason of position with reference to the main trunk or
with reference to air and sunlight, or, because of a better
start in the beginning as a result of some incidental
advantage, gain the mastery over others and crowd
them out. We have already seen that no two branches

on a plant are alike; and we are now able to understand that sports or bud-varieties are no more inexplicable than seed-varieties.

What cultivation is. — Cultivation is really but an extension or intensification of nature's methods of dealing with the plant world. The ultimate result of both nature and man is to supply more food. The variations which arise from the effects of mere cultivation, therefore, are in kind very like those which nature produces, the chief differences being that of degree. The accustomed operations of the farmer, therefore, have been powerful agents in the evolution of vegetable forms. The ways in which cultivation affords a more liberal food supply are as follows : —

1. By isolating the individual plant. The husbandman sets each plant by itself, and then protects it by destroying the weeds or plants which endeavor to crowd it out. There is a partial exception to this in the "sowed crops," like the grains, and it is noticeable that variation in these plants is usually less marked than in the "hoed crops."

2. By giving the plant the advantage of position, whereby it is allowed the most congenial exposure to sun and contour of land.

3. By increasing the fertility of the land, either by tillage or the direct application of plant-food, or both. Rich and moist soils tend to "break" the type, — or to cause initial variations, — to produce verdant colors and loss of saccharine and pungent qualities, to induce redundant growth, and to delay maturity and thereby to render plants tender to cold winter climates.

4. By thinning the tops of plants and the fruits, whereby

the remaining parts receive an amount of food in excess
of the habitual allowance.

5. By divergence of character in associated plants.
It is well known that a field planted so thickly to corn
that it cannot grow more with profit, may still grow
pumpkins between. The pumpkins and the corn are so
unlike in form that they complement each other, the one
filling the place which the other is not fitted to occupy.
We have already seen that a copse ever so full of bushes
may still grow vines. A meadow full of timothy may still
grow clover in the bottom, and land covered with apple
trees still grows weeds beneath. " The more diversed the
descendants from one species become in structure, constitution, and habits," writes Darwin, "by so much will
they be better enabled to seize on many and widely diver-
sified places in the polity of nature, and so be enabled to
increase in numbers."

Variation in climate. — The fact that any distinct
climatic region usually has plants that are very closely
related to those of other climatic regions in the same
zone, points strongly to the probable profound modification of plants by climate. And, furthermore, we should
expect that if the food environment modifies plants, the
climatic environment must have the same power. Moreover, there is abundant historical and experimental proof
that climate is capable of greatly modifying the vegetable
kingdom. There are those who contradict any great effect
of climate in the variation of plants, and acclimatization
has been even stoutly denied. These persons make the
mistake of asking that a visible modification take place
at once upon the transfer of a plant from one climate to

another, and they also err in supposing that a plant can adapt itself to a cold climate only by developing a capability to withstand more cold. Indian corn is sometimes cited as proof that plants do not become acclimatized, for it is as tender to frost now as ever, for all that we know. Yet this very plant affords a most unequivocal example of complete acclimatization, because it has shortened its period of growth fully one-half whereby it escapes the cold of the North.

The influence on plants of a change of climate, or, what may amount to the same thing, the result of a transfer of plants to new climates, is so complex and so general that no discussion of the subject can be made at this time. It will answer present purposes briefly to designate the ways in which climate modifies plants:—

1. Climate generally modifies the stature of plants. They become dwarfer in high latitudes and altitudes.

2. It modifies form. Plants tend to be broader-headed, and also more prostrate, in high latitudes and altitudes.

3. Proportionate leafiness generally increases, at the same time.

4. There is also often a gain in comparative fruitfulness following transfer towards the poles.

5. The colors of leaves, flowers, fruits, and seeds are greatly influenced by climate, there being a general tendency, in plants of temperate regions, to augmentation in intensity of colors as they are carried towards the poles.

6. There is modification in the flavor and essential ingredients of various parts, following a change of climate.

7. There is a variation in variability itself. The more difficult the climate in which a plant finds itself, the more

it tends to vary to meet the uncongenial environments. In the high North, many plants are so variable that the marks used to identify the species in other latitudes are often lost.

8. There may be a profound variation or modification in constitution and habit by which plants become acclimatized, or enabled to endure a climate at first injurious to them. This may occur by a variation in the constitution of the descendants, which enables them directly to endure more untoward conditions. It generally comes about, however, through a change in habit, by which plants, when transferred towards the poles, shorten their season of growth or even become annuals. Plants become more sensitive to spring temperatures in cold climates, so that they start relatively much earlier in the season — that is, at a lower sum-temperature — than in warm climates. Any one who has passed the springtime in both the North and South must have noticed how much more suddenly the vegetation comes forward in the North; and it is surprising how the spring-sown crops accelerate their growth in the North over those in the South.

Man's control over climate as a means of making plants to vary. — The characters that result from a change of climatic environment are peculiarly within the control of the agriculturist, for a leading factor in his business is the transfer of plants far and wide over the earth. So it has come that the staple varieties of the important grains and fruits are unlike in Europe and America and in all great geographical areas, although all the various forms may have sprung from one ancestor within historic times. A new country is stocked with varieties from the mother country; but in the course of a few generations it is found that the varieties in cultivation are unlike the ones originally introduced, and from which they came. As wild plants have become separated from each other as species in the different geographical regions, so the cultivated plants soon begin to follow similar lines of divergence. In the beginning of the colonization of this country, for example, all the varieties of apples were of European origin. But in 1817, over sixty per cent of the apples recommended for cultivation here were of American origin, that is American-grown seedlings from the original stock. At present, probably fully ninety per cent of the popular apples of the Atlantic States are American productions. The northern states of the Mississippi Valley to which most of our eastern apples are not adapted, are now witnessing a similar transformation in the adaptation and modification of the varieties introduced from the East and from Russia. The recently introduced Japanese plums are conceded to be great acquisitions to our fruit-growing, but no doubt the best results are yet to come with the origination of domestic varieties of them. So there is an irresistible tendency towards a divergence of forms in different continental or geographical regions, and much of the inevitable result is no doubt chargeable to climatic environment.

Change of seed. — We may now pause for a moment to consider two agencies or phenomena often associated with the genesis of varieties. One of these is the fact that the simple change of seed from one locality to another usually gives a larger or better product or even more marked variation. Mere transfer of seed is not of itself, however, a cause of variation. The change is beneficial because it fits together characters and environments that are not in equilibrium with each other. A plant grown for several years in one set of conditions becomes fitted to them, so to speak, and it is in a state of comparative rest. When the plant or its progeny is taken to other conditions, all the adjustments are broken up, and in the refitting to the new circumstances new or strange characters are likely to appear. We shall leave this subject for the present, expecting to give it a fuller treatment in a later chapter.

Bud-variation. — Bud-variation, or sport, is a name given to those branches which are so much unlike the normal plant in any particular that they attract attention. Many garden varieties are simply multiplications of such abnormal branches. This bud-variation is commonly held to be such an unusual and inexplicable phenomenon that it is considered apart from all the general discussions of variation. It is not, of course, a cause of variability, but only an effect of some antecedent, the same as seed-variation is. We have already seen that all the different branches, or even nodes of any plant are, in a very important sense, distinct individuals, since every one develops its own organs, each is capable of reproducing itself independently, and each is unlike every other because it is acted upon differently by environment and food supply. It is not strange, therefore, that some of these individuals should now and then depart very widely from the ordinary type, and thereby attract the attention of the gardener, who would forthwith make cuttings or set grafts from the part. Every branch is a bud-variety, just as truly as every seedling is a seed-variety, — since no seedling is ever like its parent, — and there should be no greater mystery connected with the sports of buds than there is with the varieties from seeds, for the causes that produce the one may be and probably are equally competent to produce the other (Figs. 6, 7).

Struggle for life a cause of variation. — We have seen that the world is full of plants. There is room for more only as the present individuals die. Yet nearly every species produces a great number of seeds, and makes a most strenuous effort to multiply its kind. Any one plant, if left to itself, is capable of covering the earth in a comparatively short time. A fierce struggle for a chance to live is therefore inevitable. This conflict is most apparent to the general observer in the springtime, when every "herb yielding seed after his kind, and the tree yielding fruit, whose seed was in itself, after his kind," are sending forth a host of sturdy offspring. The very land seems to be pregnant with weeds and aspiring young growths. But by midsummer the numbers may be less. The weaker and less fortunate ones have perished, and the victors have waxed stronger thereby. The annual and half of the biennial species complete their course upon the approach of winter, and the older perennial herbs are becoming weak; so in the succeeding springtime there is again a fierce combat for the vacant places.

One of the results of this conflict is the adjustment of plants to each other. We have seen how the climbing plant insinuates itself amongst the shrubberies and ties them together in an impenetrable tangle in order that

Fig. 6. — Couch-grass or quack-grass. Showing means of sexual propagation by seed and a sexual propagation by underground rootstocks. (After Clark and Fletcher.)

it, itself, may have a chance to live. So the low plants of the deep forest are such as have been plastic enough to

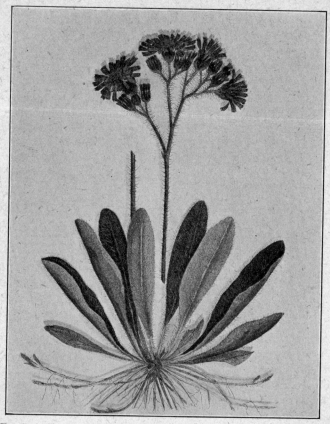

Fig. 7. — Orange hawkweed. This plant can withstand the struggle for existence. It produces immense quantities of seed and also reproduces itself by underground rootstocks. (After Clark and Fletcher.)

adapt themselves to the damp shades. Thus plants have developed companionships or divergences in character, by means of which, under the stress of circumstances, they are able to live together. Plants have adapted themselves to other plants as truly as to soil or climate; and if these latter environments are ever the sources or causes of variation, then the first must be also. We must look upon the struggle for existence, therefore, as itself a cause of individual differences, since we know that any continued pressure from without awakens an adaptive response in the form of the vegetable organisms.

D

CHAPTER III

THE CHOICE AND FIXATION OF VARIATIONS

We have now seen that every living object is unlike every other. In plants, even every branch is unlike any other branch. We have endeavored to discover some of these universal differences. We have found that they are intimately associated with the welfare of the type or species, inasmuch as they appear, for the most part, to be the means of fitting the plant to live in the conditions in which it is placed. But we have also seen that there are more individuals than can find a place to live. How, then, does nature choose the best from the poorest (or, rather, the fit from the unfit), and, having chosen them, how does she endeavor to fix them or to make them more or less stable?

"This preservation of favorable individual differences and variations, and the destruction of those which are injurious, I have called Natural Selection or the Survival of the Fittest." This is the philosophy which was propounded by Darwin, and which will carry his name to the last generation of men. It looks simple enough. Those forms which are best fitted to live, do live, because they crowd out the others. Yet, this simple principle of natural selection was the first explanation of the process of evolution that seemed to be capable of interpreting the complex phenomena of the forms of organic life. For a time, this philosophy was thought to be the one fundamental motive of the evolution or progression of life, but we are now convinced that there are other motives or forces at work; but it seems to be indisputable that natural selection is a major force underlying the evolution of plants, and it is the only one with which the person who desires to breed plants need intimately concern himself.

We must now determine what a variety is. This is a vexed question, and one which seems never to be capable of an answer that is satisfactory to the gardener. Time and again, some person has introduced what he considered to be a distinct new variety, only to find that other horticulturists dispute him and declare that it is only some old variety renamed. And yet the introducer knows that he has not renamed an old variety, but that he has propagated a form which appeared or originated on his own grounds.

What is a variety? — Now, let us see. Nature starts out with the individual to make a new form. Every individual is unlike every other one. When the individual differences are so well marked that we can readily describe and distinguish them, and so permanent that they pass down nearly intact to a few generations, we say that we have a variety. If the differences are still more marked, we say that we have a species. Where the variety ends and the species begins it may be utterly impossible to determine; and so we mark off at a certain point and say, arbitrarily, that this much is variety and that much is species. Asa Gray once said that "species are judgments." Now, if there is no hard and fast line between the variety and the species, so there is none between the individual and the variety; for a variety is only the family of descendants from some one individual. That is, the idea of variety or species rests on difference, but just how much difference shall constitute one grade or another is a matter of individual opinion. There is no standardized practice. So, when two gardeners cannot agree as to whether a given introduction is a new variety or not, they are having the same kind of difficulty that two botanists have when they cannot decide whether two plants are two species or one.

It is apparent, then, that every individual plant is a distinct variety, only that the differences between it and other individuals may be so slight that they have no practical utility and cannot be described and recorded. Just as soon as an individual plant has characters so unlike its kin that it has some commercial value, then the plant will be increased by cuttings or grafts or seeds, the brood of offspring will be given a name, and a new variety is born.

Individuals with the same general features may appear simultaneously in two or more places, and two or more men may propagate, name, and introduce them. When they are all brought together and compared, it will be said that they are all the same variety, that, according to the rules of nomenclature, the brood which chanced to be named first must "stand" or be held to be the type of the variety and the other names must become synonyms. Yet some persons may discover minor differences in them and demand that the variety be kept distinct. So the see-saw goes on — a variety is a variety so long as it answers some purpose in use or trade, and it is not a variety when it is so much like some other variety that it has no merit that the other does not possess.

As soon as a plant appears with some features which are more desirable than anything that has preceded it, therefore, it may be the beginning of a new variety. Man chooses it, and then propagates it. This is human selection. If nature did the same thing, it would be natural selection.

It must not be understood that there are no definite species in nature. Some plants are so distinct, and so constant in their characters, as to leave no doubt. But wide variability is very common, and it may obscure the relationship.

Adaptation in nature. — Now, how does nature preserve or fix this type? She does not preserve it. She simply chooses it as a beginning and gradually modifies it and shapes it into the form which she needs. She has no permanent forms. There is a general onward progression of one type either towards other types or towards extinction. We have seen that nature is constantly choosing and selecting. If she selects an individual for the beginning of a race, then she selects just as keenly from every offspring of that individual, and so on to the end of time. The process never stops. So nature fixes her forms by keeping them moving, growing, constantly developing farther away from their beginnings.

The vexed question as to whether there is an accumulative effect in variation, need not be considered here, as it is foreign to the particular point of view at this place.

Artificial selection. — Now, man does the same thing.

A plant in a cabbage row pleases him. It has a solid small head and stout stem. He stores it away for seed. Amongst the offspring, perhaps fifty per cent are as good as the parent. These are saved. So the process goes on, from season to season. In four or five generations of plants, he finds that ninety per cent of the seeds "come true." Then he names it and introduces it. It is well advertised in the seed catalogues. Many persons buy the seeds. Some of these persons will grow their own seeds, and every one of them has a different ideal in mind when selecting the seed parents. So, in the course of a few years it is found that there are really several more or less different forms under the same name. Some persons may observe this difference and legitimately introduce one or more of the forms as distinct varieties. Some other person, however, who has known the history of the stock and who is not aware that varieties pass into other forms, objects to the new names and declares that the introducer is imposing on the public.

This is the history of ninety out of every hundred varieties which are habitually propagated by seeds, like the kitchen-garden vegetables and the annual flowers. Some peculiar individual, appearing we know not why, is discovered, and seeds are saved and selection — perhaps unconscious selection — begins. After a time the variety is broken up into several, or else, if it varies only slightly, into divergent forms, the whole body or generations of the variety move onward, gradually departing from the initial type until it is no longer the same, although it may bear the same name. The life of seed varieties, in their pure and original forms, is very short. Even the best of them are usually measured by a score of years or less. They run out or pass out by variation, into other forms. The Trophy tomato is not the Trophy tomato which was introduced over forty years ago, although it bears the old name and is a direct descendant of the first stock.

Bud selection. — In plants multiplied by buds — that is, by budding, grafting, cuttings, tubers, and the like — there is less variation in the offspring than in those propagated by seeds. Yet we have seen that no two Baldwin apple trees — all of which are but divisions, more or less remote, of the same original tree — are alike, and now and then one branch of a fruit tree may "sport" or develop a strange bud-variety. We know, also, that the same variety of fruit tree takes on different characters in different geographical regions, so that the Greening apple is no longer the Greening of Rhode Island in the West and South. So, it is apparent that even when we divide a plant into many parts and distribute the members far and wide, and when there is no occasion for concerning ourselves with fixing the type, — even here there is variation. In some cases, particularly in those in which we multiply the plant by dividing abnormally developed parts, there is a tendency to scatter or to vary in many directions, and also a tendency to run out by degeneration. This is admirably true of the potato, varieties of which, in ten years or less, become so mixed in their characters, through rapid variation and deterioration, that we must return to seedling productions for a new start.

Variation and selection not entirely within man's control. — Man is only rarely the direct means of originating variations. He finds them among the normal plants of the fields and gardens. His skill and science are exercised in the selection and so-called breeding of the offspring, more than in the original genesis of the new form. It is usually only in those plants which he multiplies by simple division that he gains much immediate profit by crossing or hybridizing. It is the slow and patient care and selection, day by day, which permanently ameliorates and improves the vegetable world. Nature starts the work; man may complete it.

It is now generally held that species in nature sometimes originate suddenly, by means of "leaps." In fact, the de Vriesian view is that real species so originate, and the steps whereby a few species come into existence are called mutations. (See Chapter V.) However this may be, it is nevertheless true that these mutations are yet beyond the power of man directly to produce. Selection is still a powerful agent with which to ameliorate domestic plants.

CHAPTER IV

THE MEASUREMENT OF VARIATION

It is often desirable to describe a plant or a group of plants in exact mathematical terms. Most of the plant characters with which a breeder deals are measurable, and an individual plant may be described as having so many leaves, so many grains, and so on throughout a long list of measurements; or a group of plants may be expressed in the form of averages; likewise, the degree of resemblance or difference between plants and their offspring, or among plants of a certain group or "population." The degree or extent of correlation or association of plant characters may also be expressed mathematically.

The science of biometry. — The expression of variation and heredity by means of statistical methods is known as the science of Biometry. This method of description is now being widely employed by experimental plant-breeders. It is another tool which the breeder uses to record his progress and describe his plants. The biometrician should be cautioned to keep his use of mathematical treatment subservient to the biological facts, not forgetting that biometry is simply a means toward an end and not an end in itself. It is better first of all to become acquainted with the real plants before any mathematical treatment of their variability is attempted. It is often

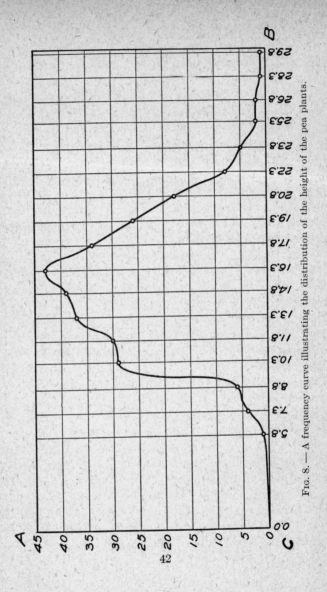

Fig. 8. — A frequency curve illustrating the distribution of the height of the pea plants.

desirable, however, to treat plants in groups by means of statistical generalizations.

Type. — In the study of any group of plants, called a "population," whether it be corn, wheat, the ray-florets of daisies, or what not, the breeder has in mind a certain type around which the individuals tend to center.

The corn breeder has in mind a certain length of an ear of corn which is his ideal type. He chooses ears of this length and plants them in his plat, and at harvest time what does he get? Not all ears of this length, but ears ranging above and below this length. The offspring will be distributed, in all probability, above and below this parental type and may possibly reach the upper and lower limits of the race. There will be a group near the average which will contain a larger number of individuals than any other and thus we have another conception of type. There is the ideal parental type which the breeder has in mind, and another type, probably different, shown by the offspring. To find the latter, the ears of corn are carefully measured and their average length determined. This average constitutes a concrete mathematical expression for the type of the offspring.

Biometrical expression of variability. — The amount and range of variability may also be well expressed statistically.

As an illustration, a number of pea plants were measured and their height was found to range from 5 to 30½ inches. A few were short and a few were tall, but most of the plants were of average height. For the sake of convenience, the plants having similar measurements were placed together in one class. When all the results had been brought together they appeared as in the following table : —

HEIGHT IN INCHES	NUMBER OF INDIVIDUALS IN EACH CLASS (f)
5.1– 6.5	1
6.6– 8	4
8.1– 9.5	6
9.6–11	29
11.1–12.5	30
12.6–14	37
14.1–15.5	39
15.6–17	43
17.1–18.5	34
18.6–20	26
20.1–21.5	18
21.6–23	8
23.1–24.5	5
24.6–26	2
26.1–27.5	2
27.6–29	1
29.1–30.5	1
	286

Here we have what is called a "frequency distribution," representing the crop as it falls into the different groups.

The curve in Fig. 8, known as the "Quetelet curve," represents the results graphically.

The frequencies, that is, the number of times each measurement appears (see column f in the table), are plotted on the axis of ordinates, line A–C, and the classes on the axis of abscissas, line C–B. For the purpose of plotting and working the data the mid-class is used, that is, 5.8 inches instead of 5.1–6.6 inches, and so forth.

Mode. — We see by inspection of the foregoing data that there is one group of the most common height, that is, there are more plants having a height of 15.6 to 17 inches (16.3) than any other class.

The group containing the greatest number of plants,

that is, of the greatest frequency, is called the *mode*. It is an excellent expression of type. When the group of plants or population which is being studied is measured and arranged with some suitable grouping, as illustrated here, we see what the variety tends to do on the whole.

Modal coefficient. — It is desirable to know what percentage of the individuals falls into this group of highest frequency, called the mode. This can be readily found by dividing the number of individuals in this class (43) by the total number (286) and multiplying by 100. This is called the *modal coefficient*, and denotes the percentage of individuals conforming to type. This modal coefficient is .15 or 15%; that is, fifteen per cent of all of the plants in this variety are found in one class.

However, as this is dependent on the system of measurement, one modal coefficient is not directly comparable with another unless the same practice of measurement has been used. Moreover, one could not compare the modal coefficient of height directly with that of weight or any other character of a different nature.

It may readily be seen that a knowledge of the distribution of plants as represented by the mode or modal coefficient is of scientific and practical importance. It enables the breeder at any time to spread out before himself a fair representation of his variety. He can see at a glance what is the prevailing type and in what direction and to what degree his breeding is extending.

Mean. — There is another conception of type known as the *mean* or average. One can understand that the average height will differ in most cases from the commonest height. The mean is most easily obtained by multiplying the mid-value of each class, say 5.8, by the number in that class, adding their products, and dividing by the total number of individuals. This is expressed by the formula M (mean) $= \dfrac{\Sigma f V}{n}$ where V represents the variables, f the frequency of each variable, n the total number of individuals, and Σ the summation of fV.

MEAN. —	V	f	fV
	5.8	1	5.8
	7.3	4	29.2
	8.8	6	52.8
	10.3	29	298.7
	11.8	30	354.0
	13.3	37	492.1
	14.8	39	577.2
	16.3	43	700.9
	17.8	34	605.2
	19.3	26	501.8
	20.8	18	374.4
	22.3	8	178.4
	23.8	5	119.0
	25.3	2	50.6
	26.8	2	53.6
	28.3	1	28.3
	29.8	1	29.8
		$n = 286$	$\Sigma = 4451.8$

Mean, $\dfrac{(\Sigma fV)}{n} = \dfrac{4451.8}{286} = 15.5$ inches.

Use of mean. — The mean gives a good average value of the character and is often more useful than the mode in expressing type. The breeder must use his judgment as to which should be used in each case, the mean or the mode.

Mathematical expression of variability. — After the average or mean of any group of plants has been determined, it is desirable to know the amount of deviation of the different individuals from the mean. This determination gives a concrete expression which is an index of the amount of variability exhibited. This variability is expressed as the *average deviation* or the *standard deviation.* The latter is ordinarily employed by mathematicians.

Average deviation. — The average deviation is determined by obtaining, first of all, the amount which each class varies from the mean and multiplying each deviation by the number of individuals concerned. For example, the column D is obtained by finding the difference between the mean, 15.5, and the variations in column V: thus in the first case the difference between 5.8 and 15.5 is -9.7 while farther down column V we find 16.3, which is greater than the mean, giving us a value of 0.8 in column D.

Now, if there were the same number of individuals in each class, the average deviation could be found by adding up the deviations in column D, and dividing by the total number of individuals in column f, but there is one individual deviating -9.7 while there are 43 deviating 0.8 and 18 deviating 5.3, and so forth. In order to overcome this the deviations are multiplied by the number of individuals giving the column fD. The sum of this column divided by the total number of individuals gives the average deviation. This is an index of variability. The average deviation is expressed by the following formula : —

$$\text{Average deviation} = \frac{\Sigma\, Df}{n}.$$

Standard deviation. — The operations for finding the standard deviation are the same as for the average deviation except that the deviations in column D are squared before multiplying by the frequency numbers (f), thus giving the columns D^2 and D^2f respectively. The sum of the latter divided by the total number of individuals and the square root of the result extracted gives the standard deviation. This can be expressed by the following formula : —

$$\sigma = \sqrt{\frac{\Sigma\, D^2 f}{n}}.$$

The details of determining the average and standard deviation are as follows : —

V	f	D	fD	D^2	D^2f
5.8	1	− 9.7	9.70	94.09	94.09
7.3	4	− 8.2	32.80	67.24	268.96
8.8	6	− 6.7	40.20	44.89	269.34
10.3	29	− 5.2	150.80	27.04	784.16
11.8	30	− 3.7	111.00	13.69	410.70
13.3	37	− 2.2	81.40	4.84	179.08
14.8	39	− 0.7	27.30	0.49	19.11
16.3	43	0.8	34.40	0.64	28.12
17.8	34	2.3	78.20	5.29	179.86
19.3	26	3.8	98.80	14.44	375.44
20.8	18	5.3	95.40	28.09	505.62
22.3	8	6.8	54.40	46.24	369.92
23.8	5	8.3	41.50	68.89	551.12
25.3	2	9.8	19.60	96.04	192.08
26.8	2	11.3	22.60	127.69	255.38
28.3	1	12.8	12.80	163.84	163.84
29.8	1	14.3	14.30	204.49	204.49
	$n = 286$		925.20		$\Sigma = 4851.31$

Average deviation $= \dfrac{925.20}{286} = 3.24$ inches.

Standard deviation, $(\sigma) = \sqrt{\dfrac{4851.31}{286}} = 4.1+$ in.

Coefficient of variability. — The average deviation or standard deviation as outlined above is always determined in the denomination of the unit in which the plant is measured; if it is height of plant in inches, the deviation will be in inches and so forth. This prohibits the careful comparison of the deviations of different plants or parts of a plant because some deviations may be in pounds or others in inches, and hence they will not be directly comparable.

It is desirable, therefore, to have an abstract expression so that the relative amount of variability of one class of organs may be directly compared with the variability of another. This is called the *coefficient of variability*. It is found by dividing the standard deviation by the mean. Thus an abstract number is found which expresses the variability. In our case the standard deviation = 4.1 inches and the mean = 15.5 inches, so that

$\dfrac{4.1}{15.5} = .264 = 26.4 \% =$ the coefficient of variability.

If the coefficient of variability of the weight of the plants had to be determined and was found to be, say, .384, it would follow at once that the height of the plant was considerably less variable than the weight.

The coefficient of variability may be expressed as follows : —

E

$$C = \frac{\sigma}{M} \times 100.$$

Probable error.[1] — It is obvious that these mathematical expressions of type and variability will be modified somewhat by the number of individuals measured. The greater the number of individuals employed, the less the error. These differences which arise from the fewness of individuals employed is known as the *probable error*. It is expressed by a pair of divergences ($\pm E$), the one above and the other below the actual value found, and indicates that the chances are even that the true value lies somewhere between the value found plus the error and the value minus the error. For example, the probable error of the mean in the problem here cited is $\pm$ .016 and is found by the formula given below. This means that

---

[1] Formulæ for probable errors: —

$$E \text{ mean} = \pm .6745 \frac{\text{standard deviation}}{\text{number of individuals}}, \text{ or } \pm .6745 \frac{\sigma}{\sqrt{n}}$$

$$E \text{ standard deviation} = \pm .6745 \frac{\text{standard deviation}}{\sqrt{2 \times \text{number of individuals}}}, \text{ or}$$

$$\pm .6745 \frac{\sigma}{\sqrt{2\,n}}$$

$$E \text{ coefficient of variability} = \pm .6745 \frac{\text{coefficient of variability}}{\sqrt{2 \times \text{number of individuals}}}$$

$$= \pm .6745 \frac{C}{\sqrt{2\,n}}$$

But when C is greater than 10% use the formula

$$EC = \pm .6745 \frac{C}{\sqrt{2\,n}} \left[1 + 2 \left(\frac{C}{100} \right)^2 \right]^{\frac{1}{2}}$$

the true mean is probably somewhere between 15.5 + .016 and 15.5 − .016 or between 15.516 and 15.484. The size of the error is generally indicative of the number of the individuals employed and the general dependability of the work.

Use of statistical methods. — The use of statistical methods enables the breeder to express quite accurately the amount of variability which would otherwise be expressed with considerable difficulty. It enables him also to keep an accurate record of his work from year to year and affords him a convenient method of comparing one year's crop with another.

It will be seen later that statistical methods may also be employed to express correlation and extent of inheritance.

CHAPTER V

MUTATIONS

THERE is endless dissimilarity in nature. No two plants and no two animals are exactly alike. There are more plants and animals than can find a place in which to live and thrive. There results a struggle for existence. Those animals or plants which, by virtue of the individual differences or peculiarities, are best fitted to the conditions in which they are placed, survive in this struggle for existence. They are "selected to live." Those that survive, propagate their peculiarities. By virtue of continued variation, and of continued selection along a certain line, the peculiarities may become augmented; finally the gulf of separation from the parental stem becomes great, and what we call a new species has originated.

Evolutionary theories of Darwin and de Vries. — This, in epitome, is the philosophy of Darwin in respect to evolution of organic forms. It contains the well-known postulate of natural selection, the principle that we know as Darwinism. This principle has had more adherents than any other hypothesis of the process of evolution. All recent hypotheses in some way relate to it. A number of them modify it, and some dispute it. The most pronounced counter-hypothesis is also the newest. It is that

52

of Professor de Vries, botanist, of Amsterdam, Holland,
who denies that natural selection is competent to produce
species, or that organic ascent is the product of small
differences gradually enlarging into great ones. According
to de Vries' view, species-characters arise suddenly, or
all at once, and they are ordinarily stable from the moment
they arise.

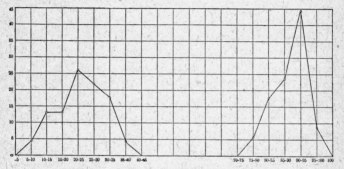

Fig. 9. — Variations in statures of *Œnothera nanella* (left), a mutant,
and *Œnothera Lamarkiana* (right), its parent. *Œnothera nanella :*
Range, 7–35 cm. ; M., 22.81 ± 1.02 cm. ; σ, 7.26 ± 0.72 cm. ; C. V.,
31.84 ± 3.16 per cent. *Œnothera Lamarkiana :* Range, 77–96 cm. ;
M., 88.68 ± 0.55 cm. ; σ, 4.76 ± 0.39 cm. ; C. V. 5.37 ± 0.44 per
cent.

De Vries conceives that variations, or differences, are of
two general categories : (1) Variations proper, or small,
fluctuating, unstable differences peculiar to the individual
(only partially transmitted to offspring) ; and (2) mutations, or differences that are usually of marked character,
appear suddenly and without transition to other forms
and are at once the starting-points of new species or races.
Variations proper may be due to the immediate environ-

ment in which the plant lives. The mutations arise from causes yet unknown, although these causes are considered to be physiological. Probably many so-called mutations are hybrids and hence not mutations in the strictest sense.

Differences between fluctuating variations and mutations: —

1. Fluctuating variations are very common and are to be found in all plants and animals. Mutations occur intermediately and are rare.

2. Fluctuating variations are thought not to be transmitted. Mutations are transmitted.

3. Fluctuating variations present a series of differences which may be plotted on a frequency curve and obey the laws of chance. Mutations or saltatory variations do not obey the laws of chance, and cannot be plotted in the form of a frequency curve.

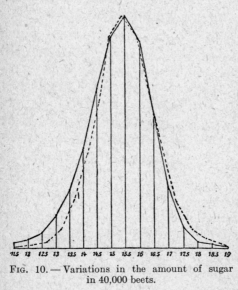

Fig. 10. — Variations in the amount of sugar in 40,000 beets.

4. Fluctuating variations do not lead to a new permanent mean of the race. Mutations cause a new mean to be

formed, around which is grouped a new series of fluctuating variations, forming a frequency curve. (See Fig. 9.)

5. In a fluctuating variation no new unit characters are added. The same characters are merely found in greater or less quantity or number (Fig. 10). Where a mutation occurs, new unit characters are added or old ones lost.

6. Fluctuating variations represent individuals or parts of them. Mutations represent groups of individuals.

In fluctuating variations, the small differences are grouped around what may be called a "center of fluctuation," which is the mean of the frequency curve. When a mutation is formed, a new center of fluctuation is established around a new mean.

Fig. 11. — *Chelidonium majus.*

History of mutation. — The first mutation was recorded in 1590. In the garden of Sprenger, an apothecary of Heidelberg, was found a peculiar form of *Chelidonium majus.* The new form appeared suddenly and without intermediates from a lot of plants which had been cultivated for many years. This mutant had "leaves cut into narrow lobes with almost linear tips, and the petals were also cut up." The new species has been constant since the first, and follows Mendel's law when crossed with *C. majus*, its parent. (See Figs. 11 and 12.)

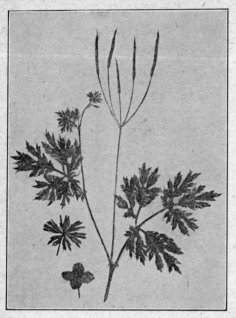

FIG. 12. — *Chelidonium laciniatum*. A flower of it to the left. Below a flower of *C. majus*.

The word "mutation" was first used in 1650 by Dr. Thomas Browne, in his book "Pseudo-doxia Epidemica." Lock quotes from Book VI, Chapter X, "Of the Blackness of Negroes," as follows : —

"We may say that men become black in the same manner that some foxes, squirrels, lions, first turned of this complexion, whereof there are a constant sort in diverse countries; that crows became pyed, all which mutations, however, they began, depend upon durable foundations and such as may continue forever."

History of the appearance of double flowers. — Double

flowers which have persisted for a long time are thought to be mutations from single types. Some of the first recorded appearances of double flowers were described in 1671 by Abraham Munting in a book called, "Waare Oeffeninge der Planten" or "True Exercises with Plants." This large book on garden plants contained a long list of double flowers which

FIG. 13. — *Anemone coronaria*, single-flowered form.

FIG. 14. — *Anemone coronaria*, semi-double-flowered form.

were found growing in gardens at that time. Double flowers of such plants as poppies, liver-leaf (*hepatica*), wallflowers (*cheiranthus*), violets, caltha, althea, colchium, and periwinkle (*vinca*), were described.

Other double forms have since been added. The double marigold (*Chrysanthemum indicum*) came from Japan; double zinnias from Mexico; and double dahlias which were first produced in Belgium in 1814, are examples.

The garden anemone (*Anemone coronaria*) is said to have been first found double in an English nursery in the first half of the last century. One flower with a single broadened stamen was observed by Williamson, owner of the nursery. The seed from this was saved separately and planted the next year. After a few generations of selection of this kind, the double flowers appeared as mutations and bred true to type (Figs. 13–15).

Fig. 15. — *Anemone coronaria*, var. *flore-pleno*. (Full double.)

The origin of the double petunia dates back to the year 1855, when it suddenly arose from ordinary seed in a garden at Lyons. Carrière reported that from this one plant all double races and varieties of petunias have been derived by natural and partly by artificial crosses, and he added that likewise other species were known at that time to produce new double varieties rapidly.

Geoffroy St. Hilaire, about 1825, expressed his belief in saltatory variations as a means of evolution. He thought that evolution does not take place entirely by the slow changes advocated by Lamark. His ideas were theoretical, however, and at that time were not borne out by experimental evidence.

Darwin recognized the appearance of sudden variations of a marked character, such as is seen in the origin of large-crested Polish fowls and short-legged Ancon sheep. He thought that these new and strange forms would be lost soon by intercrossing and, being rare, that they possessed no value. He held that the slow accumulation of minute fluctuating variations was the important factor in evolution.

De Vries' experiment with œnotheras. — De Vries became convinced long ago that Darwin's theory of the origin of species through ac- cumulation of minute changes was not the only means of creating new types. He determined to produce mutations ex- perimentally, if possible. His results in the forma- tion of a new variety of the corn marigold will be described later. After making preliminary ex- periments with some hundred species, de Vries

FIG. 16. — Hugo de Vries.

finally decided upon *Œnothera Lamarkiana* as the most suitable form to use (Figs. 17 and 18). "Only one of my tests met with expectations. This species proved to be in a state of mutation, producing new elementary forms continually, and it soon became the chief member of my experimental garden. It was one of the evening primroses." This *Œ. Lamarkiana* was found to produce a large number of mutants, both when growing wild and under cultivation.

The *Œ. Lamarkiana* plants which became the basis of

Fig. 17. — *Œnothera Lamarkiana* and *Œnothera nanella* in bloom.

future experiments were found growing wild in a field at Hilversum, near Amsterdam, Holland. Little is known of its history except that it is a native of America. It has not been found growing wild in America in recent years, although there seems to be evidence that it was seen and collected in the Southern States in the last century. The near relatives of *Œ. muricata*, which were very common in the sandy regions of Holland, are very stable; de Vries found no appreciable change in them, although he watched them for more than forty years.

Lamark's evening-primrose is grown in Europe as a cultivated plant, used principally for ornamental planting. It seeds abundantly and some of the plants have escaped cultivation. Groups of plants are found growing wild in many places. These wild plants remain in groups rather than being widely scattered, suggesting a definite

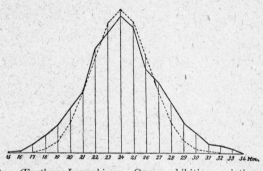

Fig. 18. — *Œnothera Lamarkiana*. Curve exhibiting variations in the length of fruits of 568 plants. The dotted line is that given by Quetelet-Galton Law.

origin for each group. *Œ. Lamarkiana* is described as a "stately plant with a stout stem, attaining often a height of 1.6 meters and more. When not crowded, the main stem is surrounded by a large circle of smaller branches, growing upwards from its base so as often to form a dense bush. These branches in their turn have numerous lateral branches. Most of them are crowded with flowers in summer, which regularly succeed each other, leaving behind them long spikes of young fruits. The flowers are large and of a bright yellow color, attracting immediate attention, even at a distance. They open towards evening, as the name indicates, and are pollinated by bumble-bees and moths. On bright days their duration is confined to one evening, but during cloudy weather they may still be found open on the following morning. Contrary to their congeners, they are dependent on visiting insects for pollination.

" In *Œ. Lamarkiana* no self-fertilization takes place. The stigmas are above the anthers in the bud, and as the style increases in length at the time of the opening of the corolla, they are elevated above the anthers and do not receive the pollen. Ordinarily the flowers remained sterile if not visited by insects or pollinated by myself, although rare instances of self-fertilization were seen."

Œ. Lamarkiana is a biennial, producing rosettes in the first year and stems in the second year. This species was found to be variable in all periods of its life cycle, — in the seedlings, the rosettes, and the stems.

De Vries pursued three methods in obtaining his mutations:—

1. Observations and studies of the plants while growing in the wild state in the fields.

2. Some of the plants were removed from the wild state and placed under cultivation. Many of the plants were self-fertilized and their seed sown under controlled conditions. By this method several mutants were found which were too weak to withstand the competition of field conditions.

3. Repetition of the sowing process for several generations, leading to the production of new forms.

De Vries divided the new types of plants into five groups, classified as follows : —

1. Retrograde varieties with negative attributes, *Œ. lævifolia*, *Œ. brevistylis*, and *Œ. nanella* (Figs. 17 and 19).

Fig. 19. — *Œnothera lata* (left), *Œnothera Lamarkiana* (middle), *Œnothera nanella* (right).

2. Progressive elementary species possessing new characters, and appearing as vigorous as the parent plant, *Œ. gigas* and *Œ. rubrinervis*.

3. Progressive elementary species, which are weaker than the parent species, *Œ. albida* and *Œ. oblonga*.

4. Organically incomplete forms, *Œ. lata* (Fig. 19).

5. Fertile but inconstant species forms, *Œ. scintillans* and *Œ. elliptica*.

The new species and varieties may be described as follows : —

Group I, retrograde varieties, which have lost some of the characters possessed by the parent, *Œ. Lamarkiana* : —

Œ. lævifolia is easily distinguished from its parent, *Œ. Lamarkiana*, by having smooth, bright leaves, without undulations. These leaves are narrower and more slender than in *Lamarkiana* and the flowers of the brighter yellow. This variety was constant from seed, showing no reversion. It is a strong-growing plant and perfectly fertile.

Œ. brevistylis is a short-styled form. The ovary of this plant is abnormally situated and is not conducive to proper fertilization. The ovary is reached by only a few pollen tubes and fertilization must be incomplete. The few seeds that are obtained reproduce this type without reversion to *Lamarkiana*. *Œ. brevistylis* may be distinguished from the other forms before blossoming as the buds are much shorter and thicker than in the other species. The presence of leaves more rounded at the tip also distinguishes this form from others before flowering.

Œ. nanella is a dwarf form, attaining often only one-fourth the height of the other types. The flowers on this dwarf form are as large as upon *Lamarkiana*, which is a striking feature. The size of the leaves is proportionate to the height of the plant, but retain the same form as the parent species. The stems are unbranched and very brittle. *Œ. nanella* is frequently produced as a mutation and is absolutely constant (Figs. 17 and 19).

Group II, progressive elementary species, possessing new characters : —

Œ. gigas is a giant form which is much larger in every respect than its parent, except in height. The stems are much larger ; internodes are shorter and the leaves more numerous than the parent species (*Œ. Lamarkiana*). The flower-buds are large and closely crowded on the spike, and when the flowers open, they make a beautiful appearance (Fig. 20).

Œ. rubrinervis is characterized by the red veins and red streaks on the fruits. This plant is as tall as *Œ. gigas*, but a little more slender. A feature of this type is the brittleness of the leaves and stems, especially in the annual individuals, of which many are found.

Many of these mutants may be recognized before the adult stage has been reached, for example, at about the age of two months. The leaves of *Œ. gigas* are broad, of a deep green, the blade sharply cut off from the stalk, all of the rosettes becoming stout and crowded with leaves. In *Œ. rubrinervis*, on the contrary, the leaves are thin, of a paler green, and with a silvery white surface ; the blades are in the form of an ellipse, acute at the apex, and gradually narrowing into the petiole.

Both of these species are quite constant and do not revert to *Œ. Lamarkiana.* However, other mutants have sprung from these two species, especially from *rubrinervis*, which is produced in greater numbers from *Lamarkiana* than is *gigas*.

F

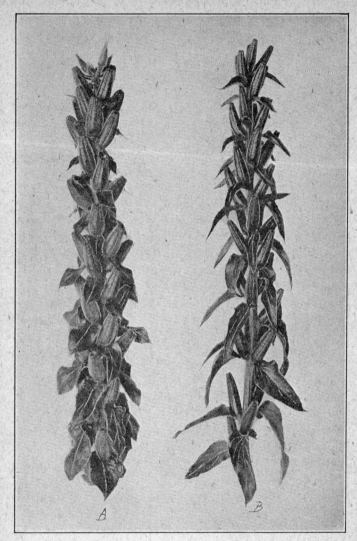

Fig. 20. — *A*, spike with almost ripe fruits of *Œnothera gigas*, a mutant species; *B*, the same of *Œnothera Lamarkiana*, its parent form.

66

Group III, progressive elementary species which make a very weak growth : —

Œ. albida has whitish, narrow leaves, apparently incapable of producing sufficient quantities of organic food, and hence are very weak. These plants are not sufficiently robust to withstand competition in the field and require transplanting into rich soil in pots in order to allow them to live through the first year so that they can produce seed the second year. When these seeds are planted they produce individuals true to type.

Œ. oblonga is a small plant about half the size of *Lamarkiana* and may be grown either as an annual or as a biennial. It is characterized by its narrow leaves, which are fleshy and of a bright green color. Another striking feature of this type is the presence of numerous little capsules covering the axis of the spike after the fading away of the petals. *Œ. oblonga* is very constant if grown from pure seed.

The forms already described are relatively very constant and never revert to the parent form. Contrasted with these constant forms, de Vries found several inconstant types as follows : —

Group IV, organically incomplete types : —

Œ. lata is characterized by the fact that only pistillate flowers are formed. The anthers seem to be robust, but they are dry, wrinkled, and nearly devoid of contents. It is a low plant with very dense and luxuriant, but brittle, foliage. It has bright yellow flowers which open only partially and remain wrinkled throughout the flowering time. *Œ. lata* may be recognized by its seedlings, which have leaves of a nearly orbicular shape and are very

sharply set off against the stalk. The mature plant
has broad sinuate leaves with rounded tips, which are
often crowded together on the summits of the stems and
branches to form rosettes. *Œ. lata* may be considered
a true mutation, and when crossed with *Œ. Lamarkiana*,
the progeny of the second generation segregates into
mendelian proportions, *lata* being recessive (Fig. 19).

Group V, perfectly fertile but inconstant species :—

Œ. scintillans is characterized by the production of
deep green leaves with smooth, shiny surfaces, "glisten-
ing in the sunshine." The plants are smaller and less
branched than the parental type. *Œ. scintillans* is a
very inconstant form ; from the seeds which are produced
in great numbers, there results not only *scintillans*, but
Lamarkiana, *oblonga*, *lata*, and *nanella*, with a predomi-
nance of the parental *Lamarkiana*. In regard to its instability, de Vries says, "The instability seems to be a
constant quality, although the words themselves are at
first sight contradictory. I mean to convey the conception that the degree of instability remains unchanged
during the successive generations."

Œ. elliptica is a very rare form both in the wild state
and in cultivation. It is characterized by having narrow
elliptical leaves and elliptical petals.

ANALYTICAL TABLE OF SEEDLINGS (After de Vries)

I. Leaves stalked.
    A. Leaves of the same breadth or
        broader.[1]
        1. Of the same breadth and shape,
            not to be distinguished as
            seedlings.

[1] " (than in Lamarkiana) " as also in the other analytical tables.

a.	1. *Œ. Lamarkiana.*
b.	2. *Œ. brevistylis.*
c.	3. *Œ. leptocarpa.*
2. Broader, pointed, with many crumples.	4. *Œ. gigas.*
3. Broader, rounded at the tip with very deep crumples, edge incurved.	
a.	5. *Œ. lata.*
b.	6. *Œ. semilata.*

B. Leaves narrower.
   1. Broadest in the middle.
      a. Very long with long stalks, with narrow veins, almost smooth.   7. *Œ. elliptica.*
      b. Small with broad leaf-stalk and broad, principal veins, very smooth, shiny dark green.   8. *Œ. scintillans.*
   2. Of equal breadth over the greater part of their length.
      a. Green.
         a. 1. Only slightly narrower, smooth without, or almost without crumples.   9. *Œ. lævifolia.*
         a. 2. Very narrow with broad leaf-stalks and broad veins which often are reddish; wrinkled.   10. *Œ. oblonga.*
      b. Whitish.
         b. 1. Crumples many, pointed, narrowing off into the stalk.   11. *Œ. albida.*
         b. 2. Crumples few, narrowing off into the stalk, wavy, brittle, veins reddish.   12. *Œ. rubrinervis.*

Fig. 21. — The cage, in Professor de Vries' Experiment Garden, showing corn and various species of *Œnothera*. Botanical Gardens, Amsterdam.

     b. 3. C r u m p l e s   f e w,
        scarcely narrowing
        into   the   stalk,
        almost grasslike.   13. *Œ. sublinearis.*

II. Leaves sessile, short and broad,
     almost heart-shaped, crumpled.   14. *Œ. nanella.*

How the mutants were produced in the garden. — Most of the types previously described were found growing wild near their parent species, *Œ. Lamarkiana.*

De Vries wished to determine whether these mutations could be produced from seed of *Œ. Lamarkiana* planted in the garden (Fig. 21). Four series of experiments were performed, lasting through five to nine generations in which thousands of individuals were grown and studied. A description is here given of one of these experiments.[1] The others were very similar. The pedigree culture began in 1886, when seed was planted in the garden from nine plants found growing wild. These nine plants constituted the first generation. The second generation flowered in 1889. This generation consisted of fifteen thousand seedlings of which ten were distinct mutations — five *lata* and five *nanella.* There were no intermediates.

The third generation of ten thousand plants produced for the first time in pedigree cultures a plant of *Œ. rubrinervis,* along with three plants of *Œ. lata* and three of *Œ. nanella.*

The fourth generation of fourteen thousand plants yielded a higher percentage of mutants. These were as follows: *oblonga* 176; *lata* 73; *nanella* 60; *albida* 15; *rubrinervis* 8; *scintillans* 1; and *gigas* 1.

[1] De Vries, "Species and Variation, their Origin by Mutation," pp. 549–575.

At this stage of the experiment, de Vries became expert in detecting variations at an early period. This accounts in part for the large number of mutants found in the fourth generation. By being able to pick out the mutating forms at an early age, a much larger number of the diverging types could be obtained in proportion to the total number of individuals.

De Vries gives the following table which represents graphically the results from eight generations of a mutating strain of *Œ. Lamarkiana*: —

MUTATING STRAINS OF Œ. LAMARKIANA

GENERA-TIONS	GIGAS	ALBIDA	OB-LONGA	RUBRI-NERVIS	LAMARK-IANA	NA-NELLA	LATA	SCINTIL-LANS
I								
II					15000	5	5	
III				1	10000	3	3	
IV	1	15	176	8	14000	60	73	1
V		25	136	20	8000	49	112	6
VI		11	29	3	1800	9	5	1
VII			9		3000	11		
VIII		5	1		1700	21	1	

De Vries' laws of mutability of the evening-primroses. — de Vries deduced certain laws from the mutations in these Œnotheras. "Obviously," he says, "they apply not only to our evening-primroses, but may be expected to be of general validity."

These laws are as follows: —

1. New elementary species appear suddenly, without intermediate steps.

The ordinary conception had been that new types of plants had been produced by the slow and gradual piling up of small fluctuating variations. The experience with the primroses shows that new types are formed in much less time than it would take by the accumulation of small variations. It is remarkable that so many different new types of forms should have been produced from the same parent and with no intermediates appearing. When *Œ. lata*, which is a pistillate form, was crossed with *Œ. Lamarkiana*, the progeny of the second generation segregated in mendelian proportion to the pure types of the parents, with no intermediates. This same absence of intermediacy is found when the progeny of the inconstant forms return each year to the parent species, *Lamarkiana*.

2. New forms spring laterally from the main stem.

This conception of the origin of new forms differs markedly from the Darwinian idea which assumes that species are slowly converted into others in the same direction and in the same degree.

In such plants as draba or helianthemum, from which mutations have been known to arise, no center or "main stem" of mutation would have been known if it had not been seen to occur in pedigree-cultures. For instance, if *gigas*, *rubrinervis*, and *Lamarkiana* had been found growing side by side in equal numbers in the wild state, it would have been impossible to tell which type had been the center of fluctuation. Many years of crossing, together with some vicinism which would probably have followed, would have been necessary to determine this. De Vries says, "According to the current belief the conversion of a group of plants growing in any locality and flowering simultaneously would be restricted to one type. In my own experiments several new species arose from the parental form at once, giving a wide range of new forms at the same time and under same conditions."

3. New elementary species attain their full constancy at once.

"Constancy is not the result of selection or of improvement. It is a quality of its own. It can neither be constrained by selection, if it is absent from the beginning, nor does it need any natural or artificial aid if it is present."

No atavism was exhibited by the primrose mutations with the exceptions of *Œ. scintillans* and *Œ. elliptica*. These latter types reproduce themselves only in part in the offspring. De Vries says that the instability in these types seems to be as permanent a quality as the stability of the other forms.

4. Some of the new strains are evidently elementary species, while others are to be considered as retrograde varieties.

Such new forms as *Œ. gigas, rubrinervis, oblonga*, and *albida* may be called new elementary species. They are not differentiated from *Lamarkiana* by one or two main features, but they differ from it in nearly all organs, and hence may be considered new elementary species. The differences exist, not only in the foliage where they are most manifest, but in the stems, flowers, seeds, and indeed, in many instances, to the minutest cell structure.

Œ. lævifolia, Œ. brevistylis, and *Œ. nanella*, on the other hand, may be considered as retrograde varieties. They seem to differ from the parental form in but one character; *lævifolia* is characterized by the loss of the crinkling of the leaves; *brevistylis*, by the partial loss of the pistil; and *nanella*, by the loss of stature.

5. The new species are produced in a large number of individuals.

It will be remembered that there were produced a large number of similar mutants in the same year, and also that the same mutations were produced in successive generations.

There is obviously some cause for the production of these mutations. Whatever the exciting cause may be, the different mutants are not affected in the same way. *Oblonga*, *nanella*, and *lata* are frequently produced, while *gigas*, *rubrinervis*, and *scintillans* are more rare. It has been found through later studies by Gates, Davis, Shull, and others that some of the types formerly thought by de Vries and others to be mutations are hybrids.

It was found also that when the mutants were crossed together, types were found in the progeny which were the same as produced by *Œ. Lamarkiana* itself. For example, *Œ. rubrinervis* was observed by de Vries to arise in the hybrid progeny of *Œ. lata × nanella; Œ. lata × brevistylis; Œ. nanella × brevistylis;* and *Œ. scintillans × nanella*.

In nature, repeated mutations are probably of far more importance than isolated ones. The competition of plants is so great that the chances of the survival of one divergent individual are much less than as if these mutants were repeatedly produced in considerable quantity.

6. Mutability is distinct from fluctuating variability.

The foregoing evidence points to the fact that new

forms are produced from quick sudden leaps. The new type is formed regardless of fluctuating variability, but the new form becomes a center of fluctuating variability similar to that around the parental form.

7. The mutations take place in nearly all directions.

De Vries says, "Some of my new types are stouter and others weaker than their parents, as shown by *gigas* and *albida*. Some have broader leaves and some narrower (*lata* and *oblonga*). Some have larger flowers (*gigas*) or deeper yellow ones (*rubrinervis*) or smaller blossoms (*scintillans*) or of a paler hue (*albida*). In some the capsules are longer (*rubrinervis*) or thicker (*gigas*) or more rounded (*lata*) or small (*oblonga*) or nearly destitute of seeds (*brevistylis*). The unevenness of the surface of the leaves may increase as in *lata* or decrease as in *lævifolia*. The tendency to become annual prevails in *rubrinervis*, but *gigas* tends to become biennial. Some are rich in pollen, while *scintillans* is poor. Some have large seeds, others small. *Lata* has become pistillate, while *brevistylis* has nearly lost the faculty to produce seeds. Some undescribed forms were quite sterile, and some I observed which produced no flowers at all."

Examples of mutations. Shirley poppy. — Lock cites [1] the Shirley poppy as a mutation from the wild field poppy (*Papaver Rhœas*) so common in England. It was first noticed in 1880 by the Rev. W. Wilks, Vicar of Shirley, near Croydon, England, in a patch of the wild forms growing in a waste corner of his garden. There suddenly appeared a solitary flower showing a very narrow border

[1] "Recent Progress in the Study of Variation, Heredity, and Evolution," p. 133.

of white. The seeds from this plant were saved and sown the next year. From this progeny of two hundred plants, four or five individuals appeared which showed the same diverging characteristics.

"From these, by further horticultural processes, the strain of Shirley poppies originated." Lock remarks, in passing, that if the original plant had been self-pollinated, a much larger proportion of the new type might have been expected to appear in the next generation.

Cupid sweet pea. — Another example of a mutation is found in the case of the Cupid sweet pea (Fig. 22). Until about fifteen years ago the only sweet peas known were the tall, climbing sorts, which grew to a height of three to six feet, depending on the richness of the soil. At this time, there was found in the seed trial grounds of Morse & Company of California, a small dwarf sweet pea plant only about six or eight inches high. This was growing in a row of the Emily Henderson variety, one of the ordinary tall sorts from which it evidently sprang. Seed of this dwarf plant was saved and grown and it was found to reproduce plants of the same dwarf character. The variety was designated "The Cupid," under which name it was introduced to the seed trade and distributed over the world. The Cupid differed from other sweet peas not only in height, but in its closely set leaves and general habit of growth. Indeed, it is as distinct from other sweet peas as are distinct species of plants in nature.

It has been found that this dwarf Cupid sweet pea mendelized with the tall ordinary sorts and appears as recessive.

Fig. 22. — Cupid sweet peas. (Photo by Beal.)

Frequency of occurrence of mutations. — In general, it may be said that the occurrence of mutations is rare.[1]

In order to obtain a clear understanding of this subject, it may be divided into four sections : —

1. Spontaneous occurrence of new varieties in the wild state.

2. Spontaneous occurrence of new species in the wild state.

3. Spontaneous occurrence of new varieties under cultivation.

4. Spontaneous occurrence of new species under cultivation.

The term "variety" as here used carries the meaning given by de Vries, — that of a group of plants differing from others in one systematic character.

Spontaneous occurrence of new varieties in the wild state.[2] — New varieties of plants are seen to occur rather rarely in the wild state. This may be due to two causes : (1) A lack of critical examination of wild plants for such spontaneous mutation ; and (2) if these mutations do occur, they are likely to meet premature death because of the severe competition to which all wild forms are subjected.

As our wild plants are being studied more critically, it is being found that they do produce a much larger number of new varieties than was formerly supposed.

In the case of the peloric toad-flax, which has been studied carefully by de Vries, the mutations are so numer-

[1] De Vries, p. 191.
[2] De Vries, "Species and Varieties, their Origin by Mutation," chapter on the Origin of Wild Species and Varieties, p. 576.

ous that they seem to be quite regular. The peloric type is known to have originated from the ordinary type at different times and in different countries, under more or less divergent conditions.

White varieties of many species of bluebells, gentians, and nearly all of the berry-bearing species in the large heather family are quite common. The same is true of the white flowers of *Brunella vulgaris, Ononis repens*, and *Thymus vulgaris.*

Spontaneous occurrence of new elementary species in the wild state. — It will be remembered that new elementary species of the *Œnothera* were found to occur in the wild state before any attempt was made to study them under cultivation. It is difficult to say how frequently these mutations occurred in the wild because unquestionably most of them were destroyed prematurely, from the competition of other plants.

The occurrence of new elementary species in the wild state seems to be much more rare than the occurrence of new varieties. This is natural, for, of course, elementary species present greater differences from the parental forms than do varieties.

The spontaneous origin of the new elementary species, *Capsella Heegeri*, in 1897, has never been observed to have been repeated since that time.[1] This new form of shepherd's purse originated in the market-place near Landau, in Germany.

Spontaneous occurrence of new elementary species and varieties under cultivation. — Whenever new forms occur spontaneously under cultivation, it should first be deter-

[1] De Vries, " Species and Varieties, their Origin by Mutation," p. 582.

mined whether they are the product of pure lines or not. If they come from pure lines, in all probability they are mutations; if not, the new forms may be a result of hybridization, which may have taken place immediately preceding the appearance of the anomaly or at a considerable time previous to its appearance.

New varieties and elementary species are seen to occur more often under cultivation for three reasons:—

1. When new forms do occur, they are more likely to be seen.

2. Because of the relative lack of competition and hence a better opportunity for preservation.

3. The transfer of plants from the wild to the cultivated state has a tendency to break the type and cause spontaneous new forms to appear. For this reason, we may expect a more frequent occurrence of mutations under cultivation.

It is commonly observed among gardeners that so-called "sports" are of very common occurrence. Some of these are monstrosities which are not inherited, but many of them are mutations and are inherited

FIG. 23.— *A, B, Linaria vulgaris;* C, D, peloric flowers.

true to type. The occurrence of double-flowered types as mutations is common.

G

Fig. 24. — *Linaria vulgaris peloria.* A richly branched stem of a plant
of the second generation. Raised in 1898 from seed of the first
generation of 1897, and photographed in August, 1900. All flowers
are peloric.

Many mutations among cultivated plants are the result
of continued selection for a period of years. This selection
assists in breaking the type and thus permits the mutation
to occur, and after the mutation has appeared, constant
selection is not necessary to keep the new variety pure.

It has been stated that the peloric type of toad-flax
is of frequent occurrence in the wild state (Figs. 23 and
24). De Vries found its appearance even more common
under cultivation than when growing wild. He planted
the seed of two toad-flax plants, one of which contained
a single peloric flower. Eighteen hundred plants were
obtained, of which seventeen, or nearly one per cent,
were wholly peloric.

The snapdragon (*Antirrhinum majus*) is also known to
produce peloric flowers from time to time as mutations
(Fig. 25). Pelorics occur sometimes in *Linaria dalmatica*
and other species of *Linaria;* in fox-glove (*Digitalis pur-*

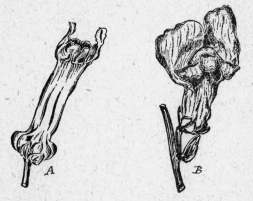

Fig. 25. — *Antirrhinum majus: A,* peloric flower from the middle of an
    otherwise normal raceme ; *B,* normal flower of the same spike.

purea), and in gloxinia. Many other instances of peloric flowers are on record, which indicates that pelorism as a mutation is frequent.

Experimental study of the origin of mutations. — De Vries has conducted a series of experiments for the purpose of observing the origin of mutations, if any should occur. One of the plants chosen for these studies was the peloric toad-flax (*Linaria vulgaris peloria*). The most accurate laboratory methods were applied. The plants were carefully isolated in his garden.

The reason for this choice of the peloric toad-flax lay in the fact that this form is known to have originated from the ordinary type at different times and in different countries under more or less divergent conditions. The ordinary toad-flax bears exceedingly unsymmetrical flowers. (See Fig. 23, *A*.) But symmetrical flowers are not uncommon in such plants as the toad-flax and snapdragon, which have similar types of flowers. In these experiments, de Vries sought to observe the birth of this anomaly in his pedigree cultures.

The experiments were begun in 1886 with normal plants; a few peloric flowers were produced, however, which is not an uncommon occurrence among plants of this genus. Throughout the next few generations, nothing more than the normal number of peloric flowers were produced.

In the third generation, among the many thousands of flowers there occurred one having five spurs. This was inbred by hand and produced a considerable quantity of seed. All other seed was discarded and this plant now became the parent of all future plants.

The next (fourth) generation contained about twenty plants having only one peloric flower among them. The plant bearing this flower, and one other plant, were saved and all others discarded. These two were bred together and produced a considerable quantity of seed.

In the next year (1894) fifty plants were in flower. Eleven of these were found to bear the normal number of peloric flowers. In addition to these eleven, there was found one plant which bore *peloric flowers only*. This was a mutation. Its appearance had been observed. It was found to breed true in future generations.

In regard to the production of this mutation, de Vries says, "Here we have the first experimental mutation of a normal into a peloric race. The facts were clear and simple : First, the ancestry was known for over a period of four generations. This ancestry was quite constant as to the peloric peculiarity remaining true to the wild type as it occurs everywhere in any country and showing in no respect any tendency to the production of a new variety.

"Second, the mutation took place at once. It was a sudden leap from the normal plants with very rare peloric flowers to a type exclusively peloric. The parents themselves had borne thousands of flowers during two summers, and these were inspected nearly every day in the hope of finding some peloric and of saving their seed separately. Only one such flower was seen. There was no visible preparation for this sudden leap.

"This leap, on the other hand, was full and complete. No reminiscence of the former condition remained. Not a single flower on the mutated plant reverted to the previous type. The whole plant departed absolutely from the old type of its progenitors."

What is true of the toad-flax is also true of the snap-dragon and other unsymmetrical flowers — the production of peloric flowers by mutation.

FIG. 26. — *Chrysanthemum segetum plenum.* One of the six inflorescences which in 1899 first exhibited true "doubling." The figure represents the parent plant of the "double" variety.

Experiments in the production of double flowers (Figs. 26–29). — De Vries performed a series of experiments with the corn marigold (*Chrysanthemum segetum*) with the object of the production of double flowers. This plant has never been known to produce double flowers. The cultivated variety (*grandiflorum*) was found to be more stable and was used as a basis of the experiments. This cultivated

form has on the average twenty-one petals on each flower.
In the population of the next generation there appeared
one plant having twenty-one petals, but on one of its
secondary heads twenty-two petals were found. This
had never been observed before. This plant was the

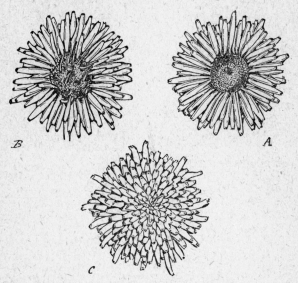

FIG. 27. — *Chrysanthemum inodorum plenissimum:* A, inflorescence with
   central disk of tube florets (*fertile*); B, with scattered tongue florets
   in the disk (half *fertile*); C, highest degree of " doubling " (*sterile*).

beginning of what developed later into the desired mutation.

This plant produced the next year (1897) plants having
thirty-four rays to the head. Next year (1898) this was
increased to forty-eight; next year (1899) to sixty-six.

During this time the means of the different generations were gradually increasing. So far there was observed a

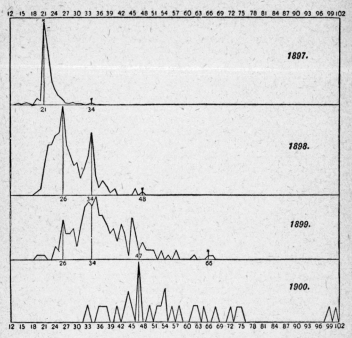

FIG. 28. — Ancestral generations of *Chrysanthemum segetum plenum.* Curves of the number of rays in the terminal inflorescence in the several individuals of the generations of 1897–1900.

rapid increase in number of petals, but no indication of doubling.

But this character soon appeared; three secondary heads on one plant in the fall of 1899 showed a few ray-florets scattered over the disk. An indication of the mutation was now seen.

The next year, 1900, the highest number of rays arose to one hundred, and reached two hundred in 1901. These

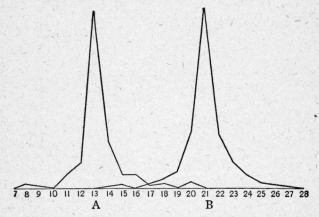

Fig. 29. — *A*, *Chrysanthemum segetum*; *B*, *Chrysanthemum segetum grandiflorum* (after purification). Curves of the races after isolation : *A*, curve of the 13-rayed race in 1894; *B*, curve of the 21-rayed race in 1897. The ordinates give the number of individuals with like number of ray-florets in the primary inflorescences of the individual plants. The number of ray-florets themselves is given below the abscissa.

heads were completely double and the mutation had appeared, not quite as suddenly, perhaps, as with toadflax, but nevertheless as surely. The new race was permanent and constant.

Complete doubleness caused sterility, so that the race had to be perpetuated from slightly inferior stock.

Here, again, was the origin of a new mutation produced in control cultures by careful laboratory methods.

What do new characters come from? — If mutations are the result of the appearance of new characters or the loss of old ones, where do these new characters come from and what causes the loss of existing ones? The answer to this question would give us the keynote to the whole situation. If breeders possessed definite knowledge of the cause of mutations, they would then have within their control a kind of variation which could be made of tremendous economic importance. The causes are evidently from an internal origin. In all probability, many so-called mutations are due to hybrid origin and in the strictest sense are not mutations at all, even though they may be bred true. Much experimental evidence is necessary to determine with certainty their cause and control.

Can mutations be produced artificially? — Must breeders passively wait for mutations to arise, or may they be produced artificially? Many experiments are now being conducted to test this. So far, experiments do not seem to have led to any definite conclusion.

Economic significance of mutations. — Agricultural and horticultural literature is full of accounts of the sudden origin, or at least the sudden finding, of exceptionally good plants which, when propagated, became the progenitors of new and valued races. So great is their number that not even an attempt to catalogue them can be made here.

The pages of "Evolution of our Native Fruits" (Bailey) are filled with examples of mutation. The experience of plant-breeders and nurserymen show the origin of many varieties in this way.

Many observing growers of cereals and other plants

have originated varieties by finding occasionally unusually good plants and propagating from them. These exceptional plants seem to bear no relationship to the others among which they are growing. Hybrid origin may account for certain of them and mutations for the others. Many of our well-known races of wheat have originated in this way. The Fultz wheat, which is a very popular and excellent race grown extensively in the Eastern States, was found in 1862 in a field of Lancaster Red by Mr. Abraham Fultz of Pennsylvania. Some beautiful heads of smoother wheat attracted his attention and they were saved and the seeds planted by themselves. These produced the wheat later named the Fultz. The Tappahannock wheat, which, in 1872, was considered to be a valuable race, was found in 1854 by a Mr. Boughton, of Essex County, Virginia. The account of its discovery as given in the Report of the Department of Agriculture for 1872 is as follows: "He noticed in his field a bunch of wheat of such growth as to attract his attention. . . . At harvest he found it to be a white wheat, at least two weeks earlier than the surrounding red wheat." Gold Coin Wheat, a seedling sport, differing from the hybrid Mediterranean in being bald and white, was found by Ira W. Green, of New York, in a field of that race and improved by selection. In the next five years the type was fixed and increased in yield about ten per cent. The American races, Wheatland Red, Pride Butte, and the well-known English races, Hopetown and Cavalier, were other accidental seedling races.

CHAPTER VI

THE PHILOSOPHY OF THE CROSSING OF PLANTS, CONSIDERED IN REFERENCE TO THEIR IMPROVEMENT UNDER CULTIVATION

It is now understood that the specific forms or groups of plants have been determined largely by the survival of the fittest in a long and severe struggle for existence. The proof that this struggle everywhere exists becomes evident on a moment's reflection. We know that all organisms are eminently variable. In fact, no two plants or animals in the world are exactly alike. We also know that a very few of the whole number of seeds which are produced in any area ever grow into plants. If all the seeds produced by the elms upon Boston Common in any fruitful year were to grow into trees, the city would become a forest as a result. If all the seeds of the rarest orchids in our woods were to grow, in a few generations of plants even our farms would be overrun. If all the rabbits which are born were to reach old age, and all their offspring were to do the same, in less than ten years every vestige of herbage would be swept from the country, and our farms would become barren.

The struggle for life. — There is, then, a wonderful
92

latent potency in these species; but the same may be said of every species of plant and animal, even of man himself. If one species of plant would overrun and usurp the land, if it increased to the fullest extent of its possibilities, what would be the result if each of the two thousand and sixty-one plants known to inhabit Middlesex County were to do the same? And then fancy the result if each of the animals from rabbits and mice to frogs and leeches were to increase without check! The plagues of Egypt would be insignificant in the comparison!

Survival of the most fit. — The fact is, the world is not big enough to hold the possible first offspring of the plants and animals at this moment living upon it. Struggle for existence, then, is inevitable, and it must be severe. It follows as a necessity that those seeds grow or those plants live which are the best fitted to grow and live, or which are fortunate enough to find a congenial foothold. It would never appear, at first thought, that much depends on the accident of falling into a congenial place, or one unoccupied by other plants or animals; but, inasmuch as scores of plants are contending for every unoccupied place, it follows that everywhere only the fittest can germinate or grow. In the greater number of cases, plants grow in a certain place because they are better fitted to grow there, to hold their own, than any other plants are; and the instances are rare in which a plant is so fortunate as to find an unoccupied place. We are likely to think that plants chance to grow where we find them, but the chance is determined by law, and, therefore, is not chance.

Flexibility as an aid to survival. — Much of the capability of a plant to persist under all this struggle depends, therefore, upon how much it varies; for the more it varies, the more likely it is to find places of least struggle. It grows under various conditions, in the sun and shade, in sand and clay, by the sea-shore or upon the hills, in the humidity of the forest, or the aridity of the plain. In some directions it very likely finds less struggle than in others, and in these directions it may expand itself, multiply, and gradually die out in other directions; so it happens that it tends to take on new forms or to undergo an evolution. In the meantime, all the intermediate forms, which are at best only indifferently adapted to their conditions, tend to disappear. In other words, gaps appear that we call "missing links." The weak links break and fall away, and what was once a chain becomes a series of rings. So the "missing links" are amongst the best proofs of evolution.

Causes of variability. — The question now arises as to the cause of these numerous variations in animals and plants. Why are no two individuals in nature exactly alike? The question is exceedingly difficult to answer. It was once said that plants vary because it is their nature to vary; that variation is a necessary function, as much as growth or fructification. This really removes the question beyond the reach of philosophy; and direct observation leads us to think that some variation, at least, is due to external circumstances. We are now looking for the cause of variation as a part of the scheme of evolution; and we are wondering whether the varied surroundings, or, as Darwin puts it, "changed conditions of life," may not actually induce variability. This conclusion would seem to follow from the fact of the severe and universal struggle in nature whereby plants are constantly forced into new and strange conditions. But there is undoubtedly much variation which has sprung from more remote causes, one of which it is our purpose to discuss here.

In the lowest plants and animals — which are merely single cells — the species multiplies by means of simple division or budding. One individual, of itself, becomes two, and the two are therefore recasts of the one. But, as organisms multiplied and conditions became more complex, that is, as struggle increased, there came a differentiation in the parts of the individual, so that one cell or one cluster of cells performed one labor and other cells performed other labor; and this tendency resulted in the development of organs. Simple division, therefore, might no longer reproduce the whole complex individual; and, as all organs are necessary to the existence of life, the organism may die if it is divided.

Origin and function of sex. — Along with this specialization came the differentiation into sex; and sex clearly has two offices: to hand over the complex organization of the parent to the offspring and also to unite the essential characters or tendencies of two beings into one. The second office is manifestly the greater, for, as it unites two organisms into one, it insures that the offspring is somewhat unlike either parent, and is therefore better fitted to seize upon any place or condition new to its kind. And as the generations increase, the tendency to variation in the offspring may be constantly greater because of the impressions of the greater number of ancestors transmitted to it. We have said that this office of sex to induce variation is more important than the mere fact of reproduction of a complex organization; for it must be borne in mind that the complexity of organization is itself a variation and adaptation made necessary by the increasing struggle for existence.

Fig. 30. — Extreme variability in the shape of the leaves of hybrid poppies. Second generation from a cross between the Bride variety of the Opium poppy and the Oriental poppy.

If, therefore, the philosophy of sex is to promote variation by the union of different individuals, it must follow that the greatest variation must come from parents considerably unlike each other in their minor characters (Fig. 30). Thus it comes that in-breeding tends to weaken a type and cross-breeding tends to strengthen it. At this point we meet that particular subject that we wish to discuss.

This preliminary discussion has been introduced because we can understand crossing only as we make it a part of the general philosophy of nature. There are the vaguest notions concerning the possibilities of crossing, some of which may be corrected by presenting the subject in its relations to the general aspects of the vegetable world.

Effects of crossing on the species. — We are now prepared to understand that crossing is good for the species, because it constantly revitalizes offspring with the strongest traits of the parents, and ever presents new combinations that enable the individuals to stand a better chance of securing a place in the polity of nature. The further discussions of the subject are such as have to do with the extent to which crossing is possible and advisable, and the general results of the operation.

The limits of crossing. — If crossing is good for the species, which philosophy and direct experiment abundantly show, it is necessary at once to find out to what extent it can be carried. Does the good increase in proportion as the cross becomes more violent or as the parents are more and more unlike? Or do we soon find a limit beyond which it is not profitable or even possible to go? If great variability is good for the species in the struggle for existence, and if crossing induces variability because of the union of unlike individuals, it would seem to follow that the more unlike the parents, the greater will be the variation in offspring and the more the type will prosper; and, carrying this thought to its logical conclusion, we shall expect to find that the most closely related plants would constantly tend to refuse to cross, because the offspring of them would be little variable

H

and, therefore, little adapted to struggle for existence; while the most widely separated plants would constantly tend to cross more and more, because their offspring would present the greatest possible degree of differences.

Swamping effects of inter-crossing. — Now, essentially this reason has been advanced to combat the evolution of plants and animals by means of natural selection; and this proposition that inter-mixing must constantly tend to obliterate all differences between plants and to prevent the establishment of well-marked types, has been called the "swamping effects of inter-crossing." It is exceedingly important that we consider this question, for it really lies at the foundation of the improvement of cultivated plants by means of crossing, as well as the persistence and evolution of varieties and species under wholly natural conditions.

What determines the limits of crossing? — We find, however, that distinct species, as a rule, refuse to cross; and the first question which naturally arises is, what is the immediate cause of the refusal of plants to cross? How does this refusal express itself? It comes about in many ways. The commonest cause is the positive refusal of a plant to allow its ovule to be impregnated by the pollen of another plant. The pollen will not "take." For instance, if we apply the pollen of a Hubbard squash to the flower of a common field pumpkin, there will be no result, — the fruit will not form. The same is true of the pear and the apple, the oat and the wheat, and most very unlike species. Or the refusal may come in the sterility of the cross or hybrid: the pollen may "take" and seeds may be formed and the seeds may grow, but the plants they produce may be wholly barren, sometimes even refusing to produce flowers as well as seeds, as in the instance of some hybrids between the Wild Goose plum and the peach. Sometimes the refusal to cross is due to some difference in the time of blooming or some incompatibility in the structure of the flowers. But it is enough for our purpose to know that there are certain characters in widely dissimilar plants which prevent inter-crossing, and that these characters are just as closely and just as much influenced by change of environment and natural selection as are size, color, reproductiveness, and other characters.

The limits of crossing tend to preserve the identity of species. — Here, then, is the sufficient answer to the proposition that inter-crossing must swamp all natural selection, and also the explanation of the varying and often restricted limits within which crossing is possible. That is, the checks to crossing have been developed through the principle of universal variability and natural selection, as has been shown by Darwin and Wallace. Plants vary in their reproductive organs and powers, as they do in other directions; and when such a variation is useful it is perpetuated, and when hurtful it is lost. Suppose that a certain well-marked individual of a species should find an unusually good place in nature, and it should multiply rapidly. Crosses would be made between its own offspring and perhaps between those offspring and itself in succeeding years; and it is fair to suppose that some of the crosses would be particularly well adapted to the conditions in which the parents grew, and these would constantly tend to perpetuate themselves, while less adaptive forms would tend similarly to disappear. Now the same thing would take place if this individual or its adaptive offspring were to cross with the main stock of the parent species; for all the offspring of such a cross which is intermediate in character and therefore less adapted to the new conditions would tend to disappear, and the two types would, as a result, become more and more fixed and the tendency to cross would constantly decrease.

The refusal to cross, the result of natural selection. — The refusal to cross, therefore, becomes a positive character of separation, and the "missing links" that result from crossing are no more or no less inexplicable than the "missing links" due to simple selection; or, to state the case more accurately, natural selection weeds out the tendency to promiscuous crossing, when it is hurtful, in the same way that it weeds out any other injurious tendency. It makes no difference in what way this tendency expresses itself, whether in some constitutional refusal to cross, — if such exists, — or infertility of offspring, or in different times of blooming: all equally come under the power of natural selection. We are likely to look upon infertility as the absence of a character, a sort of negative feature which is somehow not the legitimate field of natural selection; but such is not the case. We are perhaps led the more to this feeling because the word infertility is itself negative, and because we associate full productiveness with the positive attributes of plants. But loss of productiveness is surely no more a subject of wonder than loss of color or size, if there is some corresponding gain to be accomplished. In fact, we see, in numerous plants which propagate usually by means of runners and suckers, a very low degree of productiveness, that is, infertility.

For the production of useful hybrids, do not have the parents too diverse. — Now, if this reasoning is sound, it leads us to conclusions quite the reverse of those held by the advocates of the swamping effects of inter-crossing, and these conclusions are of the most vital importance to every man who tills the soil. The logical result is simply this: the best results of crossing are obtained, as a rule, when the cross is made between different individuals of the same variety, or at farthest, between different individuals of the same species. In other words, crosses between species are very rarely useful in nature, and it follows that the more unlike the species, the less useful will be the hybrids. This is counter to the notions of most horticulturists, and, if true, must entirely overthrow our common thinking upon this subject. But we shall be able to show that observation and experiment lead to the same conclusion to which our philosophy has brought us.

Function of the cross. — At this point, we must ask ourselves what we mean by "best results." This phrase may be taken to refer to those plants that are best fitted to survive in the struggle for existence, those that are most vigorous or most productive or most hardy, or that possess any well-marked character or characters which distinguish them in virility from their fellows. We commonly associate the term more particularly with marked vigor and productiveness; these are the characters most useful in nature and also in cultivation, the

ones which we oftenest desire to obtain. Another type
of variation that we constantly covet is something
that we call a new character, which will lead to the
production of a new cultural variety, and we are always
looking to this as the legitimate result of crossing. We
have forgotten — if, indeed, we ever knew — that the
commoner, all-pervading, more important function of the
cross is to introduce some new feature or power into the
offspring, to improve or to perpetuate an existing variety,
rather than to create a new one. Or, if a new one is
created, it comes from the gradual passing of one into
another, an inferior variety into a good one, a good one
into a superlative one. So nature usually employs crossing
in a process of slow or gradual improvement, one step
leading to another, and not in any bold or sudden creation
of new forms. And there is evidence to show that something akin to this must be done to secure the best and
most permanent results under cultivation.

Rarity of natural hybrids. — Think of the great rarity
of hybrids or pronounced crosses in nature. No doubt
all the authentic cases on record could be entered into
one or two volumes, but a list of all the individual plants
of the world could not be compressed into ten thousand
volumes. There are a few genera, in which the species
are not well defined, or in which some character of inflorescence favors promiscuous crossing, in which hybrids
are conspicuous; but even here the number of individual
hybrids is very small in comparison to the whole number
of individuals. That is, the hybrids are rare, while the
parents may be common. This is well illustrated even
in the willows and the oaks, in which, perhaps, hybrids

are better known than in any other American plants. The great genus Carex, or sedge, which occurs in great numbers and many species in almost every locality in the United States, and in which the species are particularly adapted to inter-crossing by the character of their inflorescence, furnishes but few undoubted hybrids. Among one hundred and eighty-five species and prominent varieties inhabiting the Northeastern States, there are only about a score of hybrids recorded, and all of them are rare or local, some of them having been collected but once. Species of Carex of remarkable similarity may grow side by side for years, even inter-tangled in the same clump, and yet produce no hybrid. These examples show that nature avoids hybridization, a conclusion at which we have already arrived from philosophical considerations. And we have reason to infer the same conclusion from the fact that flowers of different species are so constructed as not to invite inter-crossing. But, on the other hand, the fact that all higher plants habitually propagate by means of seeds, which is far the most expensive to the plant of all methods of propagation, while at the same time most flowers are so constructed as to prevent self-fertilization, shows that some corresponding good must come from crossing within the limits of the species or variety; and there are also philosophical reasons, as we have seen, that warrant this conclusion.

Change of seed and crossing. — Bearing in mind these good influences of crossing, let us recall another series of facts following the simple change of seed. Almost every farmer and gardener at the present day feels that an occasional change of seed results in better crops, and there are definite records to show that such is often the case. In fact, much of the rapid improvement in fruits and vegetables in recent years is probably due to the practice of buying plants and seeds so largely of dealers, by means of which the stock is often changed. Even a slight change, as between farms or neighboring villages, sometimes produces marked results, such as more vigorous plants and often more fruitful ones. We must not suppose, however, that because a small change gives a good result, a violent or very pronounced change gives a better one. There are many facts on record to show that great changes often profoundly influence plants, and when such influence results in lessened vigor or lessened productiveness, we call it an injurious one. Now, this injurious influence may result even when all the conditions in the new place are favorable to the health and development of the plant; it is an influence wholly independent, as far as we can see, of any condition which interferes injuriously with the simple processes of growth. Seeds of a native physalis, or husk-tomato, were sent from Paraguay in 1889 by Dr. Thomas Morong, then traveling in that country. It was grown from cuttings in the house and out of doors, and for two generations it failed to set fruit, even though the flowers were hand pollinated; yet the plants were healthy and grew vigorously. The third cutting-generation grown out of doors set freely. This is an instance of the fact that very great changes of conditions may injuriously affect the plant, and an equally good illustration of the power to overcome these conditions. Now there is great similarity between the effects of slight and violent changes of conditions and small and violent degrees of crossing, as both Darwin and Wallace have pointed out, and it is pertinent to this discussion to endeavor to discover why this similarity exists. It is well proved that crossing is good for the resulting off-spring, because the difference between the parents carries over new combinations of characters, or at least new powers into the crosses. It is a process of revitalization, and the more different the stocks in desirable characters within the limits of the variety, the greater may be the revitalization; and frequently the good is of a more positive kind, resulting in pronounced characters which may serve as the basis for new varieties. In the cross, therefore, a new combination of characters or a new power fit it to live better than its parents in the conditions under which they lived.

Results from change of stock. — In the case of change of stock we find the reverse, which, however, amounts to the same thing, that the same characters or powers fit the plant to live better in conditions new to it than plants which have long lived in those conditions. In either case, the good comes from the fitting together of new characters or powers and new environments. Plants which live during many generations in one place become accustomed to the place, thoroughly fitted into its conditions, and are in what Spencer calls a state of equilibrium. When either plant or conditions change, new adjustments must take place; and the plant may find an opportunity to take advantage, to expand in some direction in which it has before been held back; for plants always possess greater power than they are able to express. "These rhythmical actions or functions (of the organism)," writes Spencer, "and the various compound rhythms resulting from their combinations, are in such adjustment as to balance the actions to which the organism is subject. There is a constant or periodic genesis of forces which, in their kind, amounts, and directions, suffice to antagonize the forces which the organism has constantly or periodically to bear. If, then, there exists this state of moving equilibrium among a definite set of internal actions, exposed to a definite set of external actions, what must result if any of the external actions are changed? Of course there is no longer an equilibrium. Some force which the organism habitually generates is too great or too small to balance some incident force; and there arises a residuary force exerted by the environment on the organism, or by the organism on the environment. This residuary force, this unbalanced force, of necessity expends itself in producing some change of state in the organism."

The good results, therefore, are processes of adaptation, and when adaptation is perfect or complete, the plant may have gained no permanent advantage over its former conditions, and new crossing or another change may be necessary; yet there is often a permanent gain, as when a plant becomes visibly modified by change to another cli-mate. Now this adaptive change may express itself in two ways: either by some direct influence on the stature, vigor, or other general characters; or directly on the reproductive powers, by which some new influence is carried to the offspring. If the direct influences become hereditary, as observations seem to show may sometimes occur, the two directions of modification may amount, ultimately, to the same thing.

For the purpose of this discussion it is enough to know that crossing within the variety and change of stock within ordinary bounds are beneficial, that the results in the two cases seem to flow from essentially the same causes, and that crossing and change of stock combined may give better results than either one alone; and this benefit is expressed more in increased vigor and yield than in novel and striking variations. These processes are much more important than any mere groping after new variations, as we have already said, not only because they are surer, but because they are universal and necessary means of maintaining and improving both wild and cultivated plants. Even after one succeeds in securing and fixing the new variety, one must employ these means to a greater or less extent to maintain fertility and vigor, and to keep the variety true to its type. In the case of some garden crops, in which many seeds are produced in each fruit and in which the operation of pollination is easy, actual hand-crossing from new stock now and then may be found to be profitable. But in most cases the operation can be left to nature, if the new stock is planted among the old. Upon this point Darwin expressed himself as follows: "It is a common practice with horticulturists to obtain seeds from another place having a very different soil, so as to avoid raising plants for a long succession of generations under the same conditions; but with all the species which freely inter-crossed by the aid of the insects or the wind, it would be an incomparably better plan to obtain seeds of the required variety, which had been raised for some generations under as different conditions as possible, and sow them in alternate rows with seeds matured in the old garden. The two stocks would then intercross, with a thorough blending of their whole organizations, and with no loss of purity to the variety, and this would yield far more favorable results than a mere change of seed."

CROSSING FROM STANDPOINT OF PLANT IMPROVEMENT

The making of crosses for man's use may have a very different meaning from the effect of crossing upon the plant itself. Man removes from a plant by cultivation most of the factors which make for struggle and determines whether the plant shall survive or not. In making crosses or hybrids with a practical object in view, the welfare of the species is taken into account only sufficiently to insure vigorous plants particularly adapted to man's purposes.

Understanding of terms. — At this point it is worth while to consider a few definitions.

The Latin word *hybrida*, or *ibrida*, has been assumed to be derived from the Greek ὕβρις, an insult or outrage, and a hybrid has been supposed to be an outrage on nature, an unnatural product. The term hybrid is by many applied only to the offspring obtained by crossing two plants or animals sufficiently different to be considered by naturalists as distinct species, while the term cross is used to designate the offspring of two races or varieties of one species. A closer scrutiny of the facts, however, makes the term hybridism less isolated and more vague. The words species and genera, and still more sub-species and varieties, do not correspond with clearly marked botanical categories, and no exact line can be drawn between the various kinds of crossings from those between individuals apparently identical to those belonging to genera universally recognized as distinct. It was formerly supposed that all hybrids were more or less sterile, in contradistinction to crosses, which were thought to be very fertile. It has been found, however, that many hybrids, in the narrow sense, are very fertile, and that some crosses are nearly sterile. Since it is impossible to indicate by any two words, such as hybrid or cross, the various degrees of difference of the forms crossed, the word hybrid is now generally used as a generic term to include all organisms arising from a cross of two forms noticeably different, whether the difference be great or slight. Adjectives are sometimes used to indicate the grade of the forms crossed, such as racial hybrids, bigeneric hybrids, and so forth.

The offspring produced by the union of two plants identical in kind, but separated in descent by at least several seed generations, is often called a cross, cross-fertilized, or cross-bred plant, but it is not a hybrid, as the essential character of a hybrid is that it results from the union of plants differing more or less in kind, or, in other words, is the result of a union between different races, varieties, species, or genera. On the other hand, flowers impregnated with their own pollen, with the pollen of another flower on the same plant, or even pollen from another plant derived from the same original stock by cuttings or grafts, are said to be self-fertilized, and the offspring resulting from such unions are often termed self-fertilized plants. Strictly speaking, however, self- or close-fertilization is impregnation with pollen of the same flower. With such plants as tobacco and wheat, self-fertilization is the rule. In many cases, however, the flowers are so constructed that cross-fertilization is favored, as in corn and rye, and in some cases cross-fertilization is necessary, all possibility of self-pollinization being precluded, as in the case of hemp and other plants having the male and female flowers on separate individuals.

History of plant hybrids. — Inasmuch as the sexuality of plants was unknown, or at least very imperfectly understood, prior to the last two centuries, while a knowledge of the sex distinction of animals dates from the dawn of human history, it is not surprising that while the hybridizing of animals was well understood by the ancients, they did not know that crossing was possible with plants. Experimental proof of the sexuality of plants was published for the first time by Camerarius, December 28, 1691, and only after this discovery was the function of pollen and its necessity for seed formation understood.

The earliest recorded observation of a plant hybrid is by J. G. Gmelin toward the end of the seventeenth century; the next is that of Thomas Fairchild, who in the second decade of the eighteenth century produced the cross which is still grown in literature under the name of "Fairchild's Sweet William." It was a cross between the carnation and sweet William.

Linnæus made many experiments in the cross-fertilization of plants and produced several hybrids, but Joseph Gottlieb Kölreuter (1733–1806) laid the real foundation of our scientific knowledge of the subject. Later on, Thomas Andrew Knight, a celebrated English horticulturist, devoted much successful labor to the improvement of fruit trees and vegetables by crossing. In the second quarter of the nineteenth century, C. F. Gärtner made and published the results of a number of experiments that have not been equaled by any other worker.

What plants can be hybridized? — It is a fact of prime importance that plants so different as to be classed by botanists in widely different families never yield offspring when crossed; for example, it is impossible successfully to cross Indian corn and lilies or the apple and the walnut. Usually plants diverse enough to be considered as belonging to clearly distinct genera, even though of the same natural family, are perfectly sterile when crossed; for example, Indian corn yields no offspring when cross-pollinated with wheat, nor does wheat when crossed with oats, although all belong to the great family of grasses. Plants belonging to the different cultivated races or to natural varieties of the same species are almost invariably fertile when crossed. Indeed, as will be shown later, they are sometimes more fertile when crossed with a related species than when fertilized with their own pollen. Different species of plants closely enough related to be placed in the same genus by naturalists are very often, though by no means always, capable of being hybridized.

Gärtner found that "one of the tobaccoes, *Nicotiana acuminata,* which is not a particularly distinct species, obstinately failed to fertilize or to be fertilized by no less than eight species of Nicotiana." Darwin states that "in the same family there may be a genus, as Dianthus, in which very many species can most readily be crossed; and another genus, as Silene, in which the most persevering efforts have failed to produce, between extremely close species, a single hybrid." Again, there is considerable diversity in results in certain reciprocal crosses between

the same two species. "*Mirabilis jalapa* can easily be
fertilized by the pollen of *M. longiflora,* and the hybrids
thus produced are sufficiently fertile; but Kölreuter tried
more than two hundred times during eight following years
to fertilize reciprocally *M. longiflora* with the pollen of
M. jalapa and utterly failed," as have also many other
hybridizers. Frequently very closely related species
absolutely refuse to cross. This is true of the pumpkin
(*Cucurbita Pepo*) and squash (*C. maxima*). It is, nevertheless, true that hosts of very distinct species hybridize
readily, and a number of cases are known of species belonging to different and quite distinct genera having
hybridized, producing the so-called bigeneric hybrids.
For example, wheat and rye, and wheat and barley, belonging to closely related genera, cross with difficulty, and
Luther Burbank is said to have succeeded in obtaining a
hybrid of strawberry and raspberry. Bigeneric hybrids
are many among the orchids, even though they are highly
specialized plants; and some trigeneric hybrids are known.

Hybrids between plants belonging to different families
are very rare. The results obtained by hosts of experimenters and practical gardeners show conclusively that
the greater part of closely related species can be readily
crossed, while very distinct species, and species belonging
to distinct genera, can be crossed in only comparatively
few cases. It is impossible to predict what plants may or
may not be hybridized.

Vigor as a result of crossing. — Darwin was the first to
show that crossing within the limits of the species or
variety results in a constant revitalizing of the offspring,
and that this is the particular ultimate function of crossing

or cross-fertilization. Kölreuter, Sprengel, Knight, and others had observed many, if, indeed, not all, the facts obtained by Darwin; but they had not generalized upon them broadly, and did not conceive the relation to the complex life of the vegetable world. Darwin's results are, concisely, these: self-fertilization tends to weaken the offspring (Fig. 31); crossing between different plants of the

FIG. 31. — Inbred corn plants, showing lessened vigor of growth.
(Adapted from Yearbook.)

same variety gives a stronger and more productive offspring than arises from self-fertilization; crossing between stocks of the same variety grown in different places or under different conditions gives better offspring than crossing between different plants grown in the same place or under similar conditions; and his researches have also shown that, as a rule, flowers are so constructed as to favor cross-fertilization. In short, he found, as he expressed it, that "nature abhors perpetual self-fertilization." Some of his particular results, although often quoted, will be useful in fixing these facts in our minds.

Darwin's experiments with morning-glories. — Plants from crossed seeds of morning-glory exceeded in height those from self-fertilized seeds as 100 exceeds 76, in the first generation. Some flowers from these plants were self-pollinated and some were crossed, and in this second generation the crossed plants were to the uncrossed as 100 is to 79; the operation was again repeated, and in the third generation, the plant having been grown in midwinter, when none of them did well, 100 to 86; fifth generation, 100 to 75; sixth generation, 100 to 72; seventh generation, 100 to 81; eighth generation, 100 to 85; ninth generation, 100 to 79; tenth generation, 100 to 54. The average total gain in height of the crossed over the uncrossed was as 100 to 77, or about 30 per cent. There was a corresponding gain in fertility, or the number of seeds and seed-pods produced. Yet, striking as the results are, they were produced by simple crossing between plants grown near together, and under what would ordinarily be called uniform conditions. In order to determine the influence of crossing with fresh stock, plants of the same variety were obtained from another garden and these were crossed with the ninth generation mentioned above. The offspring of this cross exceeded those of the other crossed plants as 100 exceeds 78, in height; as 100 exceeds 57, in the number of seed-pods; and as 100 exceeds 51, in the weight of the seed-pods. In other words, crosses between fresh stock of the same variety were nearly 30 per cent more vigorous than crosses between plants grown side by side for some time and over 44 per cent more vigorous than plants from self-fertilized seeds. On the other hand, experiments showed that crosses between different flowers on the same plant gave actually poorer results than offspring of self-fertilized flowers. It is evident, from all of these figures, that nature desires crosses between plants, and, if possible, between plants grown under somewhat different conditions. All these results are exceedingly interesting and important; and there is every reason to believe that, as a rule, similar results can be obtained with all plants.

Darwin's results with other plants. — Darwin extended his investigation to many plants, only a few of which need be discussed here. Cabbage gave pronounced results. Crossed plants were to self-fertilized plants in weight as 100 is to 37. A cross was now made between these crossed plants and a plant of the same variety from another garden, and the difference in weight of the resulting offspring was the difference between 100 and 22, showing a gain of over 350 per cent, due to a cross with fresh stock. Crossed lettuce plants exceeded uncrossed in height as 100 exceeds 82. Buckwheat gave an increase in weight of seeds as 100 to 82, and in height of plants as 100 to 69. Beets gave an increase in height represented by 100 to 87. Maize, when full grown, from crossed and uncrossed seeds, gave the difference in height between 100 and 91. Canary grass gave similar results.

Increased vigor in other crosses. — Results as well marked as these have been secured on a large and what might be called a commercial scale. The first generation was raised from seeds of known parentage, the flowers from which they came having been carefully pollinated by hand. In some instances the second generations were grown from hand-crossed seeds, but in other cases the second generations were grown from seeds simply selected from the first-year patches. As the experiments have been made in the field and upon a somewhat extensive scale, it was not possible accurately to measure the plants and the fruits from individuals in all cases; but the results have been so marked as to admit of no doubt as to their character. In 1889, several hand-crosses were made among egg-plants. The fruits matured, and the seeds from them were grown in 1890. Some two hundred plants were grown, and they were characterized throughout the season by great sturdiness and vigor of growth. They grew more erect and taller than other plants near by grown from commercial seeds. It was impossible to determine productiveness, from the fact that the seasons were too short for egg-plants, and only the earliest flowers, in the large varieties, perfect their fruit, and the plant blooms continuously through the season. In order to determine how much a plant will bear, it must be grown until it ceases to bloom. When frost came, little difference could be seen in productiveness between these crossed plants and commercial plants. A dozen fruits were selected from various parts of the patch, and in 1891 about twenty-five hundred plants were grown from them. Again the plants were remarkably robust and healthy, with fine foliage, and they grew erect and tall, — an indication of vigor. They were also very productive; but, as the cross had been made between unlike varieties, and the offspring was therefore unlike either parent, an accurate comparison could not be made. But they compared well with commercial egg-plants, and undoubtedly they would have shown themselves to be more productive than common stock could they have grown a month or six weeks longer. Professor Munson, of the Maine Experiment Station, grew some of this crossed stock in 1891, and found that it was better than any commercial stock in his gardens.

In extended experiments in the crossing of pumpkins, squashes, and gourds, conducted several years, increase in productiveness due to crossing has been marked in many instances. Marked increase in productiveness has been obtained from tomato crosses even when no other results of crossing could be seen.

FIG. 32. — Hybrid walnut and parents: *m*, California black walnut (*Juglans californica*), male parent; *f*, Eastern black walnut (*J. nigra*), female parent; *h*, hybrid. Natural size. (After Burbank.)

Three factors. — Attention has been called by Willis to three factors in the gain resulting from cross-fertilization, viz. (*a*) fertility of mother plant; (*b*) vigor of offspring;

and (*c*) fertility of offspring. The relative values of these factors varies with different plants. In the carnation, for instance, factor (*a*) of cross-fertilized plants was 9 per cent greater than in self-fertilized plants, (*b*) was 16 per cent greater, and (*c*) was 54 per cent greater; in tobacco, factor (*a*) was 33 per cent less than in self-fertilized plants, but factor (*b*) was 28 per cent greater and factor (*c*) 3 per cent greater. Even when the fertility of the mother plant is greatly reduced by hybridizing with a distinct species and the hybrids themselves are sterile or very infertile, they nevertheless often show extraordinary vigor, that is, (*b*) is often greater in hybrids than in pure-bred plants, but factors (*a*) and (*c*) are usually less. In plant-breeding the importance of this increased vigor is very great (Figs. 32 and 33).

The outright production of new varieties.—The reader is waiting for a discussion of the second of the great features of crossing, — the summary production of new varieties. This is the subject that is almost universally associated with crossing in the popular mind, and even among horticulturists themselves. It is the commonest notion that the desirable characters of given parents can be definitely combined in a pronounced cross of hybrids. There are two or three philosophical reasons which somewhat oppose this doctrine, and which we will do well to consider at the outset. In the first place, nature is opposed to hybrids, for species have been bred away from each other in the ability to cross. If, therefore, there is no advantage for nature to hybridize, we may suppose that there would be little advantage for man to do so; and there would be no advantage for man did he not place the plant under condi-

FIG. 33. — A hybrid walnut (*Juglans californica nigra*), reaching double the height of ordinary trees.

tions different from nature, or desires a different set of characters. We have seen that nature's chief barriers to hybridization are total refusal of many species to unite, and entire or comparative seedlessness of offspring.

The notion is somewhat firmly rooted in the popular mind that new varieties can be produced with the greatest ease by crossing parents of given attributes. There is something captivating about the notion. It smacks of a somewhat magic power that man evokes as he passes his wand over the untamed forces of nature. But the wand is often a gilded stick, and is likely to serve no better purpose than the drum major's pretentious baton !

Let it be said further that crossing alone can accomplish comparatively little. The chief power in the evolution or progression of plants appears to be selection, or, as Darwin puts it, the law of "preservation of favorable individual differences and variations, and the destruction of those which are injurious." Selection is the force which augments, develops, and fixes types. Man must not only practice a judicious selection of parents from which the cross is to come, which is in reality but the exercise of a choice, but he must constantly select the best from among the crosses, in order to maintain a high degree of usefulness and to make any advancement ; and it sometimes happens that the selection is much more important to the cultivator than the crossing.

Further discussion of this subject naturally falls under two heads : the improvement of existing types or varieties by means of crossing, and the summary production of new varieties. As already stated, the former office is the more important, and the proposition is easy of proof. It is the chief use which nature makes of crossing, to strengthen the type.

How to overcome antipathy to crossing. — We can overcome the refusal to cross in many cases by bringing the plant under cultivation; for the character of the species becomes so changed by the wholly new conditions that its former antipathies may be overpowered. Yet, it is doubtful whether such a plant will ever acquire a complete willingness to cross. In like manner we can overcome in a measure the comparative seedlessness of hybrids, but it is very doubtful whether we can ever make such hybrids completely fruitful.

It is evident that species which have been differentiated or bred away from each other in a given locality will have more opposed qualities or powers than similar species which have arisen quite independently in places remote from each other. In the one case the species have likely struggled with each other until each one has attained to a degree of divergence which allows it to persist; while in the other case, there has been no struggle between species, but similar conditions have brought about similar results. These similar species which appear independently of each other in different places are called representative species. Islands remote from each other but similarly situated with reference to climate very often contain representative species; and the same may be said of other regions much like each other, as eastern North America and Japan. Now, it follows that, if representative species are less opposed than others, they are more likely to hybridize with good results; and this fact is remarkably well illustrated in the Kieffer and allied pears, which are hybrids between representative species of Europe and Japan; and the same may be found to be true of the common European apple and the wild crab of the Mississippi Valley. Various crabs of the Soulard type, which were once thought to constitute a distinct species, appear upon further study to be hybrids. We will also recall that the hybrid grapes which have so far proved most valuable are those obtained by Rogers between the American *Vitis Labrusca* and the European wine grape, *Vitis vinifera;* and that the attempts of Haskell and others to hybridize associated species of native grapes have given, at best, only indifferent results. To these good results from hybrids and fruit trees and vines, we shall revert presently.

Variability of hybrids. — Another theoretical point which is borne out by practice is the conclusion that, because of the great differences and lack of affinity between parents, pronounced hybrid offsprings are unstable. This is one of the greatest difficulties in the way of the summary production of new varieties by means of hybridization. It would appear, also, that, because of the unlikeness of parents, hybrid offspring must be exceedingly variable; but, as a matter of fact, in many instances the parents are so pronouncedly different that the hybrids represent a distinct type by themselves, or else they approach very nearly to the characters of one of the parents. There are, to be sure, many examples of exceedingly variable hybrid offspring, but they are usually the offspring of variable parents (Fig. 34). In other words, variability in offspring appears to follow rather as a result of variability in parents than as a result of mere unlikeness of characters. But the instability of hybrid offspring when propagated by seed is notorious. We shall see the reasons for this later when discussing mendelism. Wallace writes that "the effect of occasional crosses often results in a great amount of variability, but it also leads to instability of character, and is therefore very little employed in the production of fixed and well-marked races." We may remark again that, because of the unequal and unknown powers of the parents, we can never predict what characters will appear in the

Fig. 34. — Variation in hybrid pineapples.

hybrids, although we are now beginning to understand the reasons and to have rather definite expectations as to probabilities. This fact is well expressed by Lindley a half century ago, in the phrase, "Hybridizing is a game of chance played between man and plants."

Characteristics of crosses. — Bearing these fundamental propositions in mind, let us pursue the subject somewhat in detail. We shall find that the characters of hybrids, as compared with the characters of simple crosses between stocks of the same variety, are ambiguous, negative, and often prejudicial. Focke lays down the five following propositions concerning the character of hybrid offspring :

1. "All individuals which have come from the crossing of two pure species or races, when produced and grown under like conditions, are usually exactly like each other, or at least scarcely more different from each other than plants of the same species are." This proposition, although perhaps true in the main, appears to be too broadly and positively stated.

2. "The characters of hybrids may be different from the characters of the parents. The hybrids differ most in size and vigor and in their sexual powers.

3. "Hybrids are distinguished from their parents by their powers of vegetation or growth. Hybrids between very different species are often weak, especially when young, so that it is difficult to raise them. On the other hand, crossbreds are, as a rule, uncommonly vigorous; they are distinguished mostly in size, rapidity of growth, early flowering, productiveness, longer life, stronger reproductive power, unusual size of some special organs, and similar characteristics.

4. "Hybrids produce a less amount of pollen and fewer seeds than their parents, and they often produce none. In cross-breeds this weakening of the reproductive powers does not occur. The flowers of sterile or nearly sterile hybrids usually remain fresh a long time.

5. "Malformations and odd forms are likely to appear in hybrids, especially in the flowers."

Some of the relations between hybridization and crossing within narrow limits are stated as follows by Darwin : "It is an extraordinary fact that with many species flowers fertilized with their own pollen are either absolutely or in some degree sterile; if fertilized with pollen from another flower on the same plant, they are sometimes, though rarely, a little more fertile; if fertilized with pollen from another individual or variety of the same species, they are fully fertile; but if with pollen from a distinct species, they are sterile in all possible degrees, until utter sterility is reached. We thus have a long series with absolute sterility at the two ends; at one end due to the sexual elements not having been sufficiently differentiated, and at the other end to their having been differentiated in too great a degree, or in some peculiar manner."

Difficulties in making successful crosses. — The difficulties in the way of successful results through hybridization are, therefore, these: the difficulty of effecting the cross, infertility, instability, variability, and often weakness and monstrosity of the hybrids; and the general impossibility in most cases of predicting results. The advantage to be derived from a successful hybridization is the securing of a new variety which shall combine in some measure the most desirable features of both parents; and this advantage is often of so great moment that it is worth while to make repeated efforts and to overlook numerous failures.

Hybridization and asexual propagation. — Among the various characters of hybrid offspring, probably the most prejudicial one is their instability, their tendency to vary into new forms or to return to one or the other parent in succeeding generations. At the outset, we notice that this discouraging feature is manifested chiefly through the fact of seed-reproduction, and we thereby come

upon what is perhaps the most important practical consideration in hybridization, — the fact that the greater
number of the best hybrids in cultivation are increased
by bud-propagation, as cuttings, layers, suckers, buds, or
grafts. In fact, there are very few examples in this country
of good undoubted hybrids which are propagated with
practical certainty by means of seeds. The genera in
which the hybrids are most common are those in which
bud-propagation is the rule; as begonia, pelargonium,
orchids, gladiolus, rhododendron, roses, cannas, and the
fruits. This simply means that it is difficult to fix hybrids
so that they will come "true to seed," and makes apparent
the fact that if we desire named hybrids, we must expect
to propagate them by means of buds.

This point appears to have been overlooked by those
who contend that hybridization must necessarily swamp
all results of natural selection; for, as comparatively
few plants propagate habitually by means of buds,
whatever hybrids might have appeared would have been
speedily lost, and all the more because, by the terms of
their reasoning, the hybrids would cross with other and
dissimilar forms, and therefore lose their identity as
intermediates. Or, starting with the assumption that
hybrids are intermediates, and would therefore obliterate
specific types, we must conclude that they should have
some marked degree of stability if they are to swamp or
obliterate the characters of species; but, as all hybrids
tend to break up when propagated by seeds, it must follow
that bud-propagation would become more and more
common, and this is associated in nature with decreased
seed-production. Now, seed-production is the legitimate

function of flowers; and we must concede that, as seed-production decreased, floriferousness must have decreased; and that, therefore, pronounced inter-crossing would have obliterated the very organs upon which it depends, or have destroyed itself!

In-breeding. — But we may be met with objection that there is no inherent reason why hybrids should not become stable through seed-production by in-breeding, and we might be cited to the opinion of Darwin and others that in-breeding tends to fix any variety, whether it originates by crossing or other means. And it is a fact that in-breeding tends to fix varieties within certain limits, but those limits are often overpassed in the case of very pronounced crosses, whether cross-breeds or true hybrids. And if it is true, as all observation and experiments show, that sexual or reproductive powers of crosses are weakened as the cross becomes more violent, we shall expect less and less possibility of successful in-breeding; for in-breeding without disastrous results is possible only with comparatively strong reproductive powers. As a matter of fact, it is found in practice that it is exceedingly difficult to fix pronounced hybrids by means of in-breeding. It sometimes happens, also, that the hybrid individual that we wish to perpetuate may be infertile with itself, as has been often found in the case of squashes. It is often advised that we cross the hybrid individual which we wish to fix with another like individual, or with one of its parents. These results are often successful, but oftener they are not. In the first place, it often happens that the hybrid individuals may be so diverse that no two of them are alike; this has been the experience in many cases. And, again crossing with a parent may draw the hybrid back again to the parent form. So long ago as last century Kölreuter proved this fact with Nicotiana and Dianthus. A hybrid between *Nicotiana rustica* and *N. paniculata* was crossed with *N. paniculata* until it was indistinguishable from it; and it was then crossed with *N. rustica* until it became indistinguishable from that parent. Yet there is no other way of fixing a hybrid to be propagated by seeds than by in-breeding, and by constant attention to selection. Fortunately, it occasionally happens that a hybrid is stable, and therefore needs no fixing.

Experience with egg-plants and squashes. — Offspring of egg-plant crosses were grown in 1890, and upon some of the most promising plants some flowers were self-pollinated. But these self-pollinated seeds gave just as variable offspring in 1891 as those selected almost at random from the patch; and what was worse, none of them reproduced the parents, or "came true to seed," and all further motive for in-breeding was gone. "My labor, therefore, amounted to nothing more than my own edification. My experience in crossing pumpkins and squashes has now extended through many years; and, although I have obtained about one thousand types not named or described, I have not yet succeeded in fixing one. The difficulty here is an aggravated one, however. The species are so exceedingly variable that all the hybrid individuals may be unlike, so that there can be no crossing between identical stocks; and, if in-breeding is attempted, it may be found that the flowers will not in-breed. And the refusal to in-breed is all the more strange because the sexes are separated in different flowers on the plant. In other words, in my experience, it is very difficult to get good seeds from squashes fertilized by a flower upon the same vine. The squashes may grow normally to full maturity but be entirely hollow, or contain only empty seeds. In some instances the seeds may appear to be good, but may refuse to grow under the best conditions. Finally, a

Fig. 35.—Variation in hybrid squashes.

small number of flowers may give good seeds. I have many times observed this refusal of squashes (*Cucurbita Pepo*) to in-breed. It was first brought to my attention through efforts to fix certain types into varieties. The figures of the season's tests will sufficiently indicate the character of the problem. In 1890, one hundred and

K

eighty-five squash flowers were carefully pollinated with staminate flowers taken from the same vine that bore the pistillate flowers. Only twenty-two of these produced fruit, and of those only seven, or less than one-third, bore good seeds, and in some of these the seeds were few. Now, these twenty-two fruits represented as many different varieties, so that the inability to set fruit with pollen from the same vine is not a peculiarity of a particular variety. The records of the seeds of the seven fruits in 1891 are as follows : —

"Fruit No. 1. Four vines were obtained, with four different types, two of them being white, one yellow, and one black.

"Fruit No. 2. Twenty-three vines. Fifteen types very unlike, twelve being white and three yellow.

"Fruit No. 3. Two vines. One type of fruit, which is almost like one of the original parents.

"Fruit No. 4. Thirty-two vines. Six types, differing chiefly in size and shape.

"Fruit No. 5. Twenty vines. Nineteen types, of which ten were white, eight orange, one striped, and all very unlike.

"Fruit No. 6. Thirteen vines. Eleven types, — eight yellow, two black, one white.

"Fruit No. 7. One vine.

"These offspring were just as variable as those from flowers not in-bred and no more likely, apparently, to reproduce the parent. These tests leave me without any method of fixing a pronounced cross of squashes, and lead me to think that the legitimate process of origination of new kinds here, as, indeed, if not in general, is a more gradual process of selection, coupled, perhaps, with minor crossing.

"I will relate a definite attempt towards the fixation of a squash that I had obtained from crossing. The history of it runs back to 1887, when a cross was effected between a summer yellow crook-neck and a white bush scallop squash. In 1889 there appeared a squash of great excellence, combining the merits of summer and winter squashes with very attractive form, size, and color, and a good habit of plant. I showed the fruit to one of the most expert seedsmen of the country, and he pronounced it one of the most promising types he had ever seen; and, as he informed me that he had fixed squashes by breeding in and in, I was all the more anxious to carry out my own convictions in the same direction. It is needless to say that I was very happy over what I regarded as a great triumph. Of course, I must have a large number of plants of my new variety, that I might select the best, both for in-breeding and for crossing similar types. So I selected the very finest squash, having placed it where I could admire it for some days, and saved every seed of it. These seeds were planted on the most conspicuous knoll in my garden in 1890. It was soon evident that something was wrong. I seemed to have everything except my squash. One plant, however, bore fruits almost like the parent, and upon this I began my attempts towards in-breeding. But flower after flower failed, and I soon saw that the plant was infertile with itself. Careful search revealed two or three other plants very like this one, and I then proceeded to make crosses with them. I was equally confident that this method would succeed. When I harvested my squashes in the fall and took account of stock, I found that the seeds of my one squash had given just as many different types as there were plants, and I actually counted one hundred and ten kinds distinct enough to be named and recognized. Still confident, in 1891 I planted the seeds of my few crosses, and as the summer days grew long and the crickets chirped in the meadows, I watched the expanding squash blossoms and wondered what they would bring forth. But they

Fig. 36. — Hybrid citrange and its parents, *Citrus* (or *Poncirus*) *trifoliata* and common sweet orange.

brought only disappointment. Not one seed produced a squash like the parent. My squash had taken an unscientific leave of absence, and I do not know its whereabouts. And when the frost came and killed every ambitious blossom, my hope went out and has not yet returned!"[1]

Important hybrids of fruits and vegetables. — Let us now recall how many undoubted hybrids there are, named

[1] Bailey, "Plant-Breeding," earlier editions. See also, "A Medley of Pumpkins," Proc. Intern. Pl. Breeding Conf., New York City.

and known, among our fruits and vegetables. In grapes
there are the most. There are Rogers' hybrids, as the
Agawam, Lindley, Wilder, Salem, and Barry; and there
is some reason for supposing that the Delaware, Catawba,
and other varieties are of hybrid origin. And many
hybrids have come to notice lately through the work of

Fig. 37. — Hybrid tangelo and its parents, pomelo and tangerine.

Munson and others. But it must be remembered that
grapes are naturally exceedingly variable, and the specific
limits are not well known, and that hybridization among
them lacks much of that definiteness which ordinarily
attaches to the subject. In oranges, hybrid citranges and
tangelos made by Webber and Swingle are now reaching
considerable commercial importance (Figs. 36–39). In

Fig. 38. — Samson tangelo. $\frac{5}{6}$ natural size. (Adapted from Yearbook.)

Fig. 39.—Citranges (hybrids of orange and *Citrus trifoliata*). Top fruit *Citrus* (or *Poncirus*) *trifoliata*. Top pair, rusk citrange. Bottom pair, Willits citrange. ¾ natural size. (Reduced from colored figures in Yearbook of the Department of Agriculture.)

pears there is the Kieffer class. In apples, peaches, plums, cherries, and currants, there are no important recognized commercial hybrids. In blackberries there is the blackberry-dewberry class, represented by the Wilson Early and others. Some of the raspberries, as the Philadelphia and Shaffer, are hybrids between the red and black species. Hybrids have been produced between the raspberry and blackberry by two or three persons, but they possess no promise of economic results. It is probable that some of the gooseberries are hybrids. Among all the list of garden vegetables (plants which are propagated by seeds) there is apparently not a single important recorded hybrid; and the same is true of wheat, — unless the Carman wheat-rye varieties become prominent, — oats, the grasses, and other farm crops (Fig. 40). But among ornamental plants there are many; and it is significant that the most numerous, most marked, and most successful hybrids occur in the plants most carefully cultivated and protected, those, in other words, that are farthest removed from all untoward circumstances and an independent position. This is nowhere so well illustrated as in the case of cultivated orchids, in which hybridization has played no end of freaks, and in which, also, every individual plant is nursed and coddled.[1] With such plants the struggle for existence is reduced to its lowest terms; for it must be borne in mind that, even in the garden, plants must fight severely for a chance to live, and even then only the very best can persist, or are even allowed to try.

[1] Consult E. Bohnhof, "Dictionnaire des Orchidees Hybrides," Paris, 1905; also the recent Sanders lists.

This list of hybrids is much more meager than most catalogues and trade-lists would have us believe. It is, of course, equivalent to saying that most of the so-called hybrid fruits and vegetables are doubtful. There is every-

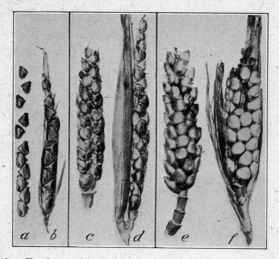

Fig. 40. — Teosinte and its hybrids with Indian corn: *a* and *b*, ears of teosinte, showing an entire absence of cob, kernels being attached to each other; *c* and *d*, ears of first-generation cross of teosinte and Indian corn; *e* and *f*, *Zea canina*, a fourth-generation hybrid of teosinte and corn. All are natural size and were grown by the Department of Agriculture in 1900 on the Potomac Flats, near Washington, D.C.

where a misconception of what a hybrid is, and how it comes to exist; and yet, perhaps because of this indefinite knowledge, there is a wide-spread feeling that a hybrid is necessarily good, while the presumption is directly the opposite. The identity of a hybrid in the popular mind rests entirely on some superficial character, and proceeds upon the assumption that it is necessarily intermediate between the parents. Hence, we find one of our popular authors asserting that, because the kohl-rabi bears its thickened part midway of its stem, it is evidently a hybrid between the cabbage and turnip, which bear respectively the thickened parts at the opposite extremities of the stem! And then there are those who confound the word hybrid with high-bred, and who build attractive castles upon the unconscious error. And thus is confusion confounded!

Influence of sex on hybrids. — But, before leaving this subject of hybridization, we must speak of the old yet common notion that there is some peculiar influence exerted by each sex in the parentage of hybrids. It was held by certain early observers, of whom the great Linnæus was one, that the female parent determines the constitution of the hybrid, while the male parent gives the external attributes, as form, size, and color. The accumulated experience of nearly a century and a half appears to contradict this proposition, and Focke, who has gone over the whole ground, positively declares that it is untrue. There are instances, to be sure, in which this old idea is affirmed, but there are others in which it is contradicted. It is usually impossible to determine beforehand which parent is the stronger. It is certain that strength does not lie in size, neither in the high development of any character. It appears to be more particularly associated with what we call fixity or stability of character, or the tendency towards invariability.

" This has been well illustrated in my own experiments

with squashes, gourds, and pumpkins. The common
little pear-shaped gourd will impress itself more strongly
upon crosses than any of the edible squashes and pumpkins
with which it will effect a cross, whether it is used as male
or female parent. It contains many dominant unit-
characters. Even the imposing and ubiquitous great
field pumpkin which every New Englander associates
with pies, is overpowered by the little gourd. Seeds from
a large and sleek pumpkin which had been fertilized by
gourd pollen produced gourds and small hard-shelled
globular fruits which were entirely inedible. A more interesting experiment was made between the handsome
green-striped Bergen fall squash and the little pear gourd.
Several flowers of the gourd were pollinated by the Bergen in 1889. The fruits raised from these seeds in 1890
were remarkably gourd-like. Some of these crosses were
pollinated again in 1890 by the Bergen, and the seeds were
grown in 1891. Here, then, were crosses into which the
gourd had gone once and the Bergen twice, and both
parents are to all appearances equally fixed, the difference
in strength, if any, attaching rather to the Bergen. Now,
the crop of 1891 still carried pronounced characters of the
gourd. Even in the fruits that most resembled the Bergen, the shells were almost flinty hard, and the flesh, even
when thick and tender, was bitter. Some of the fruits
looked so much like the Bergen that I was led to think
that the gourd had largely disappeared. The very hard
but thin paper-like shell which the gourd had laid over
the thick yellow flesh of the Bergen, I thought might
serve a useful purpose, and make the squash a better
keeper. And I found that it was a great protection, for

the squash could stand any amount of rough-handling, and was not even injured by ten degrees of frost. All this was an acquisition, and, as the squash was handsome and exceedingly productive, nothing more seemed to be desired. But it still remained to have a squash for dinner. The cook complained of the hard shell, but, once inside, the flesh was thick and attractive, and it cooked nicely. But the flavor! Dregs of quinine, gall, and boneset! The gourd was still there!"[1]

Uncertainties of pollination. — We have now seen that uncertainty follows hybridization, as well as the mere act of pollination. Between some species which are closely allied and which have large and strong flowers, four-fifths of the attempts towards cross-pollination may be successful; but such a large proportion of successes is not common, and it may be infrequent even in pollination between plants of the same species or variety. Some of the failure is due in many cases to unskillful operation, but even the most expert operators fail as often as they succeed in promiscuous pollinating. There is good reason to believe, as Darwin has shown, that the failure may be due to some selective power of individual plants, by which they refuse pollen which is, in many instances, acceptable to other plants even of the same variety or stock. The lesson to be drawn from these facts is that operations should be as many as possible, and that discouragement should not come from failure.

"Two hundred and thirty-four pollinations of gourds, pumpkins, and squashes, mostly between varieties of one species (*Cucurbita Pepo*), and including some individual

[1] Bailey, earlier editions of "Plant-Breeding."

pollinations, gave one hundred and seventeen failures and one hundred and seventeen successes. These crosses were made in varying weather, from July 28 to August 30. In some periods nearly all the operations would succeed and at other times most of them would fail. I have always regarded these experiments as among my most successful ones, and yet but half of the pollinations 'took.' But one must not understand that I actually secured seeds from even all these one hundred and seventeen fruits, for some of them turned out to be seedless, and some were destroyed by insects before they were ripe, or they were lost by accidental means. A few more than half of the successful pollinations — if by success we mean the formation and growth of fruit — really secured us seeds, or about one-fourth of the whole number of efforts.

"Twenty pollinations were made between potato flowers, and they all failed; also, seven pollinations of red peppers, four of husk tomato, two of *Nicotiana affinis* upon petunia and two of the reciprocal cross, twelve of radish, one of *Mirabilis jalapa* upon *M. longiflora* and two of the reciprocal cross, three *Convolvulus major* upon *C. minor* and one of the reciprocal, one muskmelon by squash, two muskmelons by watermelon, and one muskmelon by cucumber.

"This is but one record. Let me give another: —

"Cucumber, ninety-five efforts: fifty-two successes; forty-three failures. Tomato, forty-three efforts: nineteen successes; twenty-four failures. Egg-plant, seven efforts: one success; six failures. Pepper, fifteen efforts: one success; fourteen failures. Husk-tomato, forty-five efforts: forty-five failures. Pepino, twelve efforts: twelve failures. Petunia by *Nicotiana affinis*, eleven efforts : eleven failures. *Nicotiana affinis* by petunia, six efforts : six failures. General Grant tobacco by *Nicotiana affinis*, eleven efforts : eight successes ; three failures. *Nicotiana affinis* by General Grant tobacco, fifteen efforts : fifteen failures. General Grant tobacco by General Grant tobacco, one effort : one success. *Nicotiana affinis* by *Nicotiana affinis*, three efforts : two successes ; one failure. Tuberous begonia, five efforts : five successes.

"Total, three hundred and twelve efforts : eighty-nine successes, two hundred and twenty-three failures." [1]

Graft-hybrids. — It is well known that, when two varieties or allied species are grafted together, each retains its distinctive characters. But to this general, if not universal, rule there are on record several alleged exceptions, in which either the cion is said to have partaken of the qualities of the stock, the stock of the cion, or each to have affected the other. Supposing any of these influences to have been exerted, the resulting product would deserve to be called a graft-hybrid.

It is clearly a matter of great interest to ascertain whether such formation of hybrids by grafting is really possible ; for, even if one example of such formation could be unequivocally proved, it would show that sexual and asexual reproduction are essentially identical.

The case of Cytisus Adami (Figs. 41, 42). — The cases of alleged graft-hybridization are exceedingly few, considering the enormous number of grafts that are made every year by horticulturists and have been made for centuries.

Of these cases, one of the most celebrated is that of

[1] Bailey, earlier editions.

Fig. 41. — *Cytisus Adami*, *A*, *A'*, *A''*; *B*, a branch of *C. laburum*, *L*, *L'*, *L''*, with numerous racemes bearing ripe pods.

Adam's laburnum (*Cytisus Adami*). This plant is now flourishing in many places throughout Europe, all of the trees having been raised as cuttings from the original graft, which was made by inserting a bud of the purple

Fig. 42. — *Cytisus Adami, A, A',* bearing at *I* a bunch of twigs of
C. purpureus, P, H, and *I.*

laburnum (*Cytisus purpureus*) into a stock of the yellow (*Cytisus laburnum*). M. Adami, who made the graft at Vitry, near Paris, about 1826, has left on record that from it there sprang the existing hybrid. There can be no question as to the truly hybrid nature of the latter. It is, however, absolutely sterile, and is multiplied by grafts. It bears three kinds of flowers — some pink, others large and yellow, others small and purple. That is to say, it bore its own hybrid flowers, also those of its two parents, and the leaves and ramifications of the parts of the tree which bore these three kinds of flowers were likewise of the same three kinds and could be distinguished even in winter.

Strasburger made a careful cytological study of *Cytisus Adami*, which has been retained in cultivation ever since its origin some eighty years ago. He came to the conclusion that *Cytisus Adami* was a real sexual hybrid and not a graft-hybrid. He thinks that if the latter were true, the nuclei of the hybrid would show a double number of chromosomes. This, of course, implies that in hybrids arising otherwise than sexually, assuming that a nuclear fusion would precede the formation of such a hybrid, there would be no reduction division of the nuclei comparable to that which normally occurs before the fusion of the sexual cells in normal fertilization.

Nemec, however, thinks that a reduction division does occur and there is, therefore, no reason to expect an increase in the number of chromosomes in the cells of the hybrid. If such a reduction does occur, *Cytisus Adami* would show the same number of chromosomes as *C. laburnum*, which has the same number as *C. purpureus*.

L

Winkler's Solanum graft-hybrids. — Professor H. Winkler of Tubingen has carefully performed experiments in making graft-hybrids with the black nightshade, *Solanum nigrum*, and two varieties of the tomato, *Solanum lycopersicum*. These two species are very distinct, and indeed many botanists regard the tomato as belonging to a distinct genus lycopersicum, so that Winkler's graft-hybrids may be regarded as bigeneric hybrids. Seedlings of each were grown and reciprocal grafts made. The graft and stock united readily whether the nightshade or the tomato was used as the stock.

Naturally the majority of the shoots arising from the cut surface of the stem were either pure nightshade or pure tomato. But finally shoots were observed which were evidently of mixed origin. The first of these graft-hybrids were obviously composed of pure elements derived from the two parents. Some of these shoots were almost equally divided by a median line, on one side of which the organs — stem, leaf — were those of the nightshade, while on the other the organs were evidently derived from the tomato. It is obvious that such unusual forms, which Winkler called "Chimæra," are not hybrids in any true sense of the word, but have arisen from buds which contain the tissue of the two parent formed at the junction of the stock and graft.

Later on there developed, however, shoots which were evidently of hybrid origin. Cell fusion had unquestionably taken place. Several hybrids with different attributes were produced. These have been given different names by Professor Winkler, and may be described as follows : —

1. *Solanum tubingense* is intermediate in the size and

shape of the leaves and the color and type of the flowers between the nightshade and the tomato. The fruit is very much like that of the nightshade, but is rather larger, and although it is black there are some traces of the red or yellow color of the tomato.

2. *Solanum proteus* has very variable leaves, which, on the whole, are more divided than those of *S. tubingense*, while in the characters of the flowers and the fruit it is more like the tomato than like the nightshade.

3. *Solanum Kölreuterianum*, and

4. *Solanum Gärtnerianum.* These forms have been produced several times. The first is more like the tomato, the second more like the nightshade, but each differs in important particulars from either of the parents.

5. *Solanum Darwinianum.* The point of especial interest in connection with this form is that of all the so-called "graft-hybrids" secured by Winkler this seems to be the only one which is likely to prove a hybrid in the strict sense of the word. The fruit of this plant, unlike the others, was sterile, no perfect seeds being formed. The fruit itself is a round small berry like the fruit of the nightshade in form, but having the color and structure of the tomato.

Are these real graft-hybrids? — In all of these forms when seed was produced at all, it produced seedlings of one parent or the other, never producing the apparent hybrid.

It has been suggested by Bauer that these apparent true hybrids might be chimæras of a type which he has called "periclinal," *i.e.* the outer tissues are derived from one parent, and the inner tissues from the other, but none of the tissues themselves are of hybrid origin.

This explanation has also been applied to Cytisus hybrids in which it has been shown that the epidermal tissues were strikingly like those of *C. purpureus*, while the inner tissues were like those of *C. laburnum*.

In a later paper, Winkler arrives at the following conclusions : —

Hybrids may be arranged in two groups, sexual and graft-hybrids. The latter may be divided into three classes according to the theoretical possibility of their method of origin, viz.: (1) Fusion graft-hybrids arising from a fusion of two somatic cells derived from distinct species. (2) "Influenced" graft-hybrids which arise from specific influences of one graft component upon the other without cell fusion (as through chemical substances, translocation of cytoplasm, etc.). (3) Chimæras, in which specifically pure cells from both graft components are combined to form a new individual. These chimæras may be : (*a*) Sectorial chimæras in which the two sorts of cells in the growing point are divided by a longitudinal plane. (*b*) Periclinal chimæras in which the periclinal cell layers of the growing point are furnished respectively from one or the other parent form. (*c*) Hyper-chimæras in which the growing point is made up of a mosaic of cells derived from the two parent forms.

CHAPTER VII

HEREDITY

ALL plants arise from parents more or less like themselves. This reproduction has a visible material basis in the egg-cells and pollen-grains liberated from the parental bodies. By inheritance is meant all the qualities which have their physical basis in the fertilized egg-cell, the expression of which results in the organism. "Thus," says Thomson, "heredity is no force, no principle, but a convenient term for the genetic relation between successive organisms."

The inheritance of plants may be studied by considering parents and their offspring collectively or by studying the separate characters and their modes of transmission. The former is statistical, the latter, analytical. Studies of heredity from both points of view are being extensively conducted by the biometricians on the one hand and the mendelians on the other.

Heredity studied collectively. — "To define heredity," says Davenport, "as the direct and personal relation between the individual parent and the individual offspring is not only to restrict its meaning within too narrow limits, but to destroy its significance to the breeder and deceive him as to the actual facts of transmission during descent. 'Heredity' properly refers to the group that constitutes

149

Number of Tubers — 1909

Number of Tubers — 1910

V	1.5	3.5	5.5	7.5	9.5	11.5	13.5	15.5	17.5	19.5	21.5	23.5
1.5		1	2				1					
3.5	1	6	6	3	2	2						
5.5		4	6	8	8	5	6	1	2			
7.5		4	7	11	8	8	3	2				
9.5		2	7	17	13	15	4	1	3	1		1
11.5		2	2	14	11	14	6	3	4	2		
13.5			1	5	4	10	7	3	5		1	1
15.5	1	1	1	1	5	9	6	5	2	3	3	1
17.5				2	4	2	3	2	2	3		1
19.5			1		1	2	2			2	2	
21.5					2	1			1	1		2
23.5					2	1			1	1		
25.5						1			1			
27.5												
29.5				1								
31.5												
33.5									1			
f_{10}	2	20	33	62	60	70	38	19	22	13	6	6
$f_{10}V_{10}$	3.0	70.0	181.5	465.0	570.0	805.0	513.0	294.5	385.0	253.5	129.0	141.0
D_{10}	−9.7	−7.7	−5.7	−3.7	−1.7	+.30	2.30	4.30	6.30	8.30	10.30	12.30
D^2_{10}	94.09	59.29	32.49	13.69	2.89	.09	5.29	18.49	39.69	68.89	106.09	151.29
$D^2_{10}f_{10}$	188.18	1185.80	1072.17	848.78	173.40	6.30	201.02	351.31	873.18	895.57	636.54	907.74

25.5	27.5		41.5	43.5		f_{10}	$f_{03}V_{09}$	D_{09}	D^2_{09}	$D^2_{09}f_{09}$	ΣP
		....				4	6	−9.83	96.62	386.48	165.14
		....				20	70	−7.83	61.30	1226.00	814.32
		....				40	220	−5.83	33.98	1359.20	443.08
	1	....				44	330	−3.83	14.66	645.04	347.76
		....		1		65	617.5	−1.83	3.34	217.10	92.41
		....				58	667	0.17	.02	1.16	− 4.18
		....				37	499.5	2.17	4.70	173.90	119.56
2	1	....				41	635.5	4.17	17.38	712.58	535.01
		....				19	332.5	6.17	38.06	723.14	318.98
		....				10	195	8.17	66.74	667.40	285.95
		....				8	172	10.17	103.42	827.36	410.86
	1	....				7	164.5	12.17	148.10	1036.70	390.65
		....				2	51.0	14.17	200.78	401.56	93.52
		....				0		16.17	261.46		
		....				1	29.5	18.17	330.14	330.14	−67.22
		....				0		20.17	406.82		
1		....				2	67	22.17	491.50	983.0	456.70
3	3			1		358	4057			9690.76	4402.54
76.5	82.5			43.5		4013.0					
14.30	16.30			−32.30							
204.49	265.69			1043.29							
613.47	797.07			1043.29		9793.82					

$$M_{10} = 11.33 \pm .182$$
$$M_{09} = 11.20 \pm .182$$
$$\sigma_{09} = 5.20 \pm .130$$
$$\sigma_{10} = 5.23 \pm .131$$
$$r = \frac{4402.54}{358(5.2)(5.23)} = .452$$
$$Er = \frac{.6745(1 - r^2)}{\sqrt{n}}$$
$$= \frac{.6745(.80)}{18.9} = \pm .03$$

the parentage and the related group that constitutes
the offspring."

The coefficient of heredity. — The degree of inheritance
between a parental group of plants and their corresponding
group of offspring is determined by the use of a correlation
table. The degree of correlation or the resemblance is
determined between the parents and offspring. This may
be expressed mathematically and the result is known as
the "coefficient of heredity." The latter is, therefore,
nothing more nor less than the correlation coefficient (r)
obtained from a table in which two sets of individuals
related by descent are tabulated with respect to the same
character. The coefficient of heredity is expressed as a
decimal, somewhere between 0 and 1. The nearer 1,
the greater the closeness of resemblance between parents
and offspring, and conversely the nearer 0, the smaller
the degree of resemblance.

In the table (pp. 150–151) will be found the number of
tubers in hills of potatoes in 1909 as compared with the offspring from these hills in 1910. For example, there were 3
hills of seedling potatoes having either 7 or 8 tubers in 1909
represented in the table by the midpoint 7.5 which gave
offspring in 1910 having either 3 or 4 tubers (3.5); 8
parental hills numbering either 7 or 8 tubers in 1909 which
produced offspring in 1910 having either 5 or 6 tubers;
11 parental hills having the same number of tubers as
above which produced offspring having either 7 or 8 hills,
and so forth for each number in the table : —

Notation. —

n = Total number of individuals in the population,
equals summation of all frequencies.

f_{09} = Class frequencies of total population in 1909.

V_{09} = Value or measurement corresponding to a given frequency in 1909.

M_{09} = Mean number of potatoes per hill in 1909.

D_{09} = Deviation of number of tubers per hill from mean, 1909.

σ_{09} = Standard deviations of number of tubers per hill, 1909.

f_{10} = Class frequencies of total population in 1910.

V_{10} = Value or measurement corresponding to a given frequency in 1910.

M_{10} = Mean number of potatoes per hill in 1910.

D_{10} = Deviation of numbers of tubers per hill from mean, 1910.

σ_{10} = Standard deviation of number of tubers per hill, 1910.

r = Coefficient of correlation.

The process of finding the mean and standard deviation is the same as is given in Chapter IV, so that the only column that needs explanation is the one headed ΣP.

As an example, we will take the column on the 1910 tubers, beginning with 15.5. The figures 1, 1, 1, 1, 5, 9, 6, 5, 2, 3, 3, 1, 2, 1 are known as a horizontal array; similarly the vertical columns are known as a vertical array. We will now show how 535.01 in ΣP column is obtained.

The first number after 15.5 is 1. Going down the vertical column to column D_{10}, we find -9.7, which is multiplied by 1; the same process is gone through for each number following 15.5 and the algebraic sum is taken, which is multiplied by 4.17, found in column D_{09} opposite 15.5. So the result is as follows : —

$$4.17 + 1(-9.7) + 1(-7.7) + 1(-5.7) + 1(-3.7) + 5(-1.7) + 9(0.30) + 6(2.3) + 5(4.3) + 2(6.3) + 3(8.3) + 3(10.3) + 1(12.3) + 2(14.3) + 1(16.3) = 535.01.$$

Having obtained all the numbers in the ΣP column, the sum is taken and the coefficient of correlation is found according to the following formula : —

$$r = \frac{\Sigma P}{n(\sigma_{09})(\sigma_{10})}, \text{ or}$$

$$r = \frac{4402.54}{358(5.20)(5.23)} = .452$$

Conception of unit-characters. — Most recent studies are analytical in their nature. We now conceive of plants and animals to be composed of separately heritable units known as unit-characters. It is not possible at present to say exactly what a unit-character is, but we may call it the smallest heritable part or attribute a plant may possess. For example, the color of the flower, size and shape of leaf, height of the plant, susceptibility or immunity to disease, and so forth, may be unit-characters.

Knowledge of heredity has come through experimental breeding. — Much has been written and many conjectures made by earlier horticulturists in their attempt to classify hybrids so that inheritance could be found to proceed in an orderly and regular manner. All of these attempts had been more or less failures until Gregor Mendel, an Austrian monk, began a series of classic experiments in crossing garden peas. Mendel's work, however, was little known at the time and did not receive public recognition until many years afterwards.

Rediscovery of Mendel's work by de Vries and others. — de Vries made a thorough search of the literature of plant evolution. In an American publication [1] he saw a reference to an article on plant hybrids by G. Mendel, published in 1865 in the proceedings of a natural history of Brünn in Austria.

On looking up this paper he was astonished to find that it discussed fundamental questions of hybridization and heredity, and that it had remained practically unknown for a generation. In 1900 he published an account of it, and this was soon followed by independent discussions by Correns, Tschermak, and Bateson. In May, 1900, Bateson gave an abstract of Mendel's work before the Royal Horticultural Society of England; and later the society published a translation of Mendel's original paper. It is only within the last 10 or 12 years that a knowledge of Mendel's work has become widespread in this country. Perhaps the agencies that are most responsible for dis-

---

[1] The following extract from a letter from Professor de Vries (printed here by permission) will explain the reference in the text: "Many years ago you had the kindness to send me your article on 'Cross-breeding and Hybridizing' of 1892; and I hope it will interest you to know that it was by means of your bibliography therein that I learnt some years afterwards of the existence of Mendel's papers, which now are coming to so high credit. Without your aid I fear I should not have found them at all." My reference to Mendel in the bibliography referred to was taken from Focke's writing. I had not seen Mendel's paper. The essay, "Cross-breeding and Hybridizing," formed Chapter II of the old "Plant-Breeding"; but the bibliography that accompanied it was not reprinted until the second edition of the book. — L. H. B.

semination of the mendelian ideas in America are the instruction given by Webber and others in the Graduate School of Agriculture at Columbus, Ohio, in the summer of 1904 and the prolonged discussion before the International Conference on Plant Breeding at New York in the fall of 1902. Since that time many articles on the subject have appeared from our scientific press.

Mendel's work is important because it cuts across many of the current notions respecting hybridization. As de Vries' discussions call a halt in the current belief regarding the gradualness and slowness of evolution, so Mendel's call a halt in respect to the common opinion that the results of hybridizing are largely chance, and that hybridization is necessarily only an empirical subject. Mendel found uniformity and constancy of action in hybridization, and to explain this uniformity he proposed a theory of heredity.

One of the most significant points connected with Mendel's work is the great care he took to select plants for his experiments. He thought that hybridism is a complex and intricate subject, and that, if we are ever to discover laws, we must begin with the simplest and least complicated problems. He was aware of the general opinion that the most diverse and contradictory results are likely to follow any hybridization. He conceived that some of this diversity may be due to instability of parents rather than to the proper results of hybridizing. He also saw that he must exclude all inter-crossing in the progeny. Furthermore, the progeny must be numerous, for, since incidental and aberrant variation may arise in the plants, it is only by a study of averages of large numbers that the true results of the hybridization are to be discovered Moreover, the study must be more exact than a mere contrasting and comparing of plants : character must be compared with character.

Mendel's experiments. — The garden pea seemed to fulfill all of the requirements. Mendel chose well-marked horticultural races or varieties. He grew these two years before the experiment proper was begun in order to determine their stability or trueness to type. When the experiments were finally begun, he used only normal plants as parents, throwing out such as were weak or aberrant. Peas are self-fertile. It was to be expected that under such conditions the hybrid offspring would show uniformity of action; and it did.

In order to study the behavior of the hybrids, it was necessary to choose certain prominent marks or characters for comparison. Seven of these characters were chosen for observation. These marks pertain to seed, fruit, position of flowers, and length of stem, and they may be assumed to be representative of all other characters in the plant. These characters were paired (practically opposites) as long-stem *vs.* short-stem, round-seed *vs.* angular-seed, inflated pods *vs.* constricted pods. They were "constant" and "differentiating." Of course every parent plant possessed one or the other of every pair of contrasting characters; but in order to facilitate his studies, Mendel chose a special set of parents to illustrate each character.

The seed-shape characters were roundness and angularity — the former being the "smooth" pea of gardeners and the latter the "wrinkled" pea. Let us suppose that twenty-five flowers on round-seeded plants were cross-pollinated in the summer of 1900 with pollen from angular-seeded plants, or *vice versa*, and that an average of four seeds formed in each pod. With the death of the parent plants the old generation ended, and the 100 seeds that matured in 1900 — the year in which the cross was made — began the next generation; and these 100 seeds were hybrids. Now, all of these 100 seeds were round. Round-ness in this case was "dominant." (Dominance per-taining to the vegetative stage of the plant of course would not appear until 1901, when the seeds "grow.") These seeds are sown in the spring of 1901. If each seed be supposed to give rise to four seeds, — or 400 in all, — this next generation of seeds (produced in 1901) will show 300 round and 100 angular seeds. That is, the other seed-shape now appears in one-fourth of all the progeny; this character is said to have been "recessive" in the first hybrid generation. If the 100 angular seeds, or reces-sives, are sown in 1902, it will be found that all the progeny will be angular-seeded or will "come true"; and this occurs in all succeeding generations, providing no crossing takes place. If the 300 round seeds, or dominants, are sown in the spring of 1902, it will be found that 100 of them produce dominants only, and that 200 of them behave as before — one-fourth giving rise to recessives and three-fourths to dominants; and this occurs in all succeeding generations, providing no crossing takes place. In other words, the three-fourths of dominants in any generation are of two kinds, — one-third that produce only dominants, and two-thirds that are hybrids. That is, there is con-stantly appearing from the hybrids one-fourth that are recessives, one-fourth that are constant dominants, and one-half that are dominants to all appearances, but which in the next generation break up again into dominants and recessives. This one-half part that breaks up into the two characters are the true hybrids; but they are hybrids only in the sense that they hold each of the two parental characteristics — roundness and angularity — in their purity and not as blends or intermediates; and these two characteristics reappear in all succeeding generations in a definite mathematical ratio. Proportionally, these facts may be expressed as follows : —

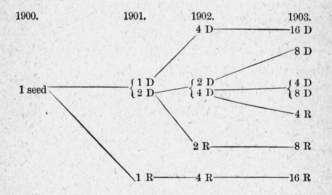

It will be seen that two-thirds of the dominants break up the following year into one-fourth constant dominants, one-fourth recessives, and one-half that again break up, the half that break up being the hybrids. This formula for the hybrids is Mendel's law. In words, it may be expressed as follows : Differentiating characters in plants reappear in their purity and in mathematical regularity in the second and succeeding hybrid offspring of these plants; the mathematical law is that each character separates in each of these generations in one-fourth of the progeny and thereafter remains true. In concise figures, it is expressed as follows:—

$$1\,D : 2\,DR : 1\,R.$$

1 *D* and 1 *R* come true, but 2 *DR* breaks up again into dominant and recessives in the ratio of 3 to 1.

Mendel found that this law holds more or less for the other characters that he studied in the pea, as well as for the seed-shape. He did not conclude, however, that it holds good for all plants, but left the subject for further investigation. It will be seen at once that it will be a very difficult matter to follow this law when many characters are to be constrasted, particularly when the characters are quantitative, or qualitative which grade into each other.

The dominant characters pertain to either parent. Some of them may come from the seed parent and some from the pollen parent. When this roundness is dominant from the male parent, there can be seen the immediate effect of pollen, the same as if the dominant roundness came from the female parent. In the case of the pea, the seed-content is embryo and we are not surprised to find this immediate effect of pollen. In those plants in which the embryo is embedded in endosperm, however, the effect of the cross-fertilization is not seen until the seed has been planted and produced a new generation. The endosperm is a part of the female parent and is not ordinarily changed by the process of cross-fertilization. In the case of a few plants, of which the Indian corn is the most conspicuous example (Fig. 43), there is double fecundation, both the embryo and endosperm being fertilized, and hence if the male parent contains dominant characters, they will be seen immediately because of the cross-fertilized endosperm. This is called Xenia and has been carefully worked out by de Vries, Webber,[1] and others.

Mendel's numerical results.[2] —

In the experiments conducted by Mendel with peas the relative numbers obtained for each pair of differentiating characters are as follows : —

Experiment 1. — Form of seed. From 253 hybrids, 7324 seeds were obtained in the second trial year. Among them were 5474 round and roundish and 1850 angular, wrinkled ones. Therefore, the ratio 2.96 is to 1 is deduced.

Experiment 2. — Color of albumen. 258 plants yielded 8023 seeds, 6022 yellow and 2001 green ; their ratio, therefore, is 3.01 to 1.

Experiment 3. — Color of seed-coats. Among 929 plants, 705 bore violet-red flowers and gray-brown seed-coats ; 224 had white flowers and white seed-coats, giving the proportion of 3.15 to 1.

Experiment 4. — Form of pods. Of 1181 plants, 882 had them simply inflated and in 299 they were constricted. Resulting ratio 2.95 to 1.

Experiment 5. — Color of unripe pods. The number

[1] Bull. 22, Div. of Veg. Phys. and Path., U. S. Dept. of Agric., 1900.

[2] The following is taken from a translation of Mendel's article as given by Bateson, and slightly revised. See Bateson-Mendel's "Principles of Heredity," Appendix.

M

Fig. 43. — Mendelism in maize. — Stowell Evergreen (sweet corn) was pollinated with Indian flour corn, giving a hybrid similar to the latter the first year. This was self-pollinated, giving the ear on the right, and pollinated with the evergreen, giving the ear on the left (Webber).

162

of trial plants was 500, of which 428 had green pods and 152 yellow pods. Consequently these stand in the ratio 2.82 to 1.

Experiment 6. — Position of flowers. Among 858 cases, 651 had inflorescence axial and 207 terminal. Ratio 3.14 to 1.

Experiment 7. — Length of stem. Out of 1064 plants in 787 cases the stem was long and in 277 short. Hence a mutual ratio of 2.84 to 1.

If the results of the whole experiment be brought together, there is found, as between the numbers of forms with the dominant and recessive characters, an average ratio of 2.98 to 1 or 3 to 1.

The following is an account of Mendel's results with peas in their third hybrid generation (F_3) : —

These forms which in the F_2 generation exhibit the recessive character do not further vary in the F_3 generation as regards this character : they remain constant in their offspring.

It is otherwise with those that possess the dominant character in the second generation. Of these, two-thirds yield offspring that display the dominant and recessive characters in the proportion of 3 to 1, and thereby show exactly the same ratio as the hybrid forms, while only one-third remain with the dominant character constant.

The separate experiments yield the following results : —

Experiment 1. — Among 665 plants which were raised from round seeds of the second generation, 193 yielded round seeds only, and remained, therefore, constant in this character; 372, however, gave both round and wrinkled seeds, in the proportion of 3 to 1. The number of the hybrids, therefore, as compared with the constants, is 1.93 to 1.

Experiment 2. — Of 509 plants which were raised from seeds whose albumen was of yellow color in the second generation, 166 yielded exclusively yellow,while 353 yielded yellow and green seeds, in the proportion of 3 to 1. There resulted, therefore, a division into hybrid and constant forms in the proportion of 2.13 to 1.

For each separate trial in the following experiments, 100 plants were selected which displayed the dominant character in the second generation, and in order to ascertain the significance of this, ten seeds of each were cultivated.

Experiment 3. — The offspring of 36 plants yielded exclusively gray-brown seed-coats, while of the offspring of 64 plants some had gray-brown and some had white.

Experiment 4. — The offspring of 29 plants had only inflated pods ; of the offspring of 71, on the other hand, some had inflated and some had constricted.

Experiment 5. — The offspring of 40 plants had only green pods ; of the offspring of 60 plants, some had green and some yellow ones.

Experiment 6. — The offspring of 33 plants had only axial flowers ; of the offspring of 67, on the other hand, some had axial and some terminal flowers.

Experiment 7. — The offspring of 28 plants inherited the long axis, and those of the 72 plants some of the long and some of the short axis.

In each of these experiments a certain number of plants came constant with the dominant character. For the determination of the proportion in which the separation of the forms with the constantly persistent character results, the first two experiments are of especial importance since in these a greater number of plants can be compared. The ratios 1.93 to 1 and 2.3 to 1 gave together almost exactly the average ratio of 2 to 1. The sixth experiment gave a quite concordant result; in the others the ratio varies more or less, as was only to be expected in view of the small number of 100 trial plants. Experiment 5, which shows the greatest departure, was repeated, and then in place of the ratio of 60 and 40 that of 65 and 35 resulted. The average ratio of 2 to 1 appears, therefore, as fixed with certainty. It is, therefore, demonstrated that, of those forms which possess the dominant character in the second generation, two-thirds have the hybrid-characters, while one-third remain constant with the dominant characters.

The ratio of 3 to 1, in accordance with which the distribution of the dominant and recessive characters results in the second generation, resolves itself, therefore, in all experiments into the ratio of $2:1:1$ if the dominant character be differentiated according to its significance as a hybrid-character or as a parental one. Since the second generation (F_2) springs directly from the seed of the first generation (F_1), it is now clear that the hybrids from seeds have one or the other of the two differentiating characters, and of those one-half develop again the hybrid form, while the other yields plants which remain constant and receive the dominant or the recessive characters, respectively, in equal numbers.

Dominance and recessiveness. — Which characters will

be dominant in any species we cannot determine until we perform the experiment; that is, there is no mark or attribute which distinguishes to us *a priori* a dominant or a recessive character. However, the mere fact as to whether the one or the other character is dominant is relatively unimportant, for constant dominance is no more a regular behavior than recessiveness is. In various subsequent experiments it has been found that even when marked dominance is not shown in the first product, the hybridization may follow the law in essential numerical results. The really important points are: (1) That the characters typically remain pure or do not blend, and (2) that their reappearance follows a numerical order.

Explanation of mendelian results. — After finding such surprising results as these, Mendel naturally endeavored to discover the reasons why. The product of his speculations is the theory of gametic purity (to use our present-day terminology), which is a partial theory of heredity. Every plant is the product of the egg, or female, cell fertilized by the sperm, or male, cell. When constant progeny is produced, it must be because the two cells, or gametes, are of like character. When inconstant progeny is produced, it must be because the sperm-cell is of one character and the egg-cell of another. When these unlike gametes come together, they will unite according to the law of mathematical probabilities, one-fourth of those of each kind coming together and one-half of those of both kinds coming together. If A and B represent the contrasting parental characteristics, they would combine as: —

$$A + A = A^2.$$
$$A + B = AB.$$
$$B + A = BA.$$
$$B + B = B^2.$$

A^2 and B^2 are equivalent only to A and B. Since both of the opposed or contrasted characters cannot be visible at the same time, we have the following: —

$$A$$
$$A^b$$
$$A^b$$
$$B$$

in which small b represents the character that for the time being is not able to express itself, or is recessive, and large B represents the same character fully expressed.

In these gametes, the unit-characters of the plants that bear them are pure. Even in hybrid plants the pollen-grains and the egg-cells are not hybrids. According to the hypothesis of gametic purity, therefore, hybrids follow natural and numerical laws; but these laws are always obscured by new crossing. True intermediate characters do not occur. If new characters appear, it is because they have been recessive or latent for a genera-tion, or because the plant has varied from other causes; they are not the proper results of hybridization, unless they are due to a reconstruction of characters. We may suppose that a new character that appears because of some internal change may be impressed on the gametes and thereby be perpetuated. The results of hybridiza-tion, according to the mendelian view, are not fundamentally a mere game of chance, but follow a law of regularity of averages; but the results are so often masked that it is sometimes impossible to recognize the law.

It is a question, of course, whether the proportional results secured by Mendel and others express a biological principle, or whether they are only the numerical proportions that may be adduced from the averages of large numbers of combinations — whether these combinations are of gametes or letters, or words, or figures. It is a fundamental necessity that certain proportions follow from "chance" combinations often repeated. But whether the "theorem of probabilities" can express a real biological fact may well be doubted. Perhaps the basis of heredity is something more than the mechanico-physical conceptions that we habitually apply to it.

Mendel's law of heredity is stated as follows by Bateson and Saunders: "The essential part of the discovery is the evidence that the germ-cells or gametes produced by cross-bred organisms may in respect of given characters be of the pure parental types and consequently incapable of transmitting the opposite character; that when such pure similar gametes of opposite sexes are united together in fertilization, the individuals so formed and their posterity are free from all taint of the cross, that there may be, in short, perfect or almost perfect discontinuity between these germs in respect of one of each pair of opposite characters."

The genetic constitutions of plants, if they are known, may be conveniently represented by formulæ containing the gametic make-up of the parents entering into their union. At least such unit-characters as are known may be represented in this manner. For example, RR may represent a plant which has been formed by the union of a red pollen-grain (pollen-grain from a pure red parent) R and a red egg-cell R. This plant if self-fertilized will always remain red. Similarly rr represents a plant which has the absence (or the opposite) of red, say, yellow. If a red plant R were crossed with a yellow plant r, the result would be a hybrid Rr. Red being dominant, the first generation hybrid, F_1, would appear as red.

The following method of squares will be found very convenient to illustrate the action of chance which governs the union of gametes to form the F_2 hybrid plants: —

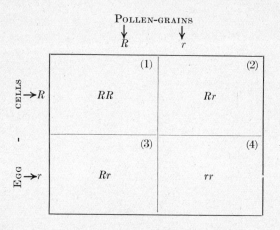

Square (1) represents a plant (RR) formed from the union of a red pollen-grain R with a red egg-cell R, and is pure red. Square (2) represents a hybrid plant (Rr) formed by r pollen-grain and R egg-cell. Square (3)

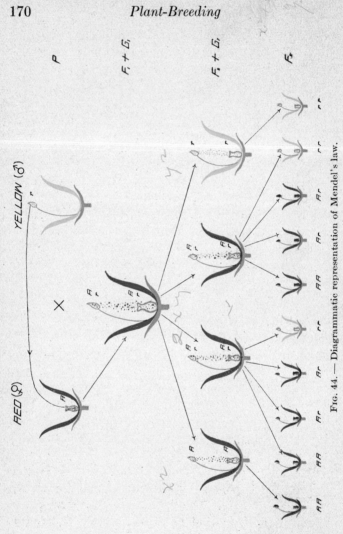

Fig. 44. — Diagrammatic representation of Mendel's law.

is the same as (2) except formed by pollen-grain R and egg-cell r, and square (4) is a pure recessive rr in which pollen-grain r united with egg-cell r.

This may be illustrated diagrammatically in another manner, as in the colored plate (Fig. 44).

Explanation of diagram. — It is assumed that a variety having red flowers (R) is crossed with another variety having yellow flowers (r). The arrow indicates the direction of the cross and also the transfer of pollen from the anthers of the yellow variety to the stigma of the red. The plants produced from these fertilized ovules will have red flowers because redness is dominant. This F_1 hybrid, however, contains both red and yellow qualities and at the time of the formation of its gametes will give rise to red and yellow pollen-grains and egg-cells. During the process of self-fertilization the law of chance will govern the union of the red and yellow egg-cells. These F_1 ovules will give rise to the plants indicated by F_2. The subsequent operations are assumed to follow regular mendelian ratios.

Mendel's results with the offspring of hybrids in which several differentiating characters are associated. — Two experiments were made with a considerable number of plants. In the first experiment the parental plants differed in the form of the seed and in the color of the albumen. Experiments with seed characters give the results in the simplest and most certain way.

Experiment 1. — Seed parent = round seeds (R) and yellow cotyledons (Y). Both dominant and hence their symbols are expressed as capital letters. Pollen parent = angular seeds (r) and green cotyledons (y). Round yellow (*RY*) × angular green (*ry*) = *RrYy* appearing as round and yellow in F_1.

Gametes of F_1 = *RY*, *Ry*, *rY*, and *ry*.

Visible types of F_2 = 9 (apparently) *RY*, 3 *Ry*, 3 *rY*, and 1 *ry*.

The following were actually found by Mendel in F_2 : —

RY, round and yellow, 315.

rY, angular and yellow, 101.

Ry, round and green, 108.

ry, angular and green, 32.

These figures stand approximately in the ratio of 9 *RY* : 3 *rY* : 3 *Ry* : 1 *ry*, but these forms, which appeared to be only four classes, were found in the next generation to be made up of nine really different classes.

From the round yellow seeds (apparently *RY*) there were obtained in the next year : —

1.	*RY*, round and yellow seeds,	38
2.	*RYy*, round, yellow and green seeds,	65
3.	*RrY*, round, yellow and angular seeds,	60
4.	*RrYy*, round, yellow and green angular, yellow and green,	138

From the round and green seeds (apparently *Ry*) were obtained : —

5.	*Ry*, round and green seeds,	35
6.	*Rry*, round angular and green seeds,	67

From the angular and yellow seeds (apparently *rY*) were obtained : —

7.	*rY*, angular and yellow seeds,	28
8.	*rYy*, angular and yellow-green seeds,	67

From the angular and green *ry* seeds were obtained : —

9.	*ry*, angular and green seeds,	30

Compare this carefully with problem 4 with special reference to the actual counts as compared with theoretical ones.

The offspring of the hybrids appeared, therefore, under nine different forms, some of them in very unequal numbers. When these are collected and coördinated, we find : —

> 38 plants with the sign RY.
> 35 plants with the sign Ry.
> 28 plants with the sign rY.
> 30 plants with the sign ry.
> 65 plants with the sign RYy.
> 68 plants with the sign rYy.
> 60 plants with the sign RrY.
> 76 plants with the sign Rry.
> 138 plants with the sign $RrYy$.

The whole of the forms may be classed into three essentially different groups. The first includes those with the signs RY (or $RRYY$, as previously designated — it is not necessary, however, to repeat the letters), Ry, rY, and ry; they possess only constant characters and do not vary again in the next generation. Each of these forms is represented, on the average, thirty-three times.

The second group includes the signs RYy, RrY, Rry, rYy; these are constant in one character and hybrid in another, and vary in the next generation only as regards the hybrid character. Each of these appears, on the average, sixty-five times. The form $RrYy$ occurs 138 times; it is hybrid in both characters and behaves as do the hybrids from which it is derived.

If the numbers in which the forms belonging to these classes appear, be compared, the ratios of 1, 2, and 4 are evidently unmistakable. The numbers 32, 65, 138 present very fair approximations to the ratio numbers of 33, 66, 132.

The developmental series consists, therefore, of nine classes of which four appear therein always once and are constant in both characters; the forms RY, ry resemble the parental forms, the two others present combinations between the conjoined characters R, r, Y, y, which combinations are likewise possibly constant. Four classes appear always twice, and are constant in one character and hybrid in the other. One class appears four times, and is hybrid in both characters. Consequently the offspring of the hybrids, if two kinds of differentiating characters are combined therein, are represented by the expression $RY — Ry — rY — ry — 2\,RYy — 2\,rYy — 2\,RrY — 2\,Rry — 4\,RrYy$.

This expression is indisputably a combination series in which the two expressions for the characters R and r, y and Y are combined. We arrive at the full number of the classes of the series by the combinations of the expressions.

The following, quoted from East, has reduced the above to a mathematical expression: "The numerical relations found are approximately the following series: AB, Ab, aB, ab, $2\,ABb$, $2\,aBb$, $2\,Aab$, $2\,AaB$, and $4\,AaBb$. This is really a combination by multiplication of the two series $(A — 2\,Aa — a) \times (B — 2\,Bb — b) = AB — Ab — aB — ab — 2\,ABb — 2\,aBb — 2\,Aab — 2\,AaB — 4\,AaBb$. The two pairs of characters behave independently of each other and as if chance only governed their combinations.

Moreover, three pairs of contrasted characters were found to behave in exactly the same manner, the number of forms found being what would theoretically be expected if the above product were multiplied by another series represented by $C - 2\ Cc - c$.

"These results can be reduced to still simpler terms, as is shown in the following table. Let N represent the number of pairs of contrasted characters in the parents. When they are crossed the second generation, when self-fertilized, shows visible differences of 2 to the nth power. These visibly different classes actually contain 3 to the nth power different classes, the phenomena of dominance obscuring part of them. Finally, when crossing to secure combinations of n characters, we must have 4 to the nth power number of individuals, to be theoretically certain of at least one individual in each class.

MENDEL'S LAW OF INHERITANCE OF UNIT-CHARACTERS

No. of Pairs of Dif. between Parents	No. of visibly Dif. Classes Each cont. One Pure Individual	No. of Actual Classes Both Pure and Hybrid	Smallest No. Offspring, allowing at least One to a Class	
n	$2\ n$	$3\ n$	$4\ n$	
1	2	3	4	Experimentally
2	4	9	16	tested by Men-
3	8	27	64	del for peas
4	16	81	256	
5	32	243	1024	Calculated
6	64	729	4096	

A is substituted for R, a for r, B for T, and b for t, and instead of writing AA and aa in the series, one of the letters is dropped."

TABLE I. — RESULTS IN F_2 WITH COMPLETE DOMINANCE IN EVERY CHARACTER-PAIR

Number of Classes and Percentage Frequency of Each Class, with Number of Dominants Left in Each Class of F_2 or Any Subsequent Generation

No. of Character-pairs	Total No. of Classes	n-0	n-1	n-2	n-3	n-4	n-5	n-6	n-7	n-8	n-9	n-10
0	1	1										
		100.00										
1	2	1	1									
		75.00	25.00									
2	4	1	2	1								
		56.25	18.75	6.25								
3	8	1	3	3	1							
		42.19	14.06	4.69	1.56							
4	16	1	4	6	4	1						
		31.64	10.55	3.52	1.17	0.391						
5	32	1	5	10	10	5	1					
		23.73	7.91	2.64	0.879	0.293	0.0977					
6	64	1	6	15	20	15	6	1				
		17.80	5.93	1.98	0.659	0.220	0.0732	0.0244				
7	128	1	7	21	35	35	21	7	1			
		13.35	4.45	1.48	0.494	0.165	0.0549	0.0183	0.00610			
8	256	1	8	28	56	70	56	28	8	1		
		10.01	3.34	1.11	0.371	0.124	0.0412	0.0137	0.00458	0.00153		
9	512	1	9	36	84	126	126	84	36	9	1	
		7.51	2.50	0.834	0.278	0.0927	0.0309	0.0103	0.00343	0.00114	0.000381	
10	1024	1	10	45	120	210	252	210	120	45	10	1
		5.63	1.88	0.626	0.209	0.0695	0.0232	0.00772	0.00257	0.000858	0.000286	0.0000954

Results involving three pairs of characters (trihybrid). —
When three allelomorphic pairs are concerned, the number of forms in the second and subsequent generations is greatly increased. For illustration, let us take a hypothetical case. Suppose we cross together a tomato having red fruit, dwarf vine, and hairy stems and leaves (the latter is hypothetical) with a variety having yellow fruit, tall vine, and smooth stems. Their formulæ would be as follows, using capitals again to represent dominant units and small letters to represent recessive units: red, dwarf, hairy (RtH) × yellow, tall, smooth (rTh), = red, tall and hairy (in appearance) $RrTtHh$. F_2 generation will be as shown in table on page 178.

In order to get a better understanding of the probable union of gametes of various kinds of crosses, the student should carefully master the method of squares, always having in mind that the use of formulæ is only a convenient method of representing plants. Each square represents a plant. (See methods as already outlined on page 169.) Capital letters will be used for dominant units and small letters for recessives as formerly. Plants having as their formulæ large and small of any letter, *i.e.* Rr, are hybrids (heterozygous) for that character, and those in which the letters are the same, *i.e.* RR, are pure (homozygous) for that character.

It will be seen that when three pairs of characters are involved, at least 64 squares are necessary to allow for the theoretically possible number of combinations to be formed. A very careful study of the table will show that there are produced 8 visible types (2^n) with proportions as follows: 27 Red Tall Hairy, RTH; 9 Red Tall smooth,

N

POLLEN-GRAINS

	RTH	RTh	RtH	Rth	rTH	rTh	rtH	rth
RTH	RR TT HH	RR TT Hh	RR Tt HH	RR Tt Hh	Rr TT HH	Rr TT Hh	Rr Tt HH	Rr Tt Hh
RTh	RR TT Hh	RR TT hh	RR Tt Hh	RR Tt hh	Rr TT HH	Rr TT hh	Rr Tt Hh	Rr Tt hh
RtH	RR Tt HH	RR Tt Hh	RR tt HH	RR tt Hh	Rr Tt HH	Rr Tt Hh	Rr tt HH	Rr tt Hh
Rth	RR Tt Hh	RR Tt hh	RR tt Hh	RR tt hh	Rr Tt HH	Rr Tt hh	Rr tt Hh	Rr tt hh
rTH	Rr TT HH	Rr TT Hh	Rr Tt HH	Rr Tt Hh	rr TT HH	rr TT Hh	rr Tt HH	rr Tt Hh
rTh	Rr TT Hh	Rr TT hh	Rr Tt Hh	Rr Tt hh	rr TT HH	rr TT hh	rr Tt Hh	rr Tt hh
rtH	Rr Tt HH	Rr Tt Hh	Rr tt HH	Rr tt Hh	rr Tt HH	rr Tt Hh	rr tt HH	rr tt Hh
rth	Rr Tt Hh	Rr Tt hh	Rr tt Hh	Rr tt hh	rr Tt HH	rr Tt hh	rr tt Hh	rr tt hh

(Left margin label: EGG-CELLS)

NOTE. It must be remembered that these are different visible types and not actual types. For example, the 27 which appear as *RTH* are not all alike, their identity is obscured of dominance.

RTh ; 9 Red dwarf Hairy, *RtH* ; 9 yellow Tall Hairy, *rTH* ; 3 Red dwarf smooth, *Rth* ; 3 yellow Tall smooth, *rTh* ; 3 yellow dwarf Hairy, *rtH* ; and 1 yellow dwarf smooth, *rth*. Of course most of the visible types are multiple, containing both pure and hybrid forms. The number of actually different types is 27 (3^n) .

Incomplete dominance. — It was stated previously that dominance is due to an unequal potency between the unit-characters associated in a cross, the dominant unit being "stronger" and covering up the weaker unit in the F_1 generation.

This is not always the rule, by any means. There are various degrees of equilibrium between the opposed units : if one is much stronger than the other, complete dominance occurs ; if they are of equal potency, we have a form in the first generation which is intermediate between the two parents. This intermediacy may lean to one parent or the other in proportion to their strength.

When intermediacy exists, the mendelian ratios are somewhat modified. Instead of having 3 : 1 ratio, we have a 1 : 2 : 1, in which the 2 represents the heterozygous or intermediate forms and the 1's represent the homozygous forms.

If we are concerned with more than one allelomorphic pair, complete dominance may occur in certain units and intermediacy or incomplete dominance in others.

The commercial carnation is a heterozygous form which is an intermediate between a single type and a type which in commerce is called a "bull-head" or a "buster." This latter is exceedingly double. When the hybrid commercial types are self-fertilized, they produce progeny in the approximate ratio of 1 single : 2 commercial doubles : 1 double-double or bull-head (Fig. 45).

Fig. 45. — Hybrid carnation (center) between a single and a burster, showing intermediacy.

The hybrids between a large, apple-shaped tomato and a small, pear-shaped one are intermediate between the parents in the first generation, as has already been noted. In all probability there are represented in the above characters more than one unit. Emerson has made similar observations in beans, gourds, and maize, Locke in maize, and Castle in rabbits.

"While it is not uncommon," says Spillman, "for a character to be dominant or recessive in a cross, it is seldom that dominance is absolute. The presence of the recessive characters can easily be detected, and in some cases very easily. Thus in the cross between bearded and smooth wheat the hybrids usually show a slight tendency to be bearded. Likewise, the cross between horned and polled cattle may have scars (hornlessness is dominant). It frequently happens that instead of either of two opposite characters being dominant, we get a form intermediate between the two parent forms. Thus, in the cross between long-headed wheat and the short-headed club wheats of the Pacific Coast, the hybrids have heads of intermediate length, though they are much more like club wheat than they are like the ordinary kinds, so that the club character is at least partially dominant. In certain crosses between red-flowered and white-flowered ornamental plants the hybrids are pink."

Presence-and-absence hypothesis. — The phenomena of mendelian inheritance may be explained in one of two ways: first, the presence of a definite substance in the germ cells of both parents representing each unit-character in the allelomorphic pair, and, second, the "presence-and-absence" hypothesis. The latter assumes that what appears to be a pair of characters is really the presence and absence of a single character.

Examples of mendelian inheritance due to the presence-and-absence of a single unit. — Red flowers may be due to the presence of red, and white flowers to its absence.

The wrinkled pea owes its character to the absence of something which the round pea possesses. Darbishire has found in the round pea that all of the sugar has been converted into starch, while only a part of it has been thus converted in the wrinkled pea and the wrinkling is primarily due to the escape of the water from the solution of sugar left over after ripening, and, consequently, in the last resort due to the absence of that which completes the conversion of the sugar into starch or, at any rate, to an insufficiency in the quantity of that substance, whatever it is. The round pea has the full share of this substance, the wrinkled pea an insufficient one. Something is absent from the wrinkled which is fully present in the round.

The same author applies the presence-and-absence hypothesis to another pair of characters in peas, the color of the cotyledons. The two characters which meet the eye are yellow and green. But the matter is not so simple as this. Bunyard has shown that there is a yellow and a green pigment *both* in the yellow and in the green cotyledon. When both are present at the same time, as in the ripe but still moist pea, the green masks the yellow. All peas, both yellow and green varieties, are green when they are eaten. Just as cooks think that all peas are round, so they think that all peas are green. It is only gardeners who sow and harvest them who know the distinction between yellow and green.

The ripe but still moist cotyledons of both yellow- and green-seeded varieties are, therefore, green. The yellow kinds become yellow as they ripen; the green do not change color during this process. The yellowing of the former is brought about by the gradual fading and disappearance of the green pigment, which thus leaves the yellow pigment (which is present in both kinds) exposed. The successive stages in the fading of the green can be easily observed. The simultaneous presence of both green and yellow pigment in yellow and in green peas has also been demonstrated.

Green-seeded varieties therefore contain two pigments in their cotyledons, a yellow and a green; neither of them fades during the process of ripening, and inasmuch as the green masks the yellow, the ripe seed is green. Yellow-seeded varieties also contain the same two pigments, but the green fades in the process of ripening, so that the ripe seed is yellow. This fading of the green pigment in the yellow pea is supposed to be brought about by the *presence* of some substance which is *absent* from the green pea. Similarly, when the apparent absence of a character is dominant, as in the case of dominance of hornlessness in cattle and of white color in swine, there is believed to be present an inhibiting factor or "inhibitor" which prevents the formation of the black pigment. In other words, it is the *presence* of the inhibitor (causing white) over its *absence* (black) which explains the phenomena of the dominance of white over black.

It is not the dominance of an absent factor, but the presence of an unseen *inhibitor*, which reacts upon the otherwise visible character, causing it to disappear.

Let us now consider another type of cause which may be explained on the basis of the presence-and-absence hypothesis. The heredity of the combs of fowls has been carefully studied by Bateson, Davenport, Punnett, and others. The latter gives an excellent description [1] of this on the presence-and-absence hypothesis.

Four types of combs are recognized; namely, rose, pea, walnut, and single. (See Fig. 46.)

[1] Punnett, "Mendelism," pp. 35, 36.

Rose and pea combs behave as simple dominants to single comb, segregating in the F_2 generation in the normal 3 : 1 ratio. What happens when the two dominants are bred together? It was found that a third type appeared as an F_1 hybrid, the so-called walnut comb. When these F_1 hybrids were bred *inter se*, four types of

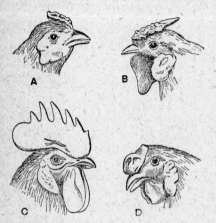

FIG. 46. — Fowls' combs: *A*, pea; *B*, rose; *C*, single; *D*, walnut.

combs were found among the F_2 progeny; namely, walnut, pea, rose, and single in the approximate ratios of 9 : 3 : 3 : 1 respectively. What is the explanation of this unusual phenomenon?

We are evidently concerned with two allelomorphic pairs of characters, which are the presence-and-absence of rose comb (R) and the presence-and-absence of pea comb (P). As suggested by Punnett, let us denote the rose comb by *RRpp* (containing the presence of rose and the absence of pea) and the pea comb by *rrPP*. When these are crossed together, the zygote *RrPp* results. This differs from either and has a walnut comb. When these F_1 hybrids are crossed together ($RrPp \times RrPp$), the following results may be graphically expressed in the series of squares : —

SPERMATOZOA

	RP	Rp	rP	rp
RP	RP RP Walnut	RP Rp Walnut	RP rP Walnut	RP rp Walnut
Rp	RP Rp Walnut	Rp Rp Rose	Rp rP Walnut	Rp rp Rose
rP	RP rP Walnut	Rp rP Walnut	rP rP Pea	rP rp Pea
rp	RP rp Walnut	Rp rp Rose	rp rP Pea	rp rp Single

OVA

Diagram to illustrate the nature of the F_2 generation from the cross of rose comb × pea comb. (After Punnett.)

All the resulting zygotes containing both rose and pea (*RP*) will be walnut; those containing rose only (*R*) and not pea (*p*) will be rose and those containing pea only (*P*) and not rose (*r*) will be pea-combed. But all individuals containing neither rose nor pea will have single combs. This was found to be a pure recessive and to breed true. The character of singleness seems to underlie all the types of comb and appears whenever allowed to do so by the absence of something representing the other kinds.

Mendelian inheritance of color. — Colors of plants or animals are generally very complex and often consist of many units of different kinds. Very rarely a certain color may be said to be due to a single unit acting alone. A knowledge of the kinds of color and the constitution of each is necessary to understand their inheritance.

1. White is due to the absence of pigment, and to the reflection of light from the cells.

2. Green color is caused by the presence of a green pigment in the chlorophyll.

3. Yellow, cream, and related colors are due to a yellow pigment either associated with green in the chloroplasts or found alone in the chromoplasts, generally the latter. Yellow may sometimes come from the cell-sap.

4. Red color may, under certain circumstances, be due to the presence of that pigment in the chromoplasts, but it is ordinarily a cell-sap color.

5. Most of the remaining colors, purple, blue, generally red, pink, etc., are due to pigments in the cell-sap.

6. Many of the colors and shades found in flowers are the result of both plastid colors and cell-sap colors acting together in various amounts.

7. Certain of the denser plastids or cell-sap colors may cover up the more delicate colors so that they cannot be seen.

8. Finally, the color in the cell-sap may be due to the relative presence of a non-nitrogenous and chemical substance anthocyanin. This is blue in an alkaline and red in acid reacting cell-sap, and, under certain conditions, also dark red, violet, dark blue, and even blackish blue. Anthocyanin can be obtained from the supersaturated cell-sap of a number of deeply colored parts of plants in a crystalline or amorphous form. Blood-colored leaves, such as those of the Copper Beach, owe their characteristic appearance to the united presence of green chlorophyll and anthocyanin. The different colors of flowers are due to the varying color of the cell-sap, to the different dis-

tribution of the cells containing the colored cell-sap, and also to the combinations of dissolved coloring matter with the yellow, orange, and red chromoplasts and the green chloroplasts. There is occasionally found in the cell-sap a yellow coloring matter known as xan-thein; it is nearly related to xanthophyll, but soluble in water.

Thus we see the plant colors are not always unit-charac-ters, such as hairiness, glabrousness, and the like. Certain colors found in plants, purple flowers, for example, are the result of the union of certain other pigments. These pigments are produced by definite units in the gametes. Color inheritance thus becomes very complicated as the results of certain crossings indicate.

White flowers in F_2 from red $\times$ cream. — Bateson points out a typical case of the paradoxical appearance of white-flowered individuals in the F_2 from the cross of a sap-colored variety with a variety having cream-colored flowers. For example, in sweet peas or stocks, when a red-flowered type is crossed with a cream, F_1 is red with-out any cream color. F_2 consists of 9 without cream, 3 reds with cream, 3 whites, 1 cream.

The red-flowered variety consists of red sap color only and the cream variety of yellow plastids only. These are inherited separately in the hybrids. The 9 reds of the F_2 hybrids have a much brighter red color than the red-creams. In the latter the red is diluted by the yellow plastids.

When the allelomorphs are correctly distinguished, the significance of this series is obvious. The operations may be shown in tabular form, thus : —

Parents . . . . Red variety ✕ Cream variety

Allelomorphs . $\begin{cases} \text{Red sap } (D) \\ \text{Colorless corpuscles } (D) \end{cases}$ Colorless sap (r) / Yellow corpuscles (r)

F_1 . . . . $\begin{cases} \text{Red sap} \\ \text{Colorless corpuscles} \end{cases}$

F_2

Red sap Colorless corpuscles	Red sap Yellow corpuscles	Colorless sap Colorless corpuscles	Colorless sap Yellow corpuscles

Appearance   9 red   3 red-cream   3 white   1 cream

The ratio 9 : 3 : 4. — The F_2 ratio, 9 : 3 : 4, is one which very frequently occurs in mendelian analysis. For example, as Tschermak found, when a pink-and-white flowered eating pea (*Pisum sativum*) is crossed with a white-flowered type, F_1 is often the original purple-flowered. Then F_2 will be

9 purple : 3 pink and white : 4 white.

In this case the factor for purple is evidently brought in by the albino. The latter contains the presence of purple, which needs a factor from the other parent to bring it out, and the absence of pink and white. The other parent contains the presence of pink and white and the absence of a factor for purple. All that is essential for the production of the ratio in F_2 is that F_1 should be heterozygous for two factors, of which one is perceptible whenever present, while the other needs the presence of the first in order that its own effects may be manifested.

Emerson's experiments with beans. — By crossing self-colored varieties of beans with white varieties, Emerson obtained in the F_1 generation, 65 mottled. In F_2 generation there were 113 mottled, 52 self-colored, and 70 white, that is, in the ratio of 6.45 : 2.97 : 4 instead of 9 : 3 : 4.

In the F_3 generation he secured the following results : —

1. All white seeds produced white seeds.
2. 7 mottled gave 22 mottled, 19 self-colored, 11 white.
3. 2 mottled yielded 13 mottled, 13 self-colored.
4. 4 mottled bore 5 mottled, 5 white.
5. 2 mottled produced 6 mottled.
6. 5 self-colored gave 63 self-colored.
7. 9 self-colored yielded 80 self-colored, 29 whites.

For the purpose of explaining the above, Emerson adopted the formula of Shull.

1. P and p for the factor presence and absence of pigment.
2. M and m for the factor presence and absence of mottling.
3. Pm = self-colored.
4. pM = white.
5. PM = mottled.

Thus he considers a self-colored variety containing the factor for pigment and having no factor for mottling. The white variety lacks the factor for pigment, but has the factor for mottling. The mottled form is originated by the presence of two factors, for the pigment and mottling.

If we follow these formulæ, we must confer to the F_1 generation the following gametic composition, $PpMm$, since F_1 hybrids will produce 9 mottled, 3 self-colored, and 4 white for the F_2 generation as seen on page 190 : —

POLLEN-GRAINS

	PM	*Pm*	*pM*	*pm*
PM	*PM* *PM* Mottled	*Pm* *PM* Mottled	*pM* *PM* Mottled	*pm* *PM* Mottled
Pm	*PM* *Pm* Mottled	*Pm* *Pm* Self	*pM* *Pm* Mottled	*pm* *Pm* Self
pM	*PM* *pM* Mottled	*Pm* *pM* Mottled	*pM* *pM* White	*pm* *pM* White
pm	*PM* *pm* Mottled	*Pm* *pm* Self	*pM* *pm* White	*pm* *pm* White

EGG-CELLS (left margin label)

The ratio of $6.45 : 2.97$, instead of $9 : 3 : 4$, seems to be chiefly due to the paucity of number treated for hybridization. Doubtless it is no small importance to study the ratio of offspring in F_3 in the light of the theoretical deduction. But here again the insufficient number of seeds informs us of its inadvisibility.

In conclusion Emerson says: "The result of most of my own experiments might be explained as due to the mendelian behavior of an allelomorphic pair, *Mm* presence and absence of mottling, *M* being visible only in the presence of *P*."

Colored forms from white $\times$ white and the $9 : 7$ ratio. — In the case of the sweet peas, Bateson has shown that the formation of color in the flowers can be proved to depend on the coexistence of *two complementary factors* in the individual.

He says that the first indication of this phenomenon

was found in the fact that two plants, each totally devoid
of color in the flowers and stems and each breeding true
to albinism may, when crossed together, give purple
flowers in F_1. The two white parents each contain a
factor which, alone, is incapable of forming color. Each
of these factors is independently transmitted in gameto-
genesis, and thus in F_2 the ratio of colored individuals to
whites is 9 : 7. This proportion depends on the fact that
a series of 16 individuals is necessary to exhibit all the
possible combinations of germ cells, for, as in any example
of hybridization involving two pairs of allelomorphs,
there will be four types of female cells and four types of
male cells produced by F_1. Of these sixteen individuals,
9 will contain both the dominant or present factors, while
of the remaining seven individuals, 3 will contain one
dominant, 3 will contain the other, and 1 will contain
neither. There will, therefore, be 9 which are colored
and 7 which are albino. In the diagram (p. 192) C
and R are the symbols representing the two complementary factors, c and r being their respective allelomorphic absences.

Absence factors. — It may be well for us in this connection
to touch upon the different conceptions of several investigators on such characters as cannot be seen without resorting
to breeding tests. Tschermak considers the appearance of
mottling in F_1 between a white and self-colored varieties
due to the presence of mottling in a latent condition in
the self-colored variety. Latency in his view is inactivity.
Shull often speaks of latent characters, but latency,
according to him, means invisibility and not dormancy or
inactivity.

POLLEN-GRAINS

	CR	Cr	cR	cr
CR	CR CR Colored	Cr CR Colored	cR CR Colored	cr CR Colored
Cr	CR Cr Colored	Cr Cr White	cR Cr Colored	cr Cr White
cR	CR cR Colored	Cr cR Colored	cR cR White	cr cR White
cr	CR cr Colored	Cr cr White	cR cr White	cr cr White

EGG-CELLS

Composition of the 9 colored and 7 albino offspring in F_2 from the cross between the albino Cr with albino cR, showing the ratio 9 colored : 7 albino.

On the other hand, Bateson advocates the undesirability of using such a terminology. He scorns the idea that there is latency of mottling or red in the white forms. Certain factors may be present which are absolutely necessary for the production of such pigments, but this fact does not lead us to contend that there are those colors latent. He emphasizes stating that "sulphate of copper is blue and chloride of copper is green, but it would be incorrect to speak of blue as latent in sulphuric acid, or of green as latent in hydrochloric acid."

Hurst seems to have difficulty to perceive a factor for absence. He brings forth three distinct views : —

1. The absence factor may be a concrete one, literally representing absence.

2. It may be nothing but presence in a latent state.

3. There may not be such a factor as the absence factor.

Of the three proposed, the first seems to be, Hurst remarks, the simplest, but it is difficult to realize and understand how such an absence factor is originated. Furthermore, he says: "There are many cases where the factor for presence is in a latent condition." The third explanation meets an objection in the fact that there is no pairing of factors in cross-breeding. Consequently, it follows that, according to this view, it is impossible to explain the phenomenon of segregation.

Mutations resulting from mendelian segregation and recombination. — It is very probable that many mutations which appear suddenly and remain constant are the result of mendelian segregation and recombination. If many unit-characters are involved, it is easily perceived how certain combinations of these would produce plants of unusual appearance which will be homozygous and breed true. Reference to Table I, p. 176, will show the great possibilities of obtaining apparently new characters by new combinations of old ones. It will be noted that when as many as 10 allelomorphs are involved, and this does not seem to be an impossible number, there is the possibility of producing 1024 different visible types.

Mutations which mendelize are constant. — The effect of swamping of mutations by crossing is prevented because of their continued identity due to the purity of the germ-cells which represent them.

Mutations may be due to three things: (*a*) the acquisition of one or more new characters, (*b*) the loss of

o

one or more characters, and (*c*) recombination of existing characters.

If the mutation is due to the addition of a new character and it remains constant, there must be present in its germ-cells some unit to represent that new character as there was in the gametes of the parent which produced it. Likewise, if a character is lost, its germinal potentiality must have become lost or entered into a latent condition.

If mutations of these types are crossed, the new gametic representatives or absences in the case of a lost character become pure in the germ-cells and reappear in the next generation.   Hence they are not lost.

If the mutation has a hybrid beginning and is due to an unusual combination of characters, this condition cannot be lost, as this certain combination which has once occurred will reproduce true if it is homozygous, or if not, it having occurred once may appear again through a like combination of unit-characters even though crossing and amphimixis may have taken place.

Mendelism in wheat. — As a specific example of evident mendelian results, W. J. Spillman, agriculturist of the Department of Agriculture, here explains some of his experiments with wheat.[1]   Mr. Spillman independently discovered numerical results, before the knowledge of the mendelian experiments had become generally known.

"The photograph (Fig. 47) shows three generations of one of my hybrid wheats. Of the three heads in the upper row, the left-hand one is the male parent (variety Valley); the right-hand one is the female parent (variety

[1] Published in fourth edition of this work, 1906; and here reproduced nearly entire for its historical as well as for its plant-breeding value.

Fig. 47. — Three generations of hybrid wheat: A 1 = male parent,
A 2 = the hybrid, A 3 = female parent; B 1–6 = the progeny of A 2;
C 1 = progeny of B 1, C 2–4 = progeny of B 2, C 5 = progeny of B 3,
C 6 and 7 = progeny of B 4, C 8–13 = progeny of B 5, C 14 and 15
= progeny of B 6. The results in the fourth generation, available
too late to include in the photograph, indicate that B 2 and B 3,
while not always separable on external appearances, are absolutely
different, the one being hybrid, the other pure.

Little Club); and the middle one is the hybrid. The
second row shows the second generation, and the third
row the third generation. Of the six types in the second
generation, the following points are important: Each

type was present in a certain proportion, which was approximately the same as in thirteen other similar cases, and the average of these fourteen cases approximated the theoretical numbers called for by Mendel's hypothesis of the disjunction of parental characters. The three at the left, being bearded, possess a character which was latent in the first generation. The fact that the beards show in these three indicates that the opposite character is absent, and they should therefore remain bearded in succeeding generations. That is, they are no longer hybrid with reference to this character. It will be observed that this was actually the case, for no beardless heads appeared in the progeny of either of these three (see lower row, first five heads). The following diagram will show the character of each of the six types in row 2. In this diagram the letters have the following meanings :—

B = bearded (written b when latent).

S = smooth (not bearded).

L = long heads.

C = Club heads (short).

I = Intermediate in length of head. (The hybrid was intermediate in this respect.)

PARENTS	FIRST GENERATION	SECOND GENERATION
		1 *BL*
		2 *BI*
BL		1 *BC*
		2 *SbL*
	SbI	4 *SbI*
		2 *SbC*
		1 *SL*
		2 *SI*
SC		1 *SC*
		16

"This diagram shows the nine types called for by Mendel's theory. Of these, *BL*, *BC*, *SL*, and *SC* are no longer hybrids — at least they have no latent characters, and will therefore reproduce true to seed. Of the remaining five types, *BI* and *SI* are hybrid only with reference to length of head, and *SbL* and *SbC* only with reference to beards; while *SbI* is hybrid with reference to both characters, as in the preceding generation.

"It will readily be seen that the types *BL* and *BC* can be separated from the others even by external appearances, and obtained in a pure state. *BL* is the type shown at the left in the second row in the picture, and all its progeny was like it, showing that it conformed to theory. *BC* is the type shown at No. 3 in the second row of heads; being pure, it should reproduce itself true to type, which it did, with an easily explained exception to be noted below. The type *BI* (shown at No. 2, row 2), being hybrid with reference to length of head, should produce again all types based on this character, and it did this, as is seen in heads 2–4, row 3. Referring again to the above diagram, it will be seen that the types *SL* and *SbL* cannot be distinguished by external characters. *SL* will of course reproduce true to type, while *SbL* will reproduce *SL*, *SbL*, and *BL*. Now *SL* and *SbL* being mixed together in the selection made in the second generation, we shall find a large percentage of *SL* mixed with some *SbL* from which it cannot be distinguished, and a small percentage of *BL* in the third generation. Heads 6 and 7, row 3, show that the types called for actually occurred. Types *SI* and *SbI* of the diagram appear alike externally, and were therefore selected together in the second generation (see head

5, row 2). Now *SI* should produce the types *SL*, *SI*, *SC*, while *SbI* should produce all nine types again (these nine types can be separated only into six by external appearance). It is therefore seen that the group represented by head 5, row 2, should produce all six types again. Heads 8–13, row 3, show these types. Types *SbC* and *SC* of the diagram are alike externally, and were hence selected together last year. Of these *SC* should produce only *SC*, while *SbC* should produce *SC*, *SbC*, and *BC*. But since *SC* and *SbC* look alike, the progeny of these two types should show only *SC* and *BC*. The last two heads in row 3 show that this actually occurred.

"In the single set of heads shown, there were two easily explained exceptions to theory. It will be seen that heads 2 and 3, row 2, differ only in length; now the group represented by head 2 varied in length from that of 1 to that of 3. In separating 2 and 3, it might easily happen that some of 3 should be placed with 2. In this case the progeny of 3 would show a few heads like 1, and this was the case. I have shown in the photograph only the heads called for by theory, for it would only lead to confusion to include the exceptions which would probably not have occurred if 2 and 3 of row 2 had been accurately separated last year. Again, in the progeny of the group represented by head 5, row 2, only five of the six types shown (row 3, heads 8–13) were found in this particular case, though all six were found in most of the others. As the missing type should constitute only $4\frac{1}{6}$ per cent of the group, and as it differed from one of the others only slightly, it is possible that it was included with the related type when the selections were made.

"I have not yet seen the data for the third generation of all these wheats, but those which are at hand are decidedly interesting. The following are the data for the third generation of the cross between Jones Winter Fife (male) and Little Club (female). The fife is long-headed and has velvet chaff (V); the Club short-headed, and has glabrous chaff (G). Velvet proved to be dominant over glabrous and the hybrids were intermediate in length. Type I of the second generation included the two types VL and VgL, since these could not be distinguished by external appearances. Seed of Type I produced in the third generation: —

	PERCENTAGE OF TYPES	
PLOT	I $= VL$	II $= GL$
1	87	13
2	81	19
Theory	$83\frac{1}{3}$	$16\frac{2}{3}$

The figures for the remaining five second-generation types are as follows: —

TYPE II $= GL$

	PERCENTAGE OF TYPES
PLOT	II
1	100
2	100
Theory	100

TYPE III $= VI$ AND VgI

PLOT	I	II	III	IV	V	VI
1	21	7	38	9	20	5
2	19	$4\frac{1}{2}$	38	12	15	$4\frac{1}{2}$
Theory	$20\frac{5}{6}$	$4\frac{1}{6}$	$41\frac{2}{3}$	$8\frac{1}{3}$	$20\frac{5}{6}$	$4\frac{1}{6}$

TYPE IV = GI

PLOT	II	IV	VI
1	28	52	20
2	31	47	22
Theory	25	50	25

TYPE V = VC AND VgC

PLOT	I	II	V	VI
1	2.4		80.0	17.6
2	4.7	2.6	79.8	12.9
Theory			$83\frac{1}{3}$	$16\frac{2}{3}$

TYPE VI = GC

PLOT	II	VI
1	7.7	92.3
2	—	100.0
Theory		100.0

"The only departures from theory of any consequence in these data are the occurrence of small amounts of Types I and II in the progeny of V, and of II in the progeny of VI. Now, Type V of the second generation (VC and VgC) differed from Type III (VI) only in being slightly shorter. If a few individuals of III had been included in V in separating the types of the second generation, we should have the actual result obtained in the third generation. Likewise, Type VI of the second generation (GC) differed from II (GI) in the same manner. Evidently a few plants of II got into the Type VI last year, and thus gave the results shown."

Mendelism summarized. — This, in barest epitome, is the teaching of Mendel. This teaching strikes at the root of two or three difficult and vital problems. It represents a new conception of the proximate mechanism of heredity, although it does not represent a complete hypothesis of heredity, since it begins with the gametes after they are formed and does not account for the constitution of the gametes, nor the way in which the parental characters are impressed upon them. This hypothesis focuses our attention along new lines, and will arouse more discussion than Weismann's hypothesis did; and it will have a much wider influence. Whether it expresses the actual means of heredity or not it is yet much too early to say; but this hypothesis is a greater contribution to science than the so-called "Mendel Law" as to the numerical results of hybridization: the hypothesis attempts to explain the "law."

One great merit of the hypothesis is the fact that its basis is a morphological unit, or at least an appreciable unit, not a mere imaginary concept. This unit should be capable of direct study, at least in some of its phases. It would seem that the mendelian hypothesis would give a new direction to cytological research.[1]

It is yet too early to say how far Mendel's law applies. We shall need to restudy the work that has been done and to do new work along more definite lines. There are relatively few former results or experiments that can be conformed to Mendel's law, because the data are not complete enough or not made from the proper point of view. We should expect the fundamental results to be masked when the plants with which we work are

[1] See, for example, "A Cytological Basis for the Mendelian Laws," Bull. Torr. Bot. Club, 29, 657 (1902), by W. A. Cannon; and other papers of this kind.

themselves unstable, when cross-fertilization is allowed to take place, or when the pairs of contrasting characters are very numerous and very complex.

Application to plant-breeding. — The wildest prophecies have been made in respect to the application of Mendel's law to the practice of plant-breeding, for the mathematical formulæ express only definiteness and precision. Unfortunately, the formulæ cannot express the indefiniteness and the unprecision which even Mendel found in his work. The greatest benefit of Mendel's work to the plant-breeder will be in improving the methods of experimenting. We can no longer be satisfied with mere "trials" in hybridizing: we must plan the work with great care, have definite ideals, "work to a line," and make accurate and statistical studies of the separate marks or characters of plants. His work suggests what we are to look for.

The time may come when the hybridizer will be able with many plants to make out beforehand plans and specifications for their breeding and for carrying these through with a large degree of exactness.

The best breeders now breed to unit-characters, for this is the significance of such expressions as "avoid breeding for antagonistic characters," "breed for one thing at a time," "know what you want," "have a definite ideal," "keep the variety up to a standard." In certain classes of plants the mendelian laws will be found to apply with great regularity, and in these we shall be able to know beforehand about what to expect (Fig. 48). The number of cases in which the law or some modification of it applies is being extended daily, both for animals and plants; but

FEMALE PARENT
VARIETY—Yellow Plum

F₁ HYBRID

MALE PARENT
VARIETY—Quarter Century

Height—*tall*
Color—*yellow*
Size—*small plum*

Height—*tall*
Color—*red*
Size—*intermediate*

Height—*dwarf*
Color—*red*
Size—*large round*

F₂ HYBRIDS

Height—*tall*
Color—*red*
Size—*small plum*

Height—*tall*
Color—*red*
Size—*intermediate*

Height—*tall*
Color—*yellow*
Size—*small plum*

Height—*dwarf*
Color—*red*
Size—*small plum*

Height—*dwarf*
Color—*red*
Size—*intermediate*

Height—*dwarf*
Color—*yellow*
Size—*small plum*

Height—*tall*
Color—*red*
Size—*large round*

Height—*tall*
Color—*yellow*
Size—*intermediate*

Height—*tall*
Color—*yellow*
Size—*large round*

Height—*dwarf*
Color—*red*
Size—*large round*

Height—*dwarf*
Color—*yellow*
Size—*intermediate*

Height—*dwarf*
Color—*yellow*
Size—*large round*

FIG. 48. — Mendelism in tomatoes. There were found in a field of *F₂* hybrids, the 12 distinct types, illustrated above. This redistribution of characters illustrates an important economic bearing of Mendel's law.

in practice we shall probably find as many exceptions to the formulæ as confirmations of them, even though the exceptions can be explained, after we find them, by Mendel's principles of heredity.

The probable limits of mendelism in the production of new varieties. — It has been said that we shall soon be able, as a result of Mendel's discoveries, to predict varieties in plant-breeding. Before considering this question, we must recall the fact that a cultural variety is a succession of plants with characters sufficiently marked and uniform to make it worth while cultivating in place of some older variety. Now and then it may be worth while to introduce some new energy or new trend into a general lot of offspring by making wholesale crosses, not expecting ever to segregate any particular variety or strain from the progeny; but these cases are rare, and the gain is indefinite and temporary. So far as our knowledge at present goes, we see no warrant for the hope that we can predict varieties with any degree of exactness, at least not beyond a very narrow effort. Following are some of the reasons that seem to argue against the probability of useful prophecy of varieties so far as the mendelian results are concerned: (1) We do not know what plants will mendelize until we try. (2) Even in plants that do not mendelize, one-half of the offspring have stable characters. But we cannot predict for even this half, for it is impossible to determine beforehand which seeds showing dominant characters (and these are three-fourths of the offspring) will "come true." Dominance, as we have seen, is of two kinds in respect to its behavior in the next generation, — constant and hybrid; and the hybrid dominance, which is twice as frequent as the other, breaks up into constant dominance, hybrid dominance, and recessiveness. (3) Mendel's law deals primarily with mere characters, not with a variety or with a plant as a whole. Every plant is a composite of a multitude of characters, and from the plant-breeder's point of view there may be as many undesirable characters as desirable ones. No plant is perfect; if it were, there would be no need of plant-breeding. The breeders want to preserve the desirable characters or traits and eliminate the undesirable ones; but under the strict interpretation of mendelism this may be difficult and perhaps impossible. The one egg gamete and the one sperm gamete that unite to make the new plant, each contains all the alternative parental characters; these various characters appear in the offspring, and all that the breeder gains is a new combination or arrangement of characters, and the undesirable attributes may be as troublesome as before. (4) The breeder usually wants wholly new characters as well as recombinations of old ones, or he wants augmented characters, and these lie outside the true mendelian categories. For example, a carnation grower wants a four-inch flower, but he has only three-inch flowers to work with, and the augmentation of characters is no part of the original mendelian law. Perhaps these augmented and new characters are to be got by means of ordinary variation and selection, or other extra-crossing means; but we know, as a matter of fact, that augmented characters do sometimes appear in hybrids. (5) New and unpredictable characters are likely to arise from the influence of environment or other causes, and very likely may be recorded in the gametes and vitiate the final results. (6) Variability itself may be a unit-character and therefore pass over. There is probably such a thing as a "tendency to vary," wholly aside from the fact of variation. (7) Many of the plants with which we need most to work in plant-breeding are themselves eminently variable, and the results, even if there is true mendelism, may be so uncertain as to be wholly unpredictable. (8) Many plants with which we must work will not close-fertilize. Some of them are monœcious or diœcious. Even if there is gametic purity in such plants, the probability is that the fact can be discovered only by a long line of scientific experimenting for that particular purpose and not by the work of the man who desires only to breed new plants. (9) A cultural variety, in any true acceptation of the term, is a series of closely related plants having a pedigree. It runs back to one individual plant, from which propagation has been made by seeds or asexual parts. Now, one can never predict just what combination of characters any plant will have, even though it be strictly mendelian. A person might have a thousand hybrids of which no one plant shows any two characters in the proportion of 3 to 1 (both seed-characters may appear in the same pod or in different pods) on the same plant, let alone all the characters as 3 to 1 or in other definite relation; and yet the total average numerical results might conform exactly to the mendelian law. Mendel's law is a law of averages. For example, in ten plants of peas, Mendel found the following ratios in respect to seed-shape and seed-color. (Similar ratios were found for other characters.)

Shape	Color	Shape	Color
3.75 : 1	2.27 : 1	4.33 : 1	3.33 : 1
3.37 : 1	4.57 : 1	3.66 : 1	2.43 : 1
3.43 : 1	2.80 : 1	2.20 : 1	4.88 : 1
1.90 : 1	2.59 : 1	4.66 : 1	3.57 : 1
2.91 : 1	1.85 : 1	3.57 : 1	2.44 : 1

Mendel reports one instance in which the ratio in seed-shape was 21 to 1, and another of 1 to 1. He also reports instances of seed-color of 32 to 1, and 1 to 1. It has been said that, because of Mendel's work, we shall be able to produce hybrid varieties with the same certainty that we produce chemical compounds. Now, a plant is made up of many combinations of many units, and these combinations are the results of mathematical chance or probability. Of course, when the offspring are numerous, all possible combinations are likely to occur; but these occurrences are essentially fortuitous. Chemical compounds are specific entities in which the parts combine by necessity with definiteness. The comparison is fallacious and the conclusion unsound.

We must remember that there are whole classes of cases of plant-breeding that do not fall under hybridization at all. Granting the de Vriesan view that selection is incompetent to produce species from individual fluctuations, it is nevertheless well established (and admitted by de Vries) that very many of our best cultural varieties have been brought to their present state of perfection by means of selection; and by selection they are maintained in their usefulness. Selection will always be a most important agency in the hands of the gardener and the plant-breeder

— none the less so now that we have challenged its rôle
in the evolution of the plant kingdom. For the time
being, the new discussions of hybridizations are likely
to overshadow all other agencies in plant-breeding; but
selection under cultivation is as important now as it was
in the days of van Mons and Darwin.

Conclusion. — Now, in conclusion, what are the great
things that we have learned from these newer studies?
(1) In the first place, we have been brought to a full stop
in respect to our ways of thinking on these evolution
subjects. (2) We are compelled to give up forever the
taxonomic idea of rigid species as a basis for studying the
process of evolution. (3) The experimental method has
finally been completely launched and set under way.
Laboratory methods, comparative morphology, embryological recapitulation, life-history studies, ecological investigations — all these means are likely to be overshad-
owed for a time by experiments in actually growing the
things under conditions of control. (4) We must study
great numbers of individuals and employ statistical
methods of comparison. (5) The doctrine of discontin-
uous evolution is now clearly before us. (6) We are
beginning to find a pathway through the bewildering maze
of hybridization.

CHAPTER VIII

HOW DOMESTIC VARIETIES ORIGINATE

"THE key is man's power of accumulative selection: nature gives successive variations; man adds them up in certain directions useful to him." This, in Darwin's phrase, is the essence of the cultivator's skill in ameliorating the vegetable kingdom. So far as man is concerned, the origin of the initial variation is largely chance, but this start or variation once given, he has the power, in most cases, to perpetuate it and to modify its characters. There, then, are two very different factors or problems in the origination of garden varieties, — the production of the first departure or variation, and the subsequent breeding of it. Persons who give little thought to the subject look upon variation as the end of their endeavors, thinking that a form comes into being with all its characters well marked and fixed. In reality, however, variation may be but the beginning in the process; selection is the end so far as the plant-breeder is concerned.

Indeterminate varieties. — There are two general classes of garden varieties in respect to the method of their origin, — those that come into existence somewhat suddenly and which require little else of the husbandman than the multiplication of them, and those that are the result of a slow evolution or direct breeding. The former are indeterminate or uncertain, and the latter are determinate or definite. The greater part of those in the first class are plants that are multiplied or divided by bud-propagation. They comprise nearly all our fruits, the woody ornamental plants, and such herbaceous genera as begonia, canna, gladiolus, lily, dahlia, carnation, chrysanthemum, and the like, — in fact, all those multiplied by grafting, cuttings, bulbs, or other asexual parts. The original plant may be either a seedling or a bud-sport. The gardener, who is always on the look-out for novelties, discovers its good qualities and propagates it.

Varieties which are habitually multiplied by buds, as in those plants that have been mentioned in the last paragraph, vary widely when grown from seeds, so that every seedling may be markedly distinct. As soon, however, as varieties are widely and exclusively propagated by seeds, they develop a capability of carrying the greater part of the individual differences down to the offspring. That is, seedlings from bud-multiplied plants do not "come true," as a rule, whilst those from seed-propagated plants do "come true." The reason of this difference will become apparent on a moment's reflection. In the seed-propagated plants, like the kitchen-garden vegetables and the annual flowers, we select the seeds and thereby eliminate all those variations which would have arisen had the discarded seeds been sown. In other words, we are constantly fixing the tendency to "come true," for this feature of plants is as much a variation as is form or color or any other attribute. Suppose, for example, that a certain variation were to receive two opposite treatments,

the seeds from one-half of the progeny being carefully
selected year by year, and all those from untypical plants
discarded, whilst in the other half all the seeds from all
the plants, whether good or bad, are saved and sown. In
the one case, it will be seen, we are fixing the tendency
to "come true," for this is all that constitutes a horticultural variety, — a brood very much like all its parents.
In the other case, we are constantly eliminating the
tendency to "come true" by allowing every modifying
agency full chance. So the very act of taking seeds only
from plants that have "come true," tends still more
strongly to fix the hereditary force within narrow limits.
Working against this restrictive force, however, are all
the agencies of environment and atavism, so that, fortunately, now and then a seed gives a "rogue," or a plant
widely unlike its parents, and this may be the start for a
new variety.

With bud-multiplied varieties, however, the case is
very different. Here every seed may be sown, as in the
illustrative case above, because the seedlings are not
wanted for themselves, but only as stocks on which
to bud or graft the desired varieties. So there is no seed
selection in the ordinary propagation of apples, pears,
peaches, and the usual orchard fruits. The seeds are
taken indiscriminately from pomace or the refuse of canning, or evaporating factories. Moreover, many such
varieties are hybrid, and when propagated by seed, split
up into many forms. But every annual garden vegetable
is always grown from seeds more or less carefully saved
from plants that possess some desired attribute. There is
no reason why the tree fruits should not reproduce them-

selves from seeds just as closely as do the annual herbs, if they were to be as carefully propagated by selected seeds through a long course of generations. There is excellent proof of this in the well-marked races or families of Russian apples. In that country, grafting had been little employed, and consequently it has been necessary to select seeds only from acceptable trees in order that the offspring might be more acceptable. So the Russian apples have come to run in groups or families, each family bearing the mark of some strong ancestor. Most of the seedlings of the Oldenburg are recognizable because of their likeness to the parent. We may thus trace an incipient tendency in our own fruits towards racial characters. The Fameuse type of apples, for example, tends to perpetuate itself; and a similar tendency is very well marked in the Damson and Green Gage plums, the Orange quince, Concord grapes, and Hill's Chili and Crawford peaches. But inasmuch as bud-multiplication is so essential in nursery practice, we can hardly hope for the time when our trees and shrubs, or even our perennial herbs, will "come true" with much certainty. In them, therefore, we get new varieties by simply sowing seeds; but in seed-propagated varieties we must depend either on chance variations or else we must resort to definite plant-breeding.

Plant-breeding. — The breeding of domestic animals is attended, for the most part, with such definite and often precise results that there has come to be a general desire to extend the same principles to plants. It is not unusual to hear well-informed people say that it is possible to breed plants with as much certainty and exactness as it is to

FIG. 49. — Pride of Georgia, a good short-staple cotton. (Natural size.)

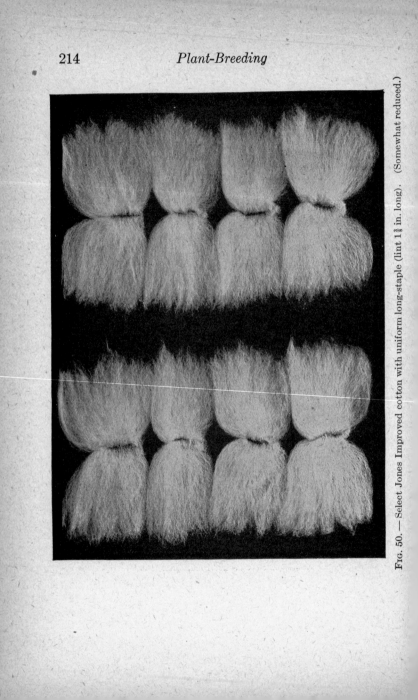

Fig. 50. — Select Jones Improved cotton with uniform long-staple (lint 1⅜ in. long). (Somewhat reduced.)

breed animals. The fact is, however, that such exactness will never be possible, because plants are very unlike animals in organization, and because, also, the objects sought in the two cases are characteristically unlike. Plants, as we have seen, are made up of a colony of potential individuals, and to breed between two plants by crossing means that we must choose the sex-parents from amongst as many individuals as there are flowers or branches on the two plants, whilst in animals we choose two definite personal parents. And these personal parents are either male or female, and the union is essential to the

Fig. 51. — Improving the tomato : A, fruit of approximately ideal form secured by crossing and selection; B, fruit showing imperfections and undesirable characters. (Yearbook, U. S. Dept. Agric.)

production of offspring, whilst in plants each parent — that is, each flower — is usually both male and female, and the union of two is not essential to the production of offspring, for the plant is capable of multiplying itself by buds. The element of chance, therefore, is one hundred, or more, to one in crossing plants as compared with crossing animals. Then, again, the plant-parents may be modified profoundly by every environmental condition of soil and temperature and sunshine, or other external conditions, since they possess no bodily tempera-

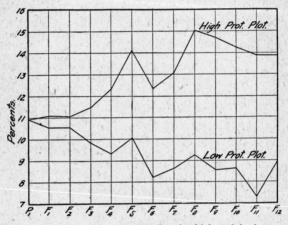

FIG. 52. — Crop averages in corn breeding for high and for low protein. Results of twelve generations. (Illinois Experiment Station.)

ture, no choice of conditions, and no volition to enable them to overcome the circumstances in which they are placed. Animals, on the contrary, have all these elements of personality, and the breeder is also able to control the conditions of their lives to a nicety. In view of all these facts, it is not strange that animals can be bred by crossing with more confidence than can plants. But there is another and even more important difference between the breeding of animals and the breeding of plants. In animals, our sole object is to secure simply one animal or one brood of offspring. In plants, our object is, in general, to secure a race or generation of

FIG. 53. — Fruit of wild elderberry.

offspring, which may be disseminated freely over the earth. In the bovine race, for example, our object in breeding is to produce one cow with given characters; in turnips, our object is to produce a new variety, the seed of which will reproduce the variety, whether sown in Pennsylvania or Ceylon. It is apparent, therefore, that any comparisons drawn between the breeding of animals and plants are likely to be fallacious.

Is there, then, any such thing as plant-breeding, any possibility that the operator can proceed with some con-

Fig. 54. — Fruit of a cultivated variety of the elderberry which appeared as a variation from the wild form.

fidence that he may obtain the ideal he has in mind? Yes, to a certain extent.

Plant-breeding by selection. — It is apparent that the very first effort on the part of the plant-breeder must be to secure individual differences; for so long as the plants

that he handles are very closely alike, so long there will
be little hope of obtaining new varieties. He must,
therefore, cause his plants to vary. In plants that
are comparatively unvariable, it is frequently impossible
to produce variations in the desired direction at once, but
it is more important to "break" the type, — that is, to

Fig. 55. — Field of wilt-resistant watermelons, growing free from disease
on infected land. (From Yearbook.)

make it depart markedly from its normal behavior in
any or many directions. If the type once begins to vary,
to break up into different forms, the operator may expect
that it will soon become plastic enough to allow of modification in the ways he desires. But whilst it is important or even necessary to break a well-marked type into
many forms, it would no doubt be unwise to encourage this

tendency after it once appears, lest the plant acquire a too strong habit of scattering. This initial variation is induced by changing the conditions in which the plant has habitually grown, as a change of seed, change of soil, tillage, varying the food supply, crossing, and the like.

As a matter of fact, however, nearly all plants that

Fig. 56. — Disease resistance in cowpeas. Showing a variety which is immune (on the left) and a susceptible variety (on the right) to cowpea wilt.

have been long cultivated are already sufficiently variable to afford a starting-point for breeding. The operator should have a vivid mental picture of the variety which he designs to obtain; then he should select that plant in his plantation which is nearest his ideal, and sow the seeds of it. From the seedlings he should again select his type, and so on, generation after generation, until the desired object is attained. It is important, if he is to make rapid progress, that he keep the same ideal in

(1) Grand Rapids, one parent used in developing improved types.

(2) Golden Queen, the other parent used in developing improved types.

(3) New loose type for the western market, secured by crossing the varieties shown in (1) and (2).

(4) New head type for eastern conditions, secured by crossing the varieties shown in (1) and (2).

FIG. 57. — Improved types of lettuce and the varieties from which they were developed.

mind year after year, otherwise there will be vacillation, and the progress of one year may be undone by a counter-direction the following year. In this way it will be found that almost any character of a plant may be either intensified or lessened within certain limits. This is man's nearest approach to the Creator in his control over the physical forms of life, and it is great and potent in proportion as it sets for itself correct ideals in the beginning and adheres to them until the end.

For examples of improvement by selection see Figs. 49–56, that represent familiar results.

RULES FOR BREEDING PLANTS

When beginning this selection or breeding for an ideal, it is important that impossible or contradictory results be avoided. Some of the cautions and suggestions that need to be considered are these : —

1. Avoid striving after features that are antagonistic or foreign to the species or genus with which you are working. Every group of plants has become endowed with certain characters or lines of development, and the cultivator will secure quicker and surer results if he works along the same lines, rather than attempt to thwart them. Nature gives the hint : let man follow it out, rather than to endeavor to create new types of characters. Consider some of the solanaceous plants for examples. There are certain types of the genus Solanum which have a natural habit of tuber-bearing, as the potato. Such species should be bred for tubers and not for fruits. There are other Solanums, however, as the egg-plants and the pepinoes, which naturally vary or develop in the direction of fruit-bearing, and these should be bred for fruits and not for tubers; and the same should be true in the related genera of tomatoes, red peppers, and physalis.

Those ambitious persons who are always looking for a tuber-bearing tomato, therefore, might better concentrate their energies on the potato, for the tomato is not developing in that direction; and even if the tomato could be made to produce tubers, it would thereby lessen its fruit production, for plants cannot maintain two diverse and profitable crops at the same time. It is more reasonable, and certainly more practicable, to grow potatoes on potato plants and tomatoes on tomato plants.

2. The quickest and most marked results are to be expected in those groups or species which are normally the most variable. There are a greater number of variations or starting-points in such species; but it also follows that the forms are less stable, the more the species is variable. Yet the variations, being very plastic, yield themselves readily to the wishes of the operator. Carrière puts the thought in this form: "The stability of forms, in any group of plants, is, in general, in inverse ratio to the number of the species which it contains, and also to the degree of its domestication."

The most variable types are the most dominant ones over the earth; that is, they occur in greater numbers and under more diverse conditions than the comparatively invariable types do. The Compositæ, or sunflower-like plants, comprise a ninth or tenth of the total species of flowering plants, and the larger part of the subordinate types or genera contain many forms or species. Aster, goldenrod, the hawkweeds, thistles, and other groups, are representative of the cosmopolitan or variable types of composites. Whenever, for any reason, any type begins to decline in variability, it usually begins to perish; it is then tending towards extinction. Monotypic genera — those which contain but a single species — are usually of local or disconnected distribution, and are probably, for the most part, vanishing remnants of a once important type. As a rule, most of our widely variable and staple cultivated species are members of large, or at least polytypic, genera. Such, for example, are the apples and pears, peaches and plums, oranges and lemons, roses, bananas, chrysanthemums, pinks, cucurbits, beans, potatoes, grapes, barley, rice, cotton. A marked exception to this statement is maize, which is immensely variable and is generally held to have come from a single species; but the genesis of maize is unknown, and it is possible that more than one species is concerned in it. Wheat is also a partial exception, although the original specific type is not understood; and the latest monographers admit three or four other species to the genus, aside from wheat. There are other exceptions, but they are mostly unimportant, and, in the main, it may be said that the dominant domestic types of plants represent markedly polytypic genera.

3. Breed for one thing at a time. The person who strives at the same time for increase or modification in prolificacy and flavor will be likely to fail in both. He should work for one object alone, simply giving sufficient attention to subsidiary objects to keep them up to normal standard. This is really equivalent to saying that there can be no such thing as the perfect all-around variety that so many people covet. Varieties must be adapted to specific uses, — one for shipping, one for canning, one for dessert, one for keeping qualities, and the like. The

more good varieties there are of any species, the more widely and successfully that species can be cultivated. A knowledge of Mendel's laws of heredity assists the breeder to secure more rapidly the proper combination of qualities and to fix them.

4. Do not desire contradictory attributes in any variety. A variety, for example, that bears the maximum number of fruits or flowers cannot be expected greatly to increase the size of those organs without loss in numbers. This is well shown in the tomato. The original tomato produced from six to ten fruits in a cluster, but as the fruits increased in size the numbers in each cluster fell to two or three. That is, increase in size proceeded somewhat at the expense of numerical productivity; yet the total weight of fruit to the plant has greatly increased. The same is true of apples and pears; for whilst these trees bear flowers in clusters, they generally bear their fruits singly. Originally, every flower normally set fruit. The reason why blackberries, currants, and grapes do not increase more markedly in size, is probably because the size of cluster has been given greater attention than the size of berry. Plants which now bear a full crop of tubers cannot be expected to increase greatly in fruit bearing, as already explained under Rule 1. This fact is illustrated in the potato, in which, as tuber-production has increased, seed-production has decreased, so that growers now complain that potatoes do not produce bolls as freely as they did years ago.

5. When selecting seeds, remember that the character of the whole plant is more important than the character of any one branch or part of the plant; and the more

Q

uniform the plant in all its parts, the greater is the likelihood that it will transmit its characters. If one is striving for larger flowers, for example, he will secure better results if he choose seeds from plants that bear large flowers throughout, than he will if he choose them from some one of the large flowering branches on a plant that bears indifferent flowers on the remaining branches, even though this given branch produces much larger flowers than those borne on the large-flowered plant. Small potatoes from productive hills give a better product than large potatoes from unproductive hills. The habit of selecting large ears from a bin of corn, or large melons from the grocer's wagon, is much less efficient in producing large products the following season than the practice of going into the fields and selecting the most uniformly large-fruited parents. A very poor plant may occasionally produce one or two very superior fruits, but the seeds are more likely to perpetuate the characters of the plant than of the fruits.

The following experiences detailed by Henri L. de Vilmorin illustrate the proposition admirably: "I tried an experiment with seeds of *Chrysanthemum carinatum* gathered on double, single, and semi-double heads, all growing on one plant, and found no difference whatever in the proportion of single and double-flowered plants. In striped verbenas, an unequal distribution of the color is often noticed; some heads are pure white, some of a self-color, and most are marked with colored stripes on white ground. I had seeds taken severally from all and tested alongside one another. The result was the same. All the seeds from one plant, whatever the color of the flower that bore them, gave the same proportion of plain and variegated flowers."

The second part of the proposition is equally as important as the first, — the fact that a plant which is uniform in all its branches or parts is more likely to transmit its general features than one which varies within itself. It is well known that bean plants often produce beans with various styles of markings on the same plant or even in the same pod, yet these variations rarely, if ever, perpetuate themselves. The same remark may be applied to variations in peas. These illustrations only add emphasis to the fact that intending plant-breeders should give greater heed than they usually do to the entire plant, rather than confine their attention to the particular part or organ which they desire to improve.

At first thought, it may look as if these facts are directly opposed to the proposition emphasized in the first chapter that every branch of a plant is a potential autonomy, but it is really a confirmation of it. The variation itself shows that the branch is measurably independent, but it is not until the conditions or causes of the variation are powerful enough to affect the entire plant that they are sufficiently impressed upon the organization of the plant to make their effects hereditary through seeds.

There is an apparent exception to the law that the character of the entire plant is more important than any one organ or part of it, in the case of the seeds themselves. That is, better results usually follow the sowing of large and heavy seeds than of small or unselected seeds from the same plant. This, however, does not affect the main proposition, for the seed is in a measure independent of

the plant body, and is not so directly influenced by environment as are the other organs. And, again, the seed
receives a part of its elements from a second or male
parent. The good results which follow the use of large
seeds are, chiefly, greater uniformity of crop, increased
vigor, often a gain in earliness and sometimes in bulk,
and usually a greater capacity for the production of
seeds. These results are probably associated less with
any innate hereditable tendencies than with the mere
vegetative strength and uniformness of the large seeds.
The large seeds usually germinate more quickly than the
small ones, provided both are equally mature, and they
push the plantlet on more vigorously. This initial
gain, coming at the most critical time in the life of the new
individual, is no doubt responsible for very much of the
result that follows. The uniformity of crop is the most
important advantage which comes of the use of large
seeds, and this is obviously the result of the elimination of
all seeds of varying degrees of maturity, of incomplete
growth and formation, and of low vitality.

Another important consideration touching the selection
of seeds, is the fact that very immature seeds give a feeble
but precocious progeny. This has long been observed
by gardeners, but Sturtevant, Arthur, and Goff have made
a critical examination of the subject. "It is not the
slightly unripe seeds that give a noticeable increase in
earliness," according to Arthur, "but very unripe seeds,
gathered from fruit (tomatoes) scarcely of full size and
still very green. Such seeds do not weigh more than
two-thirds as much as those fully ripe. They germinate
readily and are more easily affected by retarding or harm-

ful influences. If they can be brought through the early period of growth and become well established, and the foliage or fruit is not attacked by rots or blights, the grower will usually be rewarded by an earlier and more abundant crop of slightly smaller and less firm fruit. These characters will be more slightly emphasized in subsequent years by continuous seed propagation." Goff remarks that the increase in earliness in tomatoes, following the use of markedly immature seeds, "is accompanied by a marked decrease in the vigor of the plant, and in the size, firmness, and keeping quality of the fruit." These results are probably closely associated with the chemical constitution and content of the immature seeds. The organic compounds have probably not yet reached a state of stability, and therefore they respond quickly to external stimuli when placed in conditions suitable to germination; and there is little food for nourishment of the plantlet. The consequent weakness of the plantlet results in a loss of vegetative vigor, which is earliness. (See Rule 2.)

Still another feature connected with the choice of seeds is the fact that in some plants, as in various Ipomœas, for example, the color of the seed is more or less intimately associated with the color of the flower which produced them and also with the color of the flower which they will produce.

6. Plants that have any desired characteristics in common may differ widely in their ability to transmit these characters. It is usually impossible for the cultivator to determine, from the appearance of any given progeny, which is the most unvariable and the most like

its parent; but it may be said that those individuals that grow in the most usual or normal environments are most likely to perpetuate themselves. A very unusual condition, as of soil, moisture, or exposure, is not easily imitated when providing for the succeeding generation, and a return to normal conditions of environment may be expected to be followed by a more or less complete return to normal attributes on the part of the plant. If the same variation, therefore, were to occur in plants growing under widely different conditions, the operator who wishes to preserve the new form should take particular care to select his seeds from those individuals that seem to have been least influenced by the immediate conditions in which they have grown.

Again, if the same variation appears both in uncrossed and crossed plants, the best results should be expected in selecting seeds from the former. We have already seen, in the seventh chapter, how it is that crosses are unstable, and how the unstability is likely to be the greater the more violent the cross. "Cross-breeding greatly increases the chance of wide variation," writes Henri L. de Vilmorin, "but it makes the task of fixation more difficult."

It is very important, therefore, when selecting seeds from plants which seem to give promise of a new variety, to sow seeds of each plant separately, and then make the subsequent selections from the most stable generation; and it is equally important that the operator should not trust to a single plant as a starting-point, whenever he has several promising plants from which to choose.

7. The less marked the departure from the genus of

the normal type, the greater, in general, is the likelihood that it will be perpetuated, although this may not be true of sports. This is admirably illustrated in crosses. The seed-progeny of crosses between closely related varieties, or between different plants of the same variety, is more uniform and usually more easy of improvement by selection than the progeny of hybrids. In uncrossed plants, the general tendency is to resemble their parents, and the greater the number of like ancestors, the greater is the tendency to "come true." There is thought to be a tendency, though necessarily a weak one, to return to some particular ancestor, or to "date back." This is known as atavism. The so-called atavistic forms are likely to be unstable, to break up into numerous forms, or to return more or less completely to the type of the main line of the ancestry. The following statements touching some of the relations of atavism to the amelioration of plants are the results of an excellent study of heredity in lupines by Louis Levêque de Vilmorin : —

"1. The tendency to resemble its parents is generally the strongest tendency in any plant;

"2. But it is notably impaired as it comes into conflict with the tendency to resemble the general line of its ancestry.

"3. This latter tendency, or atavism, is constant, though not strong, and scarcely becomes impaired by the intervention of a series of generations in which no reversion has taken place.

"4. The tendency to resemble a near progenitor (only two or three generations removed), on the other hand, is very soon obliterated if the given progenitor is different from the bulk of its ancestors."

8. The crossing of plants should be looked upon as a means or starting-point, not as an end. We cross two flowers and sow the seeds. The resulting seedlings may be unlike either parent (see Fig. 57). Here, then, is variation. The operator should choose that plant which most nearly satisfies his ideal, and then, by selection from its progeny and the progeny of succeeding generations, gradually obtain the plant which he desires. It is only in plants which are propagated by asexual parts — as grafts, cuttings, layers, bulbs, and the like — that hybrids or crosses are commonly immediately valuable; for in these plants we really cut up and multiply the one individual plant which pleases us in the first batch of seedlings, rather than to take the offspring or seedlings of it. Thus, if any particular plant in a lot of seedlings of crosses of cannas, or plums, or hops, or strawberries, or potatoes, is valuable, we multiply that one individual. There is no reason for fixing the variety. But any satisfactory plant in a lot of seedlings of crosses of pumpkins, or wheat, or beans, must be made the parent of a new variety by sowing the seeds of it and then by selecting for seed-parents, year by year, those plants which are the best. "The unsettled forms arising from crosses," Focke writes, "are the plastic material out of which gardeners form their varieties."

But even in the fruits, and other bud-propagated plants, crossing may often be used to as good advantage for the purpose of originating variation as it may in peas or buckwheat. It only requires a longer time to fix and select variations because the plants mature so slowly.

Ordinarily, if the operator does not find satisfactory plants among the seedlings of any cross of fruit trees, he roots up the whole batch as profitless. But if he were to allow the best plants to stand and were to sow seeds from them, the second generation might produce something more to his liking. But it is generally quicker to make another cross and to try the experiment over again, than to wait for unpromising seedlings to bear. This repeated repetition of the experiment, however, — continual crossing and sowing and uprooting, — is gambling. Throwing dice to see what will turn up is a comparable proceeding. The sowing of uncrossed seed is little better. Peter M. Gideon sowed over a bushel of apple seed, and one seed produced the Wealthy apple.[1] D. B. Wier raised a million seedlings of soft maple, and one plant of the lot had finely divided leaves, and is now Wier's Cut-leaved maple. Teas' Weeping mulberry, which is now so deservedly popular, was, as Mr. Teas tells me, "merely an accidental seedling." So this explains why the production of new varieties of fruits is always chance, while a skilled man can sit in his study in the winter time and picture to himself a new bean or muskmelon, and then go out in the next three or four summers and produce it.

9. If it is desired to employ crossing as a direct means

[1] The facts in the origination of the Wealthy apple, as related to me by Mr. Gideon, are these: he first planted a bushel of apple seeds and then each year, for nine years, he planted enough to give a thousand trees. At the end of ten years, all the seedlings had perished (this was in Minnesota) except one hard seedling crab. Then a small lot of seeds of apples and crab apples was obtained in Maine, and from these the Wealthy came. There were only about fifty seeds in the batch of crab seed which gave the Wealthy; but before this variety was obtained, much over a bushel of seed had been sown.

of producing new varieties, each parent to the proposed
cross should be chosen in agreement with the rules already
specified, and also because it possesses in an emphatic
degree one or more of the qualities which it is desired to
combine; and the more uniformly and persistently the
parent presents a given character, the greater is the chance
that it will transmit that character. It has already been
said that crossing for the instant production of new varieties is most certain to give valuable results in those
species which are propagated by buds, because the initial
individual differences are not dissipated by seed reproduction. This is especially true of crossing between distinct
species; for in such violent crossing as this the offspring
is particularly likely to be unstable when propagated by
seeds. The results of hybridization appear to be most
certain in those plants grown under glass, and in which,
therefore, the selection of the seed-parents is most carefully made, and where the conditions of existence are
most uniform. The most remarkable results in hybridization yet attained are with the choicer glass-house plants,
such as orchids, begonias, anthuriums, and the like.

The more violent the cross, the less is the likelihood
that desirable offspring will follow. Species which refuse
to give satisfactory results when hybridized directly or
between the pure stocks, may give good varieties when
the "blood" has become somewhat attenuated through
previous crossings. The best results in hybridizing our
native grape with the European grape, for example, have
come from the use of one parent which is already a hybrid. Two notable examples are the Brighton and Diamond
Grapes, raised by Jacob Moore. The Brighton is a cross

of Concord (pure native) by Diana-Hamburg (hybrid of impure native and European). Diamond is a cross of Concord by Iona, the latter parent undoubtedly of impure origin, containing a trace of the European vine. T. V. Munson's Brilliant is a secondary hybrid, its parents, Lindley and Delaware, both containing hybrid blood. Others of his varieties have similar histories. Even when the cross is much attenuated — or three or four or even more times removed from a pure hybrid origin by means of subsequent crossings — it may still produce marked effects in a cross without introducing such contradictory characters as to jeopardize the value of the offspring.

Among American fruit plants there are comparatively few valuable species-hybrids. The most conspicuous are grapes, particularly the various Rogers varieties, such as Agawam, Lindley, Wilder, Barry, and others, which are hybrids of the European and native species. Other hybrids are the Keiffer and allied pears (between the common pear and the Oriental pear), probably the Transcendent and a few other crabs (between the common apple and the Siberian crab), the Soulard and kindred crabs (between the common apple and the native Western crab), a few blackberries of the Wilson Early type (between the blackberry and the dewberry), the purple-cane raspberries (between the native red and black raspberries, and possibly sometimes combined with the European raspberry), the Utah Hybrid cherry (between the Western sand cherry and the sand plum), probably some plums, and a few others. There is undoubtedly a fertile field for further work in hybridizing our fruits, particularly those of native origin, and also many of the ornamental plants; the danger is that persons are likely to expect too much from hybridization, and too little from the betterment of all the other conditions which so profoundly modify plants. Violent hybridizations generally give unsatisfactory and unreliable results; but subsequent crossings, when the "blood" of the original species to the contract is considerably attenuated, may be expected to correct or overcome the first incompatibility, as explained above.

10. Establish the ideal of the desired variety firmly in mind before any attempt is made at plant-breeding. If one is to make any progress in securing new varieties, he must first be an expert judge of the capabilities and merits of the plants with which he is dealing, otherwise he may attempt the impossible or he may obtain a variety that has no merit. Make frequent use of a score-card to familiarize yourself with all details. It is important, also, that the person bear in mind the fact that a variety which is simply as good as any other in cultivation is not worth introducing. It should be better in some particular than any other in existence. The operator must know the points of his plant, as an expert stock-breeder knows the points of an animal, and he must possess the rare judgment to determine which characters are most likely to reappear in the offspring. Inasmuch as a person can be an expert in only a few plants, it follows that he cannot expect satisfactory results in breeding any species that may chance to come before him. Persistent and uniform effort, continued over a series of years, is usually demanded for the production of really valuable varieties. Thus it often happens that one man excels all competitors in breeding a

particular class of plants. The horticulturists will recall, for example, Lemoine in the breeding of gladiolus, Eckford in peas, Crozy in cannas, Bruant in pelargoniums, and others. There are now and then varieties which arise from no effort, but because of that very fact they reflect no credit upon the so-called originator, who is really only the lucky finder. So far as the originator is concerned, such varieties are merely chance. If, however, the operator — himself an expert judge of the plant with which he deals — chooses his seeds with care and discrimination, and then proposes, if need be, to follow up his work generation after generation of plants by means of selection, the work becomes plant-breeding of the highest type.

First of all, therefore, the operator must know what he can likely get, and what will likely be worth getting. Many persons, however, begin at the other end of the problem, — they get what they can, and then let the public judge whether the effort has been worth the while.

11. Having derived a specific and correct ideal, the operator must next seek to make his plant vary in the desired direction. This may be done by crossing, or by modifying the conditions under which the plant grows. If there are any two plants that possess indications of the desired attributes, cross them; among the seedlings there may be some that may serve as starting-points for further effort.

A change in the circumstances or environment of the plant may start the desired attribute. If the plant must be dwarfer, plant it on poorer or drier soil, transfer it towards the poles, plant it late in the season, or transplant it repeatedly. Dwarf peas become climbing peas on rich, moist lands. If the plant must have large fruits, allow it more food and room, and give attention to pruning and thinning. Certain geographical regions develop certain characters in plants, as we have seen; if, therefore, the desired feature does not appear spontaneously or as a result of any other treatment, transfer the plant for a time to that region which is characterized by such attributes, if there is any such. It is not intended to convey the impression that the placing of plants on poor soil will directly cause a dwarfing which will be inherited, or large size on good soils, but if the plant already holds the characteristic of dwarfness or some other quality in a latent form, it will probably appear if the conditions are made right.

The importance of growing the plant under conditions or environments in which the desired type of characters is most frequently found, is admirably emphasized in the evolution of varieties which are adapted to forcing under glass. Within a century — and in many instances within a score of years — species that are practically unknown to glass-houses have produced varieties perfectly adapted to them. This has been accomplished by growing the most tractable existing varieties, selecting those which most completely adapt themselves to their environment and to the ideals of the operator. One of the most remarkable examples of this kind is afforded by the carnation. In Europe it was chiefly a border or outdoor plant, but within a generation it had produced hosts of excellent forcing varieties in America, where it is grown almost exclusively as a glass-house flower. So the carnation types of Europe and America have been widely unlike.

Sowing the seeds of hardy annual plants in autumn often stimulates a tendency to produce thickened roots. The plant, finding itself unable to perfect seeds, stores its reserve in the root, and it therefore tends to become biennial. In this manner, with the aid of selection and the variation of the soil, Carrière was able to produce good radishes from the wild slender-rooted charlock (*Raphanus Raphanistrum*).

Lessened vigor, so long as the plant continues to be healthy, nearly always results in a comparative increase of fruits or reproductive organs. It is an old horticultural maxim that checking growth induces fruitfulness. It is largely in consequence of this fact that plants bear heaviest when they attain approximate maturity. Trees are often thrown into bearing by girdling, heavy pruning, the attacks of borers, and various accidental injuries. The gardener knows that if he keeps his plants in vigorous growth by constantly putting them into larger pots, he will get little, or at least very late, bloom. The plant-breeder, therefore, may be able to induce the desired initial variation by attention to this principle. (See discussion of variation in relation to food supply.) Arthur has recently put the principle into this formula: "A decrease in nutrition during the period of growth of an organism favors the development of the reproductive parts at the expense of the vegetative parts."

A most important means of inducing variation is the simple change of seed, the philosophical reasons for which are explained on earlier pages. A plant becomes closely fitted or accustomed to one set of conditions, and when it is placed in new conditions, it at once makes an effort to adapt itself to them. This adaptation is variation. No doubt the free interchange of seeds between seed-merchants and customers is one of the causes of the enormous increase in varieties in recent times.

When once a novel variety appears, others of a similar kind are likely soon to follow in other places, and some persons have supposed that there is a synchronistic variation in plants, or a tendency for like variations to appear simultaneously in widely separated localities. There is perhaps some remote reason for this opinion, because there is, as Darwin expresses it, an accumulative effect of domestication or cultivation, by virtue of which plants that long remain comparatively invariable may, within a short time, when cultivation has been continued long enough, vary widely and in many directions; and it is to be expected that even when plants have long since responded to the wishes of the cultivator, an equal amount or accumulation of the force of domestication would tend to produce like effects in different places. But it is probable that by far the greater part of this synchronistic variation is simply apparent, for whenever any marked novelty appears

Fig. 58. — Wild cabbage.

the attention of all interested persons is directed to looking
for similar variations amongst their own plants.

12. The person who is wishing for new varieties should
look critically to all perennial plants, and particularly to
trees and shrubs, for bud-varieties or sports. It has
already been said that the branches of a tree may vary
among themselves in the same way in which seedlings

Fig. 59. — Curled kale. *Brassica oleracea* var. *acephala.*

vary, and for the same reason. As a rule, any marked
sport is capable of being perpetuated by bud-propagation.
The number of bud-varieties now in cultivation is really
very large. Many of the cut-leaved and colored or
variegated varieties of ornamental plants were originally
found on other trees as sports. The "mixing in the
hill" of potatoes is bud-variation. Nectarines are derived from the peach, some of them as sports and some as
seedlings. The moss-rose was probably originally a sport

R

from the Provence rose. Greening apple trees often bear Russet apples, and Russets sometimes bear Greenings.

Bud-varieties may not only come from buds, — as grafts, cuttings, and layers, — but they sometimes perpetuate themselves by seeds. Now, these seedlings are amenable to selection, just the same as any other seedlings are; the bud-variety, therefore, may give the initial starting-point for plant-breeding. But, more than this, it is sometimes possible to improve and fix the type by bud-selection as well as by seed-selection. Darwin cites this interesting testimony: "Mr. Salter brings the principle of selection to bear on variegated plants propagated by buds, and has thus greatly improved and fixed several varieties. He informs me that at first a branch often produces variegated leaves on one side alone, and that the leaves are marked only with an irregular edging, or with a few lines of white and yellow. To improve and fix such varieties, he finds it necessary to encourage the buds at the bases of the most distinctly marked leaves and to propagate from them alone. By following,

Fig. 60. — Collard.

with perseverance, this plan during three or four successive seasons a distinct and fixed variety can generally be secured." Ernest Walker, then a gardener at New Albany, Indiana, is of the opinion that the abnormal character of sports often intensifies itself if the sport is allowed to remain on the parent plant for a considerable time. He has observed this particularly in coleus, where color sports are frequent. "In these," he says, "the sport begins with a branch which may be taken off and propagated as a new variety. If left on the parent, other parts of the plant are apt to show similar variations. Indeed, I think it is not best to be in too great hurry to remove a sporting branch, for its character seems to tend to become more fixed if it remains on the plant."

Fig. 61. — Brussels sprouts.

13. The starting-point once given, all permanent progress lies in continued selection. This, as we have already pointed out, is really the key to the whole matter. In the great number of cases, the operator cannot produce the initial variation which he desires, but, by looking carefully among many plants, he may find one which shows an indication of his ideal. This plant must be carefully saved, and all of the seeds sown in a place where crossing with other types cannot take place. Of a hundred seedlings from this plant, perhaps one or two will still further emphasize the character which is sought. These,

again, are saved, and all the seeds are sown. So the operation goes on, patiently and persistently, and there is a reward at the end. This is the one fundamental practice that underlies the amelioration of plants under the touch of man; and because we know, from experience, that it is so important, we are sure, as Darwin was, that selection in nature must be a factor in the progress of the vegetable world.

But suppose this suggestion of the new variety does not appear among the batch of plants that we raise? Then sow again; vary the conditions; choose the most widely variable types; cross; at length — if the ideal is true — the suggestion will come. "Cultivation, diversification of the conditions of existence,

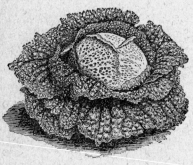

FIG. 62. — Savoy cabbage.

and repeated sowings" are the means which Verlot would employ to induce variations. But the skill and the character of the final result lie not so much in the securing of the initial start, as in the subsequent selection. Nature affords starting-points in endless numbers, but there are few men alert and skillful enough to take the hint and improve it. If we want a new tomato, we first endeavor to discover what we want. We decide that we must have one like the Acme in color, but more spherical, with a firmer flesh, and a little earlier.

Then we shall raise an acre of Acme tomatoes, and closely allied varieties; if we cannot do that, we make arrangements to inspect the neighbor's fields. We scrutinize every plant as the first fruits are ripening. Finally, one plant is found — not one fruit — which is something like the variety desired. Very well. Wait two to five years and you shall see the new variety.

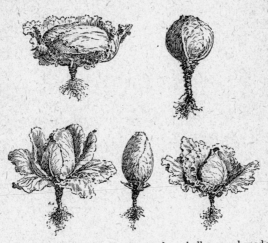

Fig. 63. — Cabbage shapes: flat; round or ball; egg-shaped; oval; conical.

Some of these initial variations possess no tendency to reproduce themselves. The seedlings of them may break up into a great diversity of forms, no form representing the parent closely. In such cases, it is generally useless to proceed further with this brood. Another start should be made with another plant. So it is always important, as we have already seen (Rule 6), to have as many starting-points as possible, to lessen the risk of failure. Whilst it requires nice judgment to choose those plants which possess the most important and the most transmissible combination of characters, the greatest skill is nevertheless required to carry forward a correct system of selection.

14. Even when the desired variety is obtained, it must be kept up to the standard by constant attention to selection. That is, there is no real stability in the forms of life. So long as the conditions of existence vary, so long will the plants make the effort to adapt themselves to the changes. No two seasons are alike; and no two fields, or even parts of fields, are alike; and there are no two cultivators who give exactly the same and equal attention to tillage, fertilizing, and the other treatment of plants. All forms or varieties, therefore, tend to "run out" by variation or gradual evolution into other forms; but because we keep the same name for all the succeeding generations, we fancy that we still have the same variety.

"In 1887 I found a single tomato plant in my garden in Michigan, that had several points of superiority over any other of the one hundred and seventy varieties I was then growing. It came from a packet of German seed of an inferior variety. The tomato was very solid, an unusually long keeper, productive, and attractive in size and appearance. The variation was so promising that I named it in a sketch of tomatoes that I published that year, calling it the Ignotum (that is, unknown), to indicate that the origin of it was no merit of my own. I sent seeds to a few friends for testing. I sowed the seeds for about five hundred plants in 1888 in an isolated patch on uniform soil. The larger part of the plants were more or less like the parent. A few reverted. A few of the best plants were selected and the seed saved. I then moved to New York and took the seed with me. This was sown in uniform soil in an isolated position in 1889. This crop, probably as a result of the careful selection of the year before and of the change of locality, was remarkably uniform and handsome. Of the 442 plants I grew that year, none reverted to the little Eiformige Dauer, the German variety from which it had come, but there was some variation in them due to different methods of treatment. I again saved the seeds, and I was now ready to introduce the variety. I therefore sold my seeds, six pounds, to V. H. Hallock & Son, Queens, New York, who introduced it in 1890. The very next year, 1891, I obtained the Ignotum from fifteen dealers and grew the plants side by side. Of the fifteen lots, eight bore small and poor fruits which were not worth growing and which could not be recognized as Ignotum! Grown from our own seeds, it still held its character well. Here, then, only a year after its introduction, half the seedsmen were selling a spurious stock. It is possible that some of this variation arose from substitution of other varieties by seedsmen, although I have yet secured no evidence of any unfair dealing. It is possible, also, that the product of some of the samples which I early sent out for testing had found their way into seedsmen's hands. But I am convinced that very much of this variation was a legitimate result of the various conditions in which the crops of 1890 had been grown, and the varying ideals of those who saved seeds. I am the more positive of this from the fact that the Ignotum tomato, as I first knew it and bred it, appears now to be lost to cultivation, although the name

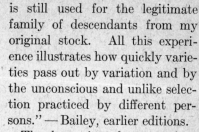

is still used for the legitimate family of descendants from my original stock. All this experience illustrates how quickly varieties pass out by variation and by the unconscious and unlike selection practiced by different persons." — Bailey, earlier editions.

The longevity of any variety is inversely proportional to the frequency of its generations. Annual plants, other conditions being the same, run out sooner than perennials, because seed-reproduction — or the generations — intervenes more frequently. Trees, on the other hand, carry their variations longer, because the seed generations — in which departures chiefly take place — are farther apart. Of all the so-called fruit plants, the strawberry runs out soonest and the varieties change the oftenest, because

Fig. 64. — Swede turnip (top) ; kohl-rabi (middle) ; cauliflower (bottom).

a new generation can be brought into fruit-bearing in two years, whilst it may require ten years or more to bring a new generation of apples or chestnuts into bearing. "Yet, my reader will remind me that the Wilson strawberry has been and is the leading variety in many places for nearly forty years, to which I reply that the Wilson of to-day is not necessarily the same as that introduced

Fig. 65. — Wild form of *Chrysanthemum morifolium*, as grown in England.

by James Wilson, simply because the name is the same. Every different soil or treatment tends to produce a different strain or variation in the Wilson strawberry, as it does in any other plant; and every grower, when setting a new plantation, chooses his plants from that part of his field which pleases him best, rather than from those plants that most nearly correspond to the original type of the Wilson. That is, the unconscious selection on the part of the grower takes no account of what the variety was, but only of what it ought to be, and this ideal differs with

Fig. 66. — Wild form of *Chrysanthemum indicum*, as grown in England.

every person. It is not surprising, therefore, to find strains of Wilson strawberry as unlike as are many named varieties; and it is to be expected that all the strains now in existence have departed considerably from the original type." — Bailey, earlier editions.

This example borrowed from the strawberry is a most important one, because it illustrates how a variety may vary and pass out of existence even though it is propagated wholly asexually or by buds. There are to-day several different types of Rhode Island Greening apple in cultivation which have probably originated from variations induced by environment and by the different ideals of propagators; and the same is true in other fruits.

All the foregoing remarks illustrate the importance of constant attention to selection if one desires to maintain the exact type of any variety which he has produced. They explain the value of the "roguing" — or systematic destruction of all "rogues" or non-typical plants — which is invariably practiced by all good seed growers. But they still more emphatically show that every variety is essentially unstable, and that the only abiding result is constant evolution, the old forms being left behind as the type expands into new and better forms. Varieties to be valuable, therefore, ought not to be rigidly fixed, and, fortunately, nature has prescribed that they cannot be.

Fig. 67. — Pompon anemone chrysanthemum.

Probably every ten years sees a marked change in every variety of any annual species which is propagated exclusively from seeds, and every century must see a like change in the tree fruits. These changes are so gradual and the original basis of comparison fades away so completely that we generally fail to recognize the evolution.

15. It is evident, therefore, that the most abiding

progress in the amelioration of plants must come as a result of the very best cultivation and the most intelligent selection and change of seed. Every reflective person must admit that the cultivation of plants — which is the fundamental conception of agriculture — has been and is

FIG. 68. — Single type.

crude and imperfect, and that there has been no conscious effort on the part of the human race to produce any given final result upon the cultivated flora. Yet, this imperfect cultivation has already modified plants so profoundly that we cannot determine the originals of many of them, and we can trace the evolution of but few. The science of rural industry is now fairly well understood in its essential fundamental principles, and the intelligence of those classes of persons who deal with plants is rapidly enlarging. The first part of the twentieth century will virtually mark a new era for agriculture, and from that time on the onward evolution of plants should proceed confidently and unchecked. Our eyes are too often dazzled by the novelties which suddenly thrust themselves upon us, and we look for some mystic power which shall enable us to produce varieties forthwith at our will. We need not so much varieties with new names as we do a general increase in productiveness and efficiency of the types we already possess; and this augmentation must come chiefly in the form of a gradual evolution under the stimulus of good care. The man who will accomplish most for the amelioration and unfolding of the forms of plants is he who fixes his eyes steadily upon the future, and, with the inspiration of a long forecast, urges the betterment of all conditions in which plants grow.

SPECIFIC EXAMPLES

The foregoing principles and discussions will become more concrete if a few actual examples of the origination of varieties are given. To begin with a very simple case, we relate the introduction of the varieties of the dewberries, for this fruit is yet little cultivated, the varieties are few, and the domestication of it is not yet fifty years old.

The dewberry and blackberry. — The dewberries are native fruits, and it is only within twenty-five years that they have become prominent among fruit-growers. The most important is the Lucretia. This was found growing wild on a plantation in

Fig. 69. — Type of pompon chrysanthemum. Grown outdoors, with no special care.

West Virginia in war time. In 1876, a few of the plants were sent to Ohio, and from this start the present stock has come. It is probable that similar wild varieties are growing to-day in many parts of the country, but they have not chanced to have been seen by persons who are interested in cultivating them. It is a form of the common wild dewberry that grows all over the Northeastern states. Just why this particular patch in West Virginia should have been so much better than the general run of the species nobody knows, but it was undoubtedly the product of some local environment or special ancestry.

Early in the seventies, T. C. Bartel, of Huey, Clinton County, Illinois, observed very excellent dewberries growing in rows between the lines of stubble in an old cornfield, where the plant had evidently been quick to avail itself of unoccupied land. This was introduced as the Bartel dewberry, and is now the second in point of prominence amongst the cultivated varieties. Other varieties have appeared in much the same way. A fruit-grower in Michigan found an extra good dewberry in a neighboring wood-lot, and introduced it under the name of Geer, in compliment to the owner of the place. In Florida an unusually good plant of the common wild dewberry of that region was discovered, and introduced by Reasoner Brothers under the name of Manatee. There are now about twenty named varieties of dewberries in cultivation as described in our horticultural writings, all of which, apparently, are chance plants from the wild.

As the dewberries become more widely grown, good seedlings will now and then appear in cultivated ground, and these will be named and sold. After a time persons will begin to sow seed for the purpose of producing new varieties; and those seedlings which chance to possess unusual merit will be propagated, and in due time introduced. This is the history of the cultivated blackberries and raspberries which have come from the wild plants in little more than half a century. These fruits are now so far developed that we no longer think of looking to the woods and copses for new varieties of promise, yet the novelties are mostly chance seedlings from cultivated varieties. A few years ago a friend purchased plants of the Snyder blackberry. When they came into bearing, he noticed that one plant was better than the others. It bore larger fruits, and the bearing season was longer. He took suckers from this plant, and from these others were taken, until he had a large plantation of the novelty, mostly selected from plants which pleased him best. The variety had such distinct merit that it was named the Mersereau, in honor of the man who recognized and propagated it.

The apple. — The original apple is not definitely known, but it was certainly a very small and inferior crabbed fruit, borne mostly in clusters. When we first find it described by historians, it was still of small value. Pliny said that some kinds were so sour as to take the edge off a knife. But better and better seedlings continued to come up about habitations, until, when printed descriptions of fruits began to be made, three or four hundred years ago, there were many named kinds in existence. The size had vastly improved, and with this increase came the reduction of the number of fruits in the cluster; so that, at the present time, whilst apple flowers are borne in clusters, the fruits are usually borne singly. That is, most of the flowers fail to set fruit, and they complete their mission when they have shed their pollen for the benefit of the one which persists.

The American colonists brought with them the staple varieties of the mother countries. But the needs of the

new country were unlike those of the old, and the tastes and fashions of the people were changing. So, as seedlings came up about the buildings and along the fences, where the seeds had been scattered, the ones that promised to satisfy the new needs were saved, and many of the old varieties were allowed to pass away. In 1817, the date of the first American fruit-book, over sixty per cent of the varieties particularly recommended for cultivation in this country were of American origin. In 1845, nearly two hundred varieties of

Fig. 70. — Japanese anemone type.

apples were described as having been fruited in this country, of which over half were of American origin. Between these two dates introduction of foreign varieties had been freely made, so that the percentage of domestic varieties had fallen. But the next thirty years saw a great change. Of 1823 varieties described in 1872, nearly or quite seventy per cent were American, and a still greater proportion of the most prized kinds were of domestic origin. In the older states, the apple had now become so completely accustomed to its environment, and the tastes of the people were so well supplied, that there was no longer much need for the in-

Fig. 71. — The small and regular anemone type.

troduction of foreign kinds. It was not so in the North-west. There the apples of the Eastern states did not thrive. The climate was too cold and too dry. Attention was turned to other countries with similar or rigorous

s

climate. In 1870, the Department of Agriculture at Washington imported cions of many varieties of apples from Russia, but these did not satisfy all fruit-growers of the Northern states. It was then conceived that the great interior plain of Russia should yield apples adapted to the upper Mississippi Valley, whilst those already imported had come from the seaboard territory. Accordingly, early in the eighties, Charles Gibb, of the province of Quebec, and Professor Budd, of Iowa, went to Russia to introduce the promising fruits of the central plain. The results have been most interesting to the pacific looker-on. There are ardent advocates of the Russian varieties, and there are others who see nothing good in them. There are those who think that all progress must come by securing seedlings from the hardiest varieties of the Eastern states; there are others who would derive everything from the Siberian

Fig. 72. — A pompon chrysanthemum. (× ⅓.)

crabs; and still others who hold that the final result lies in improving the native crabs. There has been no end of discussion and cross-purposes. In the meantime, nature is quietly doing the work. Here is a good seedling of some old variety, there a good one from some Russian, and now and then one from the crab stocks. The new varie-

Fig. 73. — Type of Japanese incurved chrysanthemum.

ties are gradually supplanting the old, so quietly that few people are aware of it; and by the time the contestants are done disputing, it will be found that there are no Russians and no Eastern apples, but a brood of Northwestern apples that have grown out of the old confusion.

All these new apples are simply seedlings, almost all of them chance trees which come up here and there wherever man has allowed nature a bit of ground upon which to make garden as she likes. In 1892, there were 878 varieties of apples offered for sale by American nurserymen, and it is doubtful if one of the whole lot was the result of any attempt on the part of the originator to produce a variety with definite qualities. And what is true of the apple is about equally true of the other fruit trees. In the small fruits and the grapes, where the generations are shorter and the results quicker, more has been done in the way of direct selection of seeds and the crossing of chosen parents; but even here, the methods are mostly haphazard. Latterly, however, the professional experimenters have begun the breeding of the apple and new varieties on a new basis have been secured; and there is now considerable literature on the subject.

Beans. — Perhaps there are no plants more tractable in the hands of the plant-breeder than the garden beans. A few years ago, a leading Eastern seedsman conceived of a new form of bean pod that would at once commend itself to his customers. He was so well convinced of the merits of this prospective variety, that he made a descriptive and "taking" name for it. He then wrote to a noted bean-raiser, describing the proposed variety and giving the name. "Can you make it for me?" he asked. "Yes, I will make you the bean," replied the grower. The seedsman then announced in his catalogue that he would soon introduce a new bean, and, in order to hold the name, he published it, along with the announcement. Two years later, I visited the bean-grower. "Did you get the bean?" I asked. "Yes, here it is." Sure enough, he had it, and it answered the requirements very well. Another seedsman would like a round-podded, stringless, green-podded bean. This same man produced it, and I went into a field of fifteen acres of it, where it was growing for seed, and the most fastidious person could not have asked for a closer approach to the ideal which the dealer had set before him some four or five years before.

How is all this done? It looks simple enough. The ideal is established first of all. The breeder revolves it in his mind, and eliminates all the impracticable and contradictory elements of it. Then he goes carefully and critically through his bean fields, particularly through those varieties most like the desired kind, and marks those plants which most nearly approach his ideal. The seeds of these are carefully saved, and they are planted in an isolated position. If he finds no promising variations among his plantations, then he must start off the variation in some other way. This is usually done by crossing those varieties which are most like the proposed kind. He has got a start; but now the care and skill begin. Year by year he selects just those plants which please him best and which he judges, from experience, will most surely carry their features over to the offspring. He starts with one plant; the next year he may have only two. If he has ten or twenty good ones, then the task is easy, for the variety has elements of permanence — that is, of hereditability — in it. But he may have no plants the second year. In that case, he begins again; for if the ideal is true, it can be attained. This particular bean-breeder upon whom many of our best seedsmen rely for new varieties, says that he has discarded fully three thousand varieties and forms as profitless. This only means that he is a most astute judge of beans, and that he knows when any type is likely to prove to be a poor breeder.

The bean also affords an excellent example of the care

which it is generally necessary to exercise to keep any variety true to the type. The person of whom we have spoken, in common with all careful seed-growers, searches his field with great pains to discover the "rogues," or those plants which vary perceptibly from the type of the given variety. The rogue may be a variation in size or habit of plant, season of maturity, color or form of pods, productiveness, susceptibility to rust, or other aberrance. In the dwarf or bush beans,

FIG. 74. — Japanese anemone chrysanthemum when fully expanded.

which are now most exclusively grown, the most frequent rogue is a climbing or half-climbing plant. This is a reversion to the ancestral type of the bean, which was no doubt a twining plant. This rogue is always destroyed even though it may be, itself, a good bean. In some cases, the men who perform the roguing are sent along every row of a whole field on their hands and knees, critically examining every plant. The effect of this continual selection is always to push the variety to greater excellence. The various "improved" strains of plants are obtained in essentially this way. If the grower has been painstaking with his roguing, he soon finds that his seed gives better and more uniform crops than the common stock of the variety. If the improvement is marked, he may dignify his strain with a distinct name, and it thereby becomes a new variety The improvement may be a very important one to a careful bean-grower and at the same time be so slight as to escape the attention of the general farmer, or even of experimenters who are not particularly skilled in judging the merits of beans.

Fig. 75. — New type with short stem, which is becoming very popular with commercial growers.

All these examples drawn from the bean are excellent illustrations of the best and most scientific plant-breeding, and the same methods — varied to suit the different needs — apply to the amelioration of all other plants. The recent dwarf lima beans may be cited as examples of accidental or fortuitous varieties, in which the preconceived ideal of the plant-breeder had no place. Four or five of these beans have attained some prominence. Henderson and Kumerle Dwarf limas were introduced in 1889, Burpee in 1890, and Barteldes in 1892 or 1893. The variety now called the Henderson was picked up thirty or more years before by a negro, who found it

growing along a roadside in Virginia. It was afterwards grown in various gardens, and about 1885 it fell into the hands of a seedsman in Richmond. Henderson purchased the stock of it in 1887, grew it in 1888, and offered it to the general public in 1889. The introduction of Henderson's bean attracted the attention of Asa Palmer, of Kennett Square, Pennsylvania, who had also been growing a dwarf lima. He called on Burpee, the well-known seedsman of Philadelphia, described his variety, and left four beans for trial. These were planted in the test grounds and were found to be valuable.   Mr. Palmer's

Fig. 76. — Incurved type.

entire stock was then purchased, — comprising over an acre, which had been carefully inspected during the season, — and Burpee Bush lima was presented to the public in the spring of 1890. Mr. Palmer's dwarf lima originated in 1883, when his entire crop of Large White (Pole) limas was destroyed by cut-worms. He went over his field to remove the poles before fitting the land for other uses, but he found one little plant, about ten inches high, which had been cut off about an inch above the ground, but which had re-rooted. It bore three pods, each containing one seed. These three seeds were planted in 1884, and two of the plants were dwarf, like the parent. By discarding all plants which had a tendency to climb, in succeeding crops, the Burpee Bush lima, as we now have it, was developed.

The Kumerle, Thorburn, or Dreer, Dwarf lima originated from occasional dwarf forms of the Challenger Pole lima, which J. W. Kumerle, of Newark, New Jersey, found growing in his field. The stock which came from these selected dwarf plants was introduced by Thorburn and Dreer, under their respective names. The singular Barteldes Bush lima came from Colorado, and is a similar dwarf sport of the old White Spanish or Dutch Runner bean. Barteldes received about a peck of the seed and introduced it sparingly. It attracted very little attention, and as the following season was dry, Barteldes himself failed to get a crop, and the variety was lost to the trade.

Cannas. — Few plants have shown more remarkable evolution in very recent years than the cannas. At the present time, the Crozy cannas — so named from Crozy, of Lyons, France, who has introduced the greater number of them — are most popular. This type is often called the French Dwarf, or the Flowering Canna, and it is marked by comparatively low stature, and very large and showy spreading flowers in many colors, whereas the cannas of former years were very tall plants, with small and late dull red narrow flowers, and they were grown for their foliage effects. How has this transformation come about?

In the first place, it should be said that there are many species of canna, and about a half-dozen of these were well known to gardeners at the opening of last century. About 1830, the cannas began to attract much attention from cultivators, and the original species were soon variously hybridized. Crossed seeds, and seeds from the successive generations of hybrids, introduced a host of new and variable forms. The first distinct fashion in cannas seems to have been tall late-flowering forms. In 1848, Année, a cultivator in France, sowed seeds of *Canna nepalensis*, a tall oriental species, and there sprung up a race of plants which has since been known as *Canna Annœi*. It is probable that this *Canna nepalensis* had become fertilized with other species growing in Année's collection, very likely with *Canna glauca*. At all events, this race of cannas became popular, and was to its time what the French dwarfs are to the present day. The plants were freely introduced into parks, beginning about 1856, but their use began to decline by 1870 or before. Descendants of this type, variously crossed and modified, are now frequently seen in parks and gardens.

The beginning of the modern race of dwarf large-flowered cannas was in 1863, when one of the smaller-flowered Costa Rican species (*Canna Warscewiczii*) was crossed upon a larger-flowered Peruvian species (*Canna iridiflora*). The offspring of this union came to be called *Canna Ehemannii*. This hybrid has been again variously crossed with other species, and modified by cultivation and selection, until the present composite type is the result. Seeds give new varieties; and any seedling which is worth saving is thereafter multiplied by divisions of the root, and the resulting plants are introduced to commerce.

The cabbage family (see Figs. 58-64). — A good illustration of unconscious improvement is to be found in cabbage, kale, collard, borecale, Brussels sprouts, kohl-rabi, and cauliflower. These probably came from a single, somewhat woody, branching perennial (*Brassica oleracea*) which is to be found growing wild on limestone bluffs in southwestern Europe. Some are a modification of the leaf, as in the cabbage and kale, others of the stem, as kohl-rabi, while in the cauliflower it is the selection of the inflorescence that has caused the peculiar modification. Some of these types have twenty and more varieties, so that there are probably over one hundred distinct forms from this one wild type.

Fig. 77. — Hairy type.

All of these forms are the result of long and patient selection of variations that were considered desirable by the gardener without any conscious attempt to produce these specific forms.

The chrysanthemum. — An excellent illustration of the appearing of a wide range of forms within the epoch of the systematic botanists is afforded by the florist's chrysanthemum (Figs. 65-79). These chrysanthemums are now so widely variable and so little referable to wild species that they have recently been named as a garden group-species, *Chrysanthemum hortorum* (Stand. Cyc. Hort. ii. 755). These plants now comprise forms single and double; pompon and giant; discoid, flat-rayed, and quilled; ball-head and reflexed; hairy-rayed; a wide range of colors; bizarre forms; and marked differences in stature and habit of plant. If one were to bring together the little pompons,

the hardy border types, the anemone-flowered, the Japanese incurved, and the slender singles, he would have difficulty in referring them to any single origin.

And yet the records show that these multitudes of forms have come from one oriental feral group, or what some botanists regard as two very similar species. The original was introduced to England about 150 years ago.

Fig. 78. — Japanese type.

In 1796 the *Botanical Magazine* figured an important large-flowered departure, marking the beginning, or practically the beginning, of the modern record and development. The plants may have been long cultivated and considerably modified in China and Japan. What are considered to be the feral forms have been introduced within very recent years. They are most unpromising looking herbs, one (*C. morifolium*) with white rays, and the other (*C. indicum*) with yellow rays. They look no more promising than many weedy composites of the fields; and yet some process has evolved a multitude of astonishing forms without our knowing how or why even though the evolution has proceeded under our eyes and within the period when plants have been under close scrutiny.

These various examples are but types of what has been and can be accomplished in a given group of plants. There is nothing mysterious about the subject, so far as the cultivator is concerned. He simply sets his ideal, makes sure that it does not contradict any of the fundamental laws of development of the plant with which he is to work, then patiently and persistently keeps at his task. He must have good judgment, skill, and inspiration, but he does not need genius.

FIG. 79. — Reflexed type.

"In the improvement of plants," writes Henri L. de Vilmorin, "the action of man, much like influences which act in the wild state, only brings about slow and gradual changes, often scarcely noticeable at first. But if the efforts towards the desired end be kept on steadily, the changes will soon become greater and greater, and the last stages of the improvement will become much more rapid than the first ones."

CHAPTER IX

POLLINATION: OR HOW TO CROSS PLANTS

POLLINATION is the act of conveying pollen from the anther to the stigma. It is the manual part of the crossing of plants. The word fertilization is often used in a like sense, although erroneously; for it is the office of the pollen, not of the operator, to fertilize or fecundate that part of the flower which is to develop into a seed.

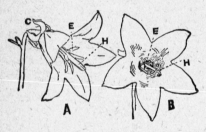

FIG. 80. — Bellflower.

The structure of the flower. — The chief requirement in pollinating flowers is to know the parts of the flower itself. The conspicuous or showy part of the flower is the envelope, which is endlessly modified in size, form, and color. This envelope covers the inner or essential organs, and it also attracts insects, which often perform the labor of pollination. This floral envelope is usually of two series or parts, — an outer and commonly green series known as the calyx, and an inner and usually more showy series known as the corolla. These two series are well shown in the bellflower, Fig. 80. The calyx, with

its reflexed lobes, is at *C*, and the large bell-form part
is the corolla. When the calyx is composed of separate
parts or leaves, each part is called a sepal; in like manner
each separate part of the corolla is a petal. In the lily,
Fig. 81, there is no distinction between calyx and corolla;
or, it may be said, the calyx
is wanting. These envelopes
of the flower are often much
disguised. This is particularly true in the orchids, one
of which, a lady-slipper, is
illustrated in Fig. 82. The
sepals are seen at *DD*. They
are apparently only two, but
there is reason to believe that
the lower sepal is really made
up of a union of two. The
three inner leaves are the
petals, the lower one, *H*,
being enlarged into the sac
or slipper.

The most important organs
of the flower, however, to

FIG. 81. — Flower of white lily.

one who wishes to make crosses, are the so-called sexual
organs, the stamens and pistils. They can be readily
distinguished in the lily, Fig. 81. The six bodies shown
at *S* are the ends of the stamens, or so-called male organs.
These stamens generally have a stalk or stem, known as
a filament, and the enlarged tip as the anther. It is in
this anther that the pollen is borne. The pollen is usually made up of very minute yellow or brownish grains,

although it is sometimes in the form of a more or less glutinous or adhesive mass, as in the milk-weeds and orchids. The irritating dust which falls from the corn tassels at the later cultivatings is the pollen.

The pistil, or so-called female organ, is shown at *OP*, Fig. 81. The enlarged portion at *O* is the ovary, which develops into the seed-pod. The stigma, or the enlarged and roughened part which receives the pollen, is at *P*. Between these two parts is the slender style, a part that is absent in many flowers.

FIG. 82. — Flower of greenhouse cypripedium.

The stamens and pistils are known as the essential organs of the flower, for, whilst the calyx and corolla may be entirely absent, either one or both of these organs is present; and these are the parts that are directly concerned in the reproduction of the species. Like the floral envelopes, these essential organs are often modified, so much so that botanists are sometimes perplexed to distinguish them from each other or from modified forms of the petals or sepals. The particular features of these organs which the plant-breeder must be able to distinguish are the anther and the stigma; for the anther bears the pollen and the stigma must receive it. In Fig. 80, the stamens are shown at *E*. In the flower *A*, which has just

Fig. 83. — Flower of night-blooming cereus.

expanded, these stamens are rigid and in condition to shed the pollen, but in the flower *B*, they have shed the pollen and have collapsed. The stigma in this case is

T

divided into three parts, but when the flower first opens, these parts are closed together, *H* in flower *A*, so that it is impossible that they receive any pollen from the same flower; when the stamens have withered, however, as in *B*, the stigma, *H*, spreads open and is ready to receive any pollen which may be brought to it by insects or

Fig. 84. — Flower of the shrubby hibiscus (*Hibiscus syriacus*).

other agencies. In this case, the ovary or young seed-pod, which is in the bottom of the flower, is not shown in the engraving.

Some of the particular forms of essential organs are well illustrated in the accompanying photographs. In the night-blooming cereus, Fig. 83, the many-rayed stigma is shown just below the center of the mouth of the flower, and the numerous stamens are arranged in a circular form outside of it. The many petals and numerous spreading sepals are also well shown. The hibiscus, Fig. 84, has a central column with the anthers hanging upon it, and a large stigma raised beyond them. The wild bugbane, or cimicifuga, is seen in Fig. 85, natural size. Here is a long spike or cluster of flowers. At the top are the unopened buds, in the center the expanded flowers with the floral envelopes fallen away, — the fringe-like stamens very prominent, — and below are seen the pistils, the stamens having fallen. These pistils will now ripen into pods, but the tip-like stigma may still be seen on them. The stamens and the long protruding style are also shown in the fuchsia, Fig. 94. The essential organs of orchids are curiously disguised. They are combined into a single body. In the lady-slipper, Fig. 82, the lip-like stigma is shown at *P.* On either side, at its base, is an anther, *S.* Pro-

FIG. 85. — Bugbane (*Cimicifuga racemosa*).

jecting over the stigma is a greenish ladle-like body, *T*, which is a transformed and sterile anther. In all lady-slippers, these organs are essentially the same as in the drawing, although they vary much in size and shape· but in most other orchids, the two side anthers, *S*, are wholly wanting, and the terminal organ, *T*, is a pollen-bearing anther. In numerous plants, there are many distinct pistils in each flower. Such is the case in the strawberry, where each little yellow "seed" on the ripened berry represents a pistil; and the blackberry and the raspberry,

Fig. 86. — Blossom of flowering raspberry (*Rubus odoratus*).

where each little grain or drupelet of the fruit stands for the same organ. A flowering raspberry is illustrated natural size in Fig. 86, for the purpose of showing the ring of many anthers near the center of the flower, inside of which, in the very center, is a little head of pistils.

It frequently occurs that the stamens and pistils are borne in different flowers, rather than together in the same flower, as they are in the examples we have studied. In these cases the flower is said to be staminate, or male or sterile, in one case, and pistillate, female or fer-

Fig. 87. — Squash flowers of each sex.

tile, in the other case. If these two kinds of flowers are borne together on the same plant, as in pumpkins, melons, cucumbers, chestnuts, oaks, and begonias, the plant is said to be monœcious; but if the staminate and pistillate flowers are on entirely different plants, as in willows and poplars, the plant is diœcious. The two kinds of squash flowers are shown in Fig. 87. The pistillate flower is on the left, and it is at once distinguished by the ovary or little squash below the colored part, or corolla of the flower. The lobed stigma is seen in the center. The staminate flower is on the right. It has a longer

Fig. 88. — Flowers of clematis (*Clematis virginiana*).

stem, no ovary, and the anthers are united into a conspicuous cone in the center. The flowers expand early in the morning. Insects carry pollen to the pistillate flower, which then begins to set its fruit, whilst the staminate flower dies. The flower of the common wild clematis is shown in Fig. 88. On the right are the sterile flowers, which are wholly staminate. On the left, the flowers with larger sepals — the petals are absent — have a cone of pistils in the center, and a few short and sterile stamens spreading from the base of the cone. These different flowers are borne on different plants in this species of clematis, and the plants are therefore practically diœcious, because the stamens of the pistillate flowers generally bear no pollen. A similar mixed arrangement occurs in some strawberries, except that there are no purely staminate flowers. There are purely pistillate varieties, others, as the Crescent, with a few nearly or quite abortive stamens at the base of the cone of pistils, and others in which the flowers are perfect or hermaphrodites, that is, containing the two sexes.

The compositous flowers — as the asters, daisies, goldenrods, sunflowers, dahlias, zinnias, chrysanthemums, and their kin — need to be considered in still a different category. In these plants, the head, or so-called flower, is an aggregation of several or many small flowers or florets. Each seed in a sunflower head, for example, represents a distinct flower. Sometimes all of these flowers are perfect, — contain the two sexes, — and sometimes they are pistillate or staminate in different parts of the head; and in some cases the plants are diœcious. In many plants of the composite family, the flowers near the border of the head are unlike those of the center or disk, in having a long ray-like corolla; and these ray-flowers are frequently of different form from the others in the character of the essential organs. Very frequently the ray-flowers are pistillate, whilst the disk flowers are generally hermaphrodite. The anthers in these plants are united in a ring closely about the style and below the stigma.

The ovary, as we have seen, ripens into the pod, berry,

or other fruit; but it is not able to bear seeds until it is assisted by the pollen. The pollen falls upon the roughish or sticky surface of the stigma, and there germinates or sends a minute tube downwards through the style and finally reaches the ovule, which, when fertilized, rapidly ripens into the seed. The nature of this fecundation is not germane to the present subject; but it may be said that only one pollen-grain is necessary to the fertilization of a single ovule, but the addition of a superabundance of pollen greatly stimulates the growth of the fleshy or enveloping parts of the fruit. It is important that the person who desires to cross plants should become familiar with the stigma when it is "ripe," receptive, or ready to receive the pollen. This condition is usually indicated by the glutinous or sticky or moist condition of the stigma, or in those stigmas which are not glutinous it is told by the appearing of a distinctly roughened or papillose condition. This receptive condition generally occurs about as soon as the flower opens. If pollen is withheld, the stigma will remain receptive much longer than when fertilization has taken place, — in some flowers for two or three days.

The pollen is discharged from the anther in various ways, but it most commonly escapes through a chink or crack in the side of the anther. Sometimes it escapes through pores at one end of the anther; and in other cases there are more elaborate mechanisms to admit of its discharge. In most plants, the anthers and stigma in the same flower mature at different times, so that close-fertilization or in-breeding is avoided. This is well illustrated in the bellflower, Fig. 80. Here the anthers wither and die before the stigmatic lobes open. In other cases, the stigma matures first, although this is not the usual condition.

Manipulating the flowers. — We are now familiar with the essential principles in the pollination of flowers. Before a person proceeds to operate on a flower with which he is unfamiliar, he should carefully study its structure, so as to be able to locate the different organs, and to discover when the pollen and the stigma are ready for work.

The first and last rule in the pollinating of plants is this: Exercise every precaution to prevent any other pollination than that which you design to give. The anthers, therefore, must be removed from the flower before it opens. This removal of the anthers is known as emasculation. Just as soon as this is done, tie up the flower securely in a bag to protect it from foreign pollen, which may be brought by winds or insects. As soon as the stigma is ripe, remove the bag and apply the desired pollen, placing the bag on the flower again, where it must remain until the seeds begin to form. The stigma may be receptive the day following emasculation, or, perhaps, not until a week afterwards. Much depends on the age of the bud when emasculation takes place. It is commonly best to delay emasculation as long as possible and not have the flower open; but the operator must be sure that the anthers do not discharge or that insects do not get into the flower before he has emasculated it. The bud at *B*, in Fig. 82, is nearly ready to emasculate. The older buds on the top of the spike of bugbane, Fig. 85, are ready to operate; and so is the bud seen at the left in Fig. 86.

The manner of emasculating the flower varies with the operator. It is a common practice to clip off the anthers with a pair of small scissors, or to hook them out with a bent pin or a crochet hook. There are disadvantages in any of these methods, because the anthers are likely

Fig. 89. — Tobacco flowers, showing the parts of the flower, a bud ready to be emasculated, and an emasculated subject.

to drop into the bottom of the corolla, where it is sometimes difficult to rescue them; and if one uses tweezers, there is always danger that the anthers may be crushed and that some of the pollen may adhere to the instrument and contaminate future crosses. We may therefore cut the corolla completely off just above the ovary, with a pair of small, long-handled surgeon's scissors (see Fig. 91), removing everything but the pistil. The operation is explained in Fig. 89, which shows the tobacco flower

FIG. 90. — Zinnia flowers; the upper head ready for emasculation, the lower one showing the operation performed.

The flower at the left shows the pin-head stigma in the center of the throat, and the five anthers surrounding it. The second flower is spread open for the purpose of showing these organs. The third figure is a bud in

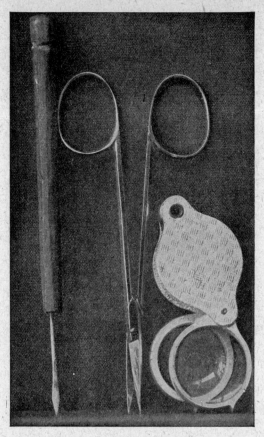

Fig. 91. — Instruments used in pollinating flowers, natural size. Pin
scalpel, scissors, lens.

the right condition for operation. The right-hand figure
shows this bud cut around with the points of the scissors,

leaving only the pistil. The line at *W*, in Fig. 81, shows where the flower of the lily might be cut off.

The method for a compositous flower is shown in the picture of the zinnia, Fig. 90. In this plant the outer flowers of the head are pistillate, whilst those of the disk are perfect. It is only necessary, therefore, to remove the central stamen-bearing flowers before any of them open, and to cover the flower up before any of the pistils near the border have protruded themselves. The upper head in Fig. 90 shows the untreated sample, while the lower one shows the same with the cone of central flowers pulled out. This treated head should now be covered,

FIG. 92. — Ladle for pollinating house tomatoes.

to await the maturing of the stigmas. In many compositous plants, however, the case is not so simple as this, because all the flowers are perfect. In such cases, nearly all the florets should be removed from the head, and a few remaining ones emasculated in essentially the same method as described for the tobacco, Fig. 89.

Whenever flowers are borne in clusters, nearly all of them should be removed and the attention confined to only two or three of them. One is then more certain of getting seeds to set. In some cases, like the apple cluster, only one or two flowers of any cluster ever set fruit, and the operator should then choose the two or three strongest and most promising buds, and cut all the others off.

Flowers that bear no stamens, as the pistillate flowers of squashes, strawberries, and many other plants, of course do not require emasculating. They should be tied up while in bud, however, to prevent the access of any foreign pollen. Indian corn is a case in point. The pistillate flowers are on the ear, each kernel of corn representing a single flower. The silks are the stigmas. If it is desired to cross corn, therefore, the ear should be covered before any silks are protruded, and the pollen should be applied some days later, when the silks are fully grown. The staminate or male flowers are in the tassel.

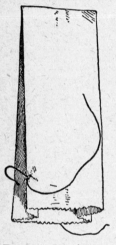

Fig. 93. — Bag for covering the flowers.

The pollen should be derived from a flower which has also been protected from wind and insects, because foreign pollen may have been dropped upon an anther by an insect visitor, and it may be unknowingly transferred by the operator. The pollen-bearing parent needs no operation, of course, but the flower should have been tied up in a bag when it was in bud. The pollen is best obtained by picking off a ripe anther and crushing it upon the thumb-nail. Then it is transferred to the stigma by a tiny scalpel made by hammering out the small end of a pin, as shown, full size, at the left in Fig. 91. The stigma should be entirely covered with the pollen, if possible. It is often advised to use a camel's-hair brush to transfer pollen,

but much of the pollen sticks amongst the hairs of the
brush and is ready to contaminate a future cross; and
when the pollen is scarce it cannot be conserved to ad-

Fig. 94. — Fuchsias, showing the stamens and pistils, and a bud ready
to be emasculated.

vantage by a brush.   In some cases the pollen is discharged
so freely that the anther may be rubbed upon the stigma,
or even shaken over it, but in most instances it will be

necessary actually to place the pollen upon the stigma with some hand instrument. When pollinating house-grown melons and cucumbers, the staminate flower is broken off, the corolla stripped back, and the anther-cone inserted into the pistillate flower, where it is allowed to remain until it dries and falls away. In pollinating house tomatoes, an implement shown in Fig. 92, one-third size, is used. This is simply a watch-glass, *T*, secured to a

Fig. 95. — Fuchsia flower emasculated.

handle. When the house is dry, at midday, the watch-glass is held under the flowers, which are tapped, and the pollen falls into the glass. The glass is then held up under another flower until the stigma rests in the pollen. It should be said, however, that this pollination of tomatoes is for the purpose of making the fruit set in the absence of insects, not to effect a cross. If the latter purpose were the object sought, the flowers which are to bear the seeds would need to be emasculated.

Sometimes it is impossible to secure the pollen at the time the stigma is ready. In some cases of this kind, the intended parents can be grown under glass so as to bring them into bloom at the same time. In other cases, it is necessary to keep the pollen for some time. The length of time that pollen will keep varies with the species and probably also with the strength and vigor of the plants that bear it. As a rule, it will not keep more than a week or two, and, in general, it may be said that the fresher it is, the better it may be expected to act. It is best kept in dry and tight paper bags, such as are used for covering the flowers.

Fig. 96. — Fuchsia flower tied up after emasculation.

Something more should be said about the bags which are used for covering the flowers. It has been found that light transparent oiled paper bags are the best. For

U

small flowers use the two-ounce bags and for larger flowers use the four-ounce size. If oiled bags are not available, the ordinary manilla bags may be used. When they are still flat, as they come from the packages, a hole is made near the opening, and a string is passed through it and then tied at one of the folds, as shown in Fig. 93. The bag is then ready for use. Before it is put on the flower, the lower end of it is dipped in water to soften it so that

Fig. 97. — Tomato and quince, showing how the sepals were cut off in emasculating.

it can be puckered tightly about the stem and thereby prevent the entrance of any insect. A bag is put upon the seed-bearing flower when emasculation is performed, and upon the intended pollen parent when the flower is still in bud. The bag may be removed from the emasculated flower from time to time to examine the stigma, and again when the pollen is applied; but it should not be taken off permanently until the pod or fruit begins to grow.

By way of recapitulation, let us consider the crossing

of a fuchsia flower. In Fig. 94 two flowers are shown in full bloom, with the long style and the eight shorter stamens. The single bud is just the right age to emasculate. We therefore cut off the two flowers and emasculate the bud, as in Fig. 95. The pollen of another flower is applied and the bag is tied on, as seen in Fig. 96. The best label is a small merchandise tag, and this records the staminate parent and the date.

It will be seen that in the operation of emasculating the fuchsia flower we cut off the sepals as well as the petals. In some plants the calyx adheres to the full-grown fruit, as on the apple, pear, quince, gooseberry, or persists at the base of the fruit, as in the tomato, pea, raspberry. In these fruits, therefore, the cutting away of the calyx leaves an indelible mark which

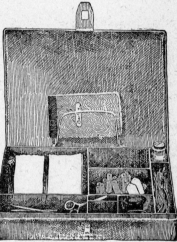

Fig. 98. — Pollinating kit.

at once distinguishes the fruits which have been crossed, even if the labels are lost. In Fig. 97 a tomato and quince are shown thus marked.

All the foregoing remarks do not apply to the crossing of ferns, lycopodes, and the like, because these plants have no flowers; yet cross-fertilization may take place

in them. When the spores of these flowerless plants are
sown, a thin green tissue, or prothallus, appears and
spreads over the ground. In this tissue the separate
sex-organs appear, and after fecundation takes place,
the fern, as we commonly understand it, springs forth.
Thereafter, this fern lives an asexual life and produces
spores year after year; but it is only in this primitive
prothallic stage that fertilization takes place, once in the
life time of the plant.

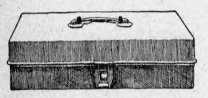

If these plants are to
be crossed, the only
procedure open to the
gardener is to sow the
spores of the intended
parents together in
the hope that a nat-
ural mixing may take

Fig. 99. — Pollinating kit.

place.   There are various well-authenticated fern hybrids.

The pollination of flowers is such a simple work that
few implements are required for its easy performance.
Great care is more important than any number of tools.
Every one who expects to cross plants should provide himself with the three instruments shown in Fig. 91, — a pin
scalpel, sharp-pointed scissors, and a large hand-lens. If
one contemplates much experimenting in this direction,
however, it is economy of time to have some sort of box
in which there are compartments for the various necessi-
ties. These various compartments suggest at once whatever
accessories are wanting, and they hold a sufficient supply
for several hundred operations.   There should be a com-

partment for bags, string, lens, scissors, and pencils, tags, note-book, and the like. Figs. 98 and 99 show a convenient case for an experimenter, and one that has been used with satisfaction for several years. This kit is twelve inches long, nine inches wide, and three inches deep.

CHAPTER X

THE FORWARD MOVEMENT IN PLANT-BREEDING

THE first specific interest in cultivated plants was in the gross kinds or species. As the contact with plants became more intimate, various indefinite form-groups were recognized within the limits of the species. Gradually, with the intensifying of domestication and cultivation, very particular groups appeared and were recognized. These smaller groups came finally to be designated by names, and the idea of the definite and homogeneous cultural variety came into existence. The variety-conception is really a late one in the development of the human race. It is practically only within the past two centuries that cultivated varieties of plants have been recognized as being worthy of receiving designative names. It is within this period, also, that most of the great breeds of animals have been defined and separately named.

All this measures the increasing intimacy of our contact with domesticated plants and animals. It is a record of our progress. The peoples that are most advanced in the cultivation of any plant are the ones that have the most named varieties of that plant. In Japan, to this day, the plums are said to pass under ill-defined class names. We have introduced these classes, have sorted out the particular forms that promise to be of value to us, and have given them specific American names. Some time ago a native professor in Japan wrote me asking for cions of these plums, in order that he might introduce Japanese plums into Japan. The Russian apples are designated to some extent by class names; in fact, it was not until the appearance of Regel's work, about a generation ago, that Russian pomology may be said to have begun. What constitutes a variety is increasingly more difficult to define, because we are constantly differentiating on smaller points. The growth of the variety-conception is really the growth of the power of analysis.

The earlier recognized varieties seem to have come into existence unchallenged. There is very little record of inquiry as to how or why or even where they originated. That is, the quest of the origin arose long after the recognition of the variety as a variety. Even after inquisitive search into origins had begun, there was little effort to produce these varieties. The describing of varieties and the search into their histories was a special work of the nineteenth century. One has only to consult such American works as Downing's "Fruits and Fruit Trees of America," and Burr's "Field and Garden Vegetables of America," to see how carefully and methodically the descriptions and synonymy of the varieties were worked out. These are types of excellent pieces of editorial and formal systematic work.

Systematic improvement of plants. — There have been isolated efforts at producing varieties for many years. These efforts began before the time of the general discussion of organic evolution. In fact, it was on such experiments that Darwin drew heavily in some of his most important writing. Roughly speaking, however, the conception that the kinds of plants can be definitely modified and varied by man is a product of the last half century. We now think that there is such a possibility as plant-breeding. It is really a more modern conception, so far as its general acceptance is concerned, than animal-breeding. But both animal-breeding and plant-breeding are the results of a new attitude toward the forms of life — a conviction that the very structure, habits, and attributes are amenable to change and control by man. This is really one of the great new attitudes of the modern world.

The term plant-breeding itself is new. It occurs only in the most recent supplements of dictionaries. Before this term came into use, such words as " improvement " and " amelioration " of plants were employed, although cross-breeding had long been current. The early writings of Verlot and Carrière were under the title of " production and fixation of varieties of plants." The term plant-breeding carries the conception of a definite purpose in the producing of new forms and attributes of plants, by crossing, selection, and whatever other means may be useful.

One of the "signs of the times" in North America is the attention that is being given to the practical breeding of plants. A host of persons is actually at work. There are professorships devoted to the subject. Many societies are giving special attention to the practical improvement of plants. Results are accumulating rapidly with very many kinds of plants, and the literature is growing rapidly.

Eventually, of course, we shall be able to formulate somewhat definite statements as to how to proceed to secure desired results, and then the literature of plant-breeding can be intelligently rewritten. However, there is no hope that plant-breeding can ever proceed with such exactness as to enable us to produce forthwith the things that we desire, in the way in which the mechanician devises new machines, notwithstanding all the suggestions of persons who write with much self-assurance. For all that we can now see, plant-breeding will always be an experimental process. It is this very experimental uncertainty of the work that gives it much of its charm to inquisitive and sensitive minds.

The plant-breeder should aim toward definite ideals. — Now, plant-breeding is worthy of the name only as it sets definite ideals and is able to attain them. Merely to produce new things is of no merit; that was done long before man was evolved. A child can "produce" a new variety, but it may learn nothing and contribute nothing in producing it. In many "new" things that are produced there may be dispute as to whether they are new, and as to whether they are distinct enough to be named and therefore to be ranked as varieties at all. This is not science, nor even breeding: it is playing and guessing. What does the world care whether John Jones produces "Jones' Giant Beardless Wheat"? But it does care if he produces wheat having a half of one per cent more protein. We must give up the production of mere "varieties"; we must breed for certain definite attributes that will make the new generation of plants more efficient for certain purposes: this is the new out-look in plant-breeding.

Plant improvement a serious business. — In considering
the American achievement in plant-breeding, we must
divest ourselves at the outset of all idea of "wonder," and
"miracle," and other nonsense, which has been so much
written into the subject in very recent time. Plant-
breeding is a plain and serious business, to be conducted
by carefully trained persons in a painstaking and methodical way. It is not magic. There are persons who have
unusual native judgment as to the merits and capabilities
of plants and who develop great manual skill; but they
are plain and modest citizens, nevertheless, and their
methods are perfectly normal and scrutable. The wonder-
mongers are the reporters, not the plant-breeders.

It is a curious psychological phenomenon that the popu-
lace, or a certain part of it, seems to lose its head now and
then. This phenomenon is not peculiar to politics. It
enters those domains that are compassed by fact and that
in ordinary times are dominated by common sense.
Plant-breeding has been seized of this sensationalism.
Newspapers, magazines, and books have spread the most
wonderful tales. The lay writers have at last awakened
to the fact that great progress is making in agricultural
subjects, and, with a fragmentary and superficial view
here and there, have written of the subjects with all the
enthusiasm and partiality of new discovery. We have
now in mind not only the inflated writing about plant-
breeding, which constitutes a regrettable contribution to
current horticultural literature, but also that general
tendency to exploit everything that is capable of high
coloring. The agricultural historian, when he takes account of the exploitations of the present day, will recall other

stages in which we seem temporarily to have lost our better judgment, of which the *Morus multicaulis* craze and the lightning-rod boom are examples in two past generations.

Having now warned our readers that we have nothing marvelous in store, we shall proceed to indicate some of the ways in which American plant-breeders are working, fully conscious that the space at our disposal is much too little to allow of any adequate presentation of the subject. It may not be out of place to call the reader's attention to the three foundations on which rests the increased productiveness of crops and animals : —

The enrichment of the land ;

The tillage and care ;

The producing of better varieties and strains.

We have long given careful attention to the first two ; now we are studying the third with new enthusiasm and purpose.

The results of plant-breeding effort. — Happily, we are not without abundant accomplishment in this new field. The last ten years has seen a remarkable specialization in the producing of plants that are adapted to particular needs. The days of merely crossing and sowing the seeds to see what will turn up are already past with those who are engaged seriously in the work. The old method was hit-and-miss, and the result was to take what good luck put in our way : the new method proceeds definitely and directly, and the result is the necessary outcome of the line of effort. The crux of the new ideal is efficiency in one particular attribute in the product of the breeding. These attributes are measurable ; the kinds of results are foreseen in the plan.

State plant-breeding associations. — One of the most significant advances in popular interest in plant improvement is the banding together of persons in many of the states and provinces in an organized effort to improve plants, especially field crops. This line of effort has been largely brought about at the suggestion of some officer of the state agricultural college, who is often an expert plant-breeder himself, and usually acts as secretary of the association. These associations have done great good in arousing interest in plant-breeding.

The Wisconsin Association, known as the Wisconsin Agricultural Improvement Association, was established Feb. 22, 1901, and now has a paid-up membership of over 2000 persons, consisting of "all former, present, and future students and instructors of the Wisconsin College of Agriculture," also "any person residing within the state having completed a course in agriculture in any college equivalent to that given by the Wisconsin University." More recently the county agricultural schools have been admitted to membership and honorary members may be elected by a majority vote at any annual or special meeting of the association.

The association has organized some 44 county suborders, which are smaller units conducting an active work in more restricted areas. These county orders contain approximately 4000 members. Any one interested in agriculture may unite with the county order. They have become live centers which stand behind all agricultural activities and lend a helping hand in making agricultural and other resources of the county known far and near. As a result of the association there has been established in the neighborhood of 2000 seed-grain centers where pure-bred seed barley may be obtained. It is estimated that over seventy-five per cent of the seed barley of Wisconsin is of one distinct variety.

Another series of organizations, to be known as "township organizations," has been planned. These are smaller groups within the county orders. Three are already in existence. This scheme of organization brings the activities of the association to practically every farmer of the state.

Starting out primarily as breeding associations, their activities have extended in many directions. An alfalfa order has been established which is closely affiliated with the main association : its object is "to promote the alfalfa interests of the state in general,"

1st. By coöperating with the Department of Agronomy and the Wisconsin Agricultural Experiment Association in growing, experimenting, and in the wide dissemination of alfalfa ;

2d. By having alfalfa exhibits at agricultural fairs ;

3d. By having annual meetings in order to report and discuss topics beneficial to the members of the order ;

4th. By distributing literature and information bearing upon the production of alfalfa for seed and forage.

The alfalfa order was organized three years ago and now has a membership of 1200. In 1914, 50 tons of alfalfa seed were sent out for experimental purposes.

The association receives state aid, $5000 a year, and some of the county orders receive financial aid from the county. The annual dues of members is fifty cents.

One of the principal aims of the Wisconsin association

is to place pure-bred seed on the market. This seed is to bear the seal of the association.

It is estimated that members of the association sell over three hundred thousand dollars' worth of pure-bred seed a year. The members are in close touch with the breeding work of the experiment station and test, propagate, and disseminate the improved grains which are produced on the station farm.

The association prints an annual report of over one hundred pages containing the progress of the members in improving seed grain and much valuable information concerning plant-breeding in general. Such titles as the following appear in recent annual reports: —

Dissemination of Pure Bred Seed Grains, Through the Coöperation of Students in the Country Schools, J. C. Brockert.

Necessity of Thorough Preparation of Pure Bred Seed Grain for the General Trade, Wm. R. Leonard.

County Order of Experiment Association as Factor to Promote Dissemination of Pure Bred Grain, R. A. Moore.

Importance of Testing Our Pure Seed Grains Previous to Sowing Season's Crop, H. L. Post.

Importance of the Farm Inspection Work, and How Shall It Be Carried Out? E. B. Skewes.

Growing and Preparing Seed Grains and Forage Plants for Exhibition, O. R. Frauenheim.

Wheat Breeding — The Value of the Individual, F. H. Demaree.

In this connection, mention should be made of the Wisconsin Potato Growers' Association, an active and growing organization whose object is to improve the seed and table potatoes of Wisconsin by breeding and to guarantee variety shipments true to name and free from disease. This association, like its sister organization, does business on a large scale and has at present nearly 300 members. "Potato Special" trains have been run throughout the state under its auspices and that of the State College of Agriculture, and several very successful potato exhibits have been held.

This association has done much to standardize certain commercial varieties of potatoes and to put seed on the market which is true to name. Its members found our varieties badly mixed up and containing many distinct types. This purifying of varieties is the first step toward careful and systematic breeding.

A Minnesota association, known as the "Minnesota Field Crop Breeders' Association," has been organized with a similar plan and objects as the Wisconsin associations. It publishes an elaborate annual report giving information concerning the work of the association as a whole and the activities of the county sections, of which there are many. One of the functions of the association, besides encouraging the production and sale of pure-bred seeds, is to stage elaborate exhibits of farm products at the state and other fairs.

In some states, notably Illinois, Ohio, and New York, associations of breeders have been established on a different membership basis. They have chosen to have smaller associations consisting of persons who bind themselves to follow certain rules and regulations laid down by the association. The Illinois Seed-corn Breeders' Association is such an organization. Its members grow certain varieties of corn recognized by the association and offer these for sale with the approval and backing of the association.

The Ohio and New York associations laid out elaborate plans of breeding for their members to follow, but it was found that farmers were not ready for such work and as a result the Ohio association has never been very large and the New York association has abandoned this plan and is turning its attention to bringing the farmers and seedsmen into closer relations, encouraging the farmer to demand a better product and the seedsmen to produce one.

Other plant-breeding associations. — The most notable breeders' associations are the Canadian Seed Growers' Association and the Swedish Seed Association.

The former has an elaborate system of inspection of all seeds sold by members of the association under the supervision of a permanent, salaried secretary. The results are noteworthy. The standard of seed grain has been tremendously raised in Canada and much better crops are the result. Canadian seed grain is now in demand all over the world. The Canadian experiment stations are leading in this work by carefully and systematically producing improved varieties on their experimental farms and distributing them to members of the association who grow them, keeping up a careful selection from year to year and offering them for sale.

The Swedish association has an interesting history and an enviable record. It has done more, probably, than any other organization to reshape our conception and methods of selection. Dr. Nilsson and his associates have started on a large scale the principle of individual selection in contrast to the older method of mass selection which is now largely given up. The group of scientists at Svalöf have not only shown their ability to produce practical results, but they have also elaborated scientific principles.

The founding of the station at Svalöf is wholly due to the private initiative of a group of Swedish farmers. The purpose of the association has always been to produce practical results, to breed better grains for local use.

But the station has been fortunate from the first in having in its employ expert botanists whose skill has not only produced many noteworthy new varieties, but who have elaborated scientific principles of far-reaching importance. These men have been given a free hand to pursue their work without such distracting activities as teaching, comparative field trials, commercial analyses, and the like. This fact together with an unrestricted organization, a well-selected program, and an expert corps of assistants accounts for the wonderful success of this station.

This Swedish seed association has two groups of members: those who are permanent after having paid $28 once for all; and those who pay annually $1.40.

The association has an annual budget of about $40,000 derived from dues of members, contributions from agricultural associations, government aid, and sale of pedigreed seed. Funds from the last two sources have increased very rapidly in recent years. Gifts of various kinds amounting to $77,000 have been set aside for buildings.

Accordingly, the society now has at its disposal a large and well-equipped establishment, comprising two connected buildings serving as laboratories (Fig. 100), a house

x

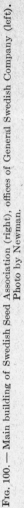

FIG. 100. — Main building of Swedish Seed Association (right), offices of General Swedish Company (left).
Photo by Newman.

for preparatory work, with a little farm and a dwelling house; it also owns 40 acres of land, of which special cultures and seed multiplication plots occupy 25 acres. Despite this, it has been found necessary to make most of the cultural experiments on the wide fields of the huge property adjoining, in order to give the different cereals, occupying in all about 30 acres a year, their proper place in the rotation of crops, which is found absolutely necessary for a normal development.

The program of work in Sweden was, at first, vague and uncertain. Theorizing scientists were attempting to solve problems for practical farmers and nobody had blazed the trail. The starting-point of the work was naturally the method of selection in vogue at the time, that is, the Darwinian method of "methodical selection" or of "mass selection" as it is now called. By this system, a selection of seed was made from a large number of plants and the whole thrown together and sown "en masse" in a single plot. But it soon became evident that this method of selection was not yielding the results which the Swedish farmers demanded — better varieties which would be constant. The method of selection was therefore changed and in two years the difficulties were being overcome by the new method.

This new method consisted of testing individual plants and their progeny instead of making, at once, a composite test of many plants. This plan of individual selection has proved itself. The results were convincing. It left no doubt as to the fact that the only true starting-point for the fixation of different types must be plants taken one by one.

This Swedish discovery has changed the outlook on the problem of plant-breeding, especially the methods of selection. It could be easily demonstrated that there existed in any cultural variety of plants a large number of independent forms having widely divergent qualities and a practical value that was quite useful. It was found, moreover, that most of the descendants or "pedigree culture" of single individuals were constant.

In employing the old method of "mass selection," they were working blindly without knowing how or when or even whether they were going to reach a stability of type; on the other hand the method of pedigreed culture or "individual selection" eliminated the fear of failure because of the appearance of the hitherto unsurmountable variations. The varieties are already there, and fixed from the beginning of the work; the only difficulty is to learn to recognize them and to place the proper valuations upon them.

The success of this method of breeding at Svalöf has profoundly modified the method of selection in this country. The principle almost universally applied now is the method of individual selection. Thus we hear about plant-to-row, head-to-row, ear-to-row, or tuber-unit testing, depending upon the plant used.

This method of selection is by no means the only one used for plant improvement at the Swedish station, hybridization also plays an important part in the work.

The work has grown very rapidly and has now been split up into different departments with an expert in charge of each.

Commercial breeding agencies. — The chief among commercial breeding agencies are, of course, the professional seedsmen. The demand for "novelties" is ever present and the seedsman must meet it. Therefore every seedsman's catalogue each spring features them, giving them a prominent place and often painted in radiant colors. Everybody knows that novelties are often no better than the old standard sorts. But this demand for something new seems to be inherent.

It does not seem to be the common practice among American seedsmen to produce their own novelties by precise and recognized plant-breeding methods. Many of them are purchased abroad and others are accidental discoveries picked up here and there.

Our standard sorts of seeds of all kinds are being gradually improved, but usually not by any particular up-to-date methods, except in certain unusual or exceptional instances. The seedsmen, however, carefully rogue their fields to eliminate divergent plants in an attempt to produce seed of more importance.

Recently, however, the American Seed Trade Association, consisting of the better class of seedsmen of the United States, has begun a general movement for improving crops by methods such as are used by careful breeders at the agricultural experiment stations. A committee on crop improvement has been organized whose duties are to ascertain, so far as possible, how the seed trade can be most helpful in these movements for better bred seed, and to bring about a close harmony between the seedsmen and the plant-breeding experts of the agricultural experiment stations.

Many seedsmen feel, at present, that the extra cost

entailed in producing pedigreed seed will not be adequately paid for by the average American buyer. There is probably much justification for this feeling. Two things should be done — to educate the buying public to the importance of better seed and the justification for its greater cost, and also to devise methods whereby this seed may be more cheaply and economically produced. The agricultural colleges through various channels are doing much to solve these two difficulties.

Work of the council of grain exchanges. — The National Council of Grain Exchanges is the associated body of the various grain exchanges or boards of trade of this country. This organization is interested in a larger yield of better grain. It has a crop improvement committee which is very active in grain-improvement work, including grain-breeding. This committee is conducting a very extensive publicity campaign in an attempt to induce farmers to use select seed and improve their crops. The executive work is done by a secretary, who acts as general manager, and an agronomist, who is an expert plant-breeder and advises concerning the technical features of the work, most of which is done through the county agents. To aid in this work, the committee publishes a monthly publication called *The County Agent*, a paper filled with terse information concerning all phases of farm improvement work. The secretary and agronomist have large funds at their disposal, which are being used to bring about concerted action by farming communities for the improvement of seed grain.

United States Department of Agriculture and state experiment stations. — The most methodical plant-breeding is now being done by officers of the experiment stations in the United States and Canada, and by the United States Department of Agriculture. In most of the experiment stations there is at least one person interested in improving horticultural plants and others interested in field crops; as there is an experiment station in every state and territory and in the provinces of Canada, it will be seen that there are several hundred persons who, by their profession, are directly concerned in plant-breeding, aside from a number of persons in the federal Department of Agriculture who devote themselves exclusively to this subject. The work is extended, also, into the hands of various assistants in the different institutions; so that it is probably no exaggeration to say that three to four hundred professional investigators are now giving attention, for a greater or less part of their time, to measures for improving American crop production by means of breeding.

The breeding enterprises of the federal Department of Agriculture were formerly confined to investigators in the Plant-Breeding Laboratory. But the work has grown to such an extent and breeding now touches so many phases of plant work that the former organization, as such, has been discontinued, and breeding is taken up in connection with many other departments. There is now more of a tendency for the administrative divisions to group themselves around the crops such as corn, cotton, wheat, vegetables, and so forth, rather than processes such as plant-breeding, or culture.

The work of the federal investigators has been tremendously important both from the standpoint of original research and the production of improved varieties and strains for dissemination.

The success of the cotton-breeding experiments is noteworthy. These have been conducted with the object of increasing the length and strength of lint; and an early variety to avoid the ravages of the boll-weevil is desired. The famous long-stapled Sea Island Cotton has been much used for hybridizing with the upland cottons to increase the length of lint of the latter. The length has been increased very considerably by this method and the varieties have been made more uniform, an important factor in ginning.

The work of Webber and Swingle in producing new types of oranges which are resistant to cold is exceedingly important. Various varieties of the common sweet orange were crossed with *Poncirus* (or *Citrus*) *trifoliata*, a hardy hedge orange, and hybrids have been produced which are called " citranges." These will grow some four hundred miles farther north than the present orange belt, which is no small factor in orange-growing. These hybrids are too bitter to be eaten out-of-hand, but they make an excellent ade; many of them have more juice than lemons.

A cross has also been made between the pomelo or grapefruit and the tangerine. A hybrid was produced which combines the easily removable rind of the tangerine and has the flavor, not of the pomelo, but of the sweet orange. A fruit of this kind, combining these characteristics so well, bids fair to play an important part in orange-growing of the future.

The division of Plant Introduction has contributed no small part to breeding work. Through its activities, a great many plants have been imported from all over the world which have formed rich material for the plant-breeder to take and improve, and many other varieties have been introduced which have immediately become valuable without further improvement. Such plants as durum wheat, Japanese kinshu rice, Swedish select oats, Washington navel orange, cold-resistant varieties of alfalfa, Russian apples, varieties of dates for Southern California and Arizona, drought-resistant olives, Egyptian cotton, and very many others have added millions to our agricultural wealth.

The work of Orton and his associates in breeding plants resistant to disease forms an important chapter in this work. They have been successful in waging war on wilt of cotton, cowpeas, watermelons (see Figs. 55 and 56), and other crops by means of breeding to obtain wilt-resistant strains. The only successful method of combating certain maladies seems to be in this way. Strains of disease-resistant asparagus and of rust-resistant cereals have reached economic importance.

Many great sections of the United States which are now nearly barren could be made productive if varieties of plants could be developed which are resistant to drought and alkali. This work has occupied the attention of a large corps of plant-breeders and not without results. The experts from eighteen state experiment stations besides the men from Washington are engaged in this work. As a result, varieties of wheat and other cereals, alfalfa, nuts, olives, and various fruits have been developed which will grow in parts of this great region and are of considerable economic importance.

Work of the state agricultural experiment stations. —
Investigators in the state experiment stations have always
taken an active part in plant-breeding work. Five years
ago, in an admirable editorial in the Experiment Station
Record, Dr. Allen says as follows: "The list of projects conducted by the experiment stations under the
Adams fund includes sixty-three which fall under the head
of investigations in breeding (eleven of these relate to the
breeding of animals). This relatively large number indicates the popularity of the subject, and an evident feeling
that it not only presents large research possibility, but is
a line in which investigation is greatly needed. The
attention which is being given to breeding is encouraging
and the number of enterprises suggests the possibility of
material additions to the general understanding of its
various phases."

The experiments subsequent to that time have, to a
considerable extent, justified the hope of "material
additions to the general understanding of its various
phases." Numerous bulletins have been published which
have added to that knowledge, and the experiment station
men have written many articles which have appeared in
various serial publications.

The lines of work which have received the greatest
attention and in which the most constructive work has
been done are the application of Mendel's laws to economic
plants and the elucidation of individual selection and pure-
line breeding. Not only have important practical results
been obtained in improving our economic plants, but a
considerable amount of material of scientific value has
been accumulated.

The experiments with corn at the Illinois and other experiment stations and those with timothy at the Cornell station stand out prominently as examples of pieces of scientific research which, at the same time, have tremendous economic importance.

There is scarcely an economic crop but is receiving some attention by the plant-breeders of our experiment stations, and bulletins are appearing frequently dealing with this phase of the work.

Many experiment stations, such as Wisconsin, Minnesota, Ohio, New York, and Kansas, are also busily engaged in producing superior varieties upon their own grounds for distribution to their constituents.

The old-time very prevalent variety tests are still made, but these are now supplemented by variety improvement and careful studies of variety adaptation.

Beside the large amount of practical work which most of the stations are doing, there are a large number of breeding projects prosecuted by them, and which are destined to become of scientific importance.

The following projects have been reported by Dr. Allen of the federal Office of Experiment Stations as now conducted at the different stations : —

Breeding Corn — Alabama Station.
Breeding Experiments with Cotton — Alabama Station.
Breeding Oats — Alabama Station.
Wheat Breeding Investigations — Kansas Station.
Alfalfa Breeding Investigations — Kansas Station.
Analysis of Cellular Structure of Hybrids — Maine Station.
Experimental Modification of the Hereditary Process — Maine Station.

Breeding Alfalfa with Reference to the Extreme and Sub-tropical Conditions of Arizona — Arizona Station.

Cotton Breeding — Arkansas Station.

Nicotiana Hybrids — California Station.

Improvement of Dent, Flint, and Sweet Corn in Yield and Feeding Value, by Breeding Work in Six Different Localities — Connecticut (State) Station.

Breeding Investigations with Tobacco — Connecticut (State) Station.

Zenia in Maize and Hereditary Transmission of Various Characters — Connecticut (State) Station.

The Effect of Variations in Physical Characters and Chemical Composition of the Corn Kernel upon the Vigor of the Plant — Delaware Station.

Plant Breeding — Florida Station.

Investigation of Mendelian Laws in Application to the Cotton Plant — Georgia Station.

Inheritance of Contrasted Characters — Mississippi Station.

Study of the Correlation of Characters and of Inheritance in Pure Lines and Varieties — Montana Station.

Degree of Close Breeding in Maize — Nebraska Station.

Plant Breeding Work with Pure Lines of Cereals — New Mexico Station.

Place Variation with Cotton — North Carolina Station.

The Increase and Fixation of Desirable Properties in Plants — Ohio Station.

Breeding Drought-resistant Corn; Study of Qualities of Drought Resistance — Oklahoma Station.

Breeding Sorghums, especially Kafir Corn, Milo Maize, and Broom Corn, to secure more Drought-resistant Types — Oklahoma Station.

Fundamental Study of Inheritance in Cotton — Texas Station.

Comparative Study of Durum, Poulard, and Bread Wheats — Arizona Station.

Study of Principles Underlying the Development of Disease Resistance or Immunity in Farm Crops — North Dakota Station.

Effects of Pollen from Barren Stalks of Corn — South Carolina Station.

Breeding a Strain of Peaches resistant to Brown Rot — Alabama Station.

Biological Analysis of Papago Sweet Corn for the Synthesis of Desirable Characters — Arizona Station.

Principles relating to Transmission of Characters in the Apple as affected by Selection and by Crossing — Illinois Station.

Apple Breeding — Iowa Station.

Investigations upon Asparagus — Massachusetts Station.

Study of the Principles of Heredity underlying Disease and Climatic Resistance in the Apple, Plum, and Strawberry — Minnesota Station.

Heredity in Plants — Nebraska Station.

Studies of Heredity in Vegetables, especially Squashes and Tomatoes — New Hampshire Station.

Carnation Breeding — New Hampshire Station.

Nature of the Inheritance and Correlation of Structural Characters in Crosses — New Jersey Station.

Improvement of Mexican Chili by Breeding and Selection — New Mexico Station.

Investigation of the Laws of Inheritance in Hybridization — New York (Cornell) Station.

An Investigation of Mutation and Other Types of Variation in Wild and Cultivated Plants, to determine their Value in Plant Breeding — New York (Cornell) Station.

Influence of Environment in producing Variation of Value to the Breeder — New York (Cornell) Station.

Study of Transmission of Characters in Hybrids of Rotundifolia Grapes — North Carolina Station.

A Study of the Fecundation of the Rotundifolia Grapes — South Carolina Station.

Improvement of Hardy Wild Fruits of the Northwest by Breeding and Crossing — South Dakota Station.

The Breeding of Apple and Pear Varieties for Resistance to Blight — Tennessee Station.

Breeding Work with Blackberry — Texas Station.

Breeding Experiments with Apples — Virginia Station.

Mendelism of the Hybrids of Blackberries and Raspberries, particularly with Reference to Leaf Structure and Habits of Growth — Washington Station.

Pollination of the Apple — West Virginia Station.

Investigation of Mendel's Law as applied to Hybridizing the White with the Black Varieties of Muscadine Grape — Georgia Station.

Apple Breeding Investigations — Idaho Station.

Effects of Fertilizers on Cell Structure of Crops and their Relations to Mutations in Fruits, Vegetables, and Flowers — Maryland Station.

Investigations on "Double Flower" and Sterility in Blackberries and Dewberries — North Carolina Station.

Pollination of the Apple and Conditions affecting It — Oregon Station.

In addition to the work of the experiment station men, very much highly valuable work is under way by such men as East at Harvard, Shull at Cold Spring Harbor, Harper and Stout at the New York Botanical Garden, Bradley Moore Davis at the University of Pennsylvania, B. M. Duggar at the Missouri Botanical Garden, and many others. This research is undertaken by well-trained specialists who are producing the very highest type of fundamental constructive results.

Fig. 101. — Gardens at Luther Burbank's.

Fig. 102. — Some of Burbank's frames and garden beds.

Instruction in plant-breeding in the United States. — One of the most, if not the most, significant advances that plant-breeding has made in recent years is the increase in the amount of instruction given in the agricultural colleges and other agricultural schools.

Formerly, the only teaching of this subject was in connection with a course of horticulture, probably, and the breeding was likely to receive minor consideration.

All of this has been changed. Strong courses are given in this subject in all of the agricultural colleges. Some go so far as to have separate departments or divisions in which the staff devotes all of its time to plant-breeding instruction and investigations. It is estimated that over two thousand students receive regular plant-breeding instruction each year in this country. This is bound to have tremendous influence upon practical plant improvement on the farms of the country. Plant-breeding holds a very prominent place in the instruction given to short-term students, as it should, and in the form of various extension enterprises.

Luther Burbank. — In addition to the large number of plant-breeders who have some official connection with the state experiment stations or the federal government, there has always been a number of men who have maintained private plant-breeding establishments. Chief among these is Luther Burbank. He will always be given a prominent place in American horticulture because of the many and valuable varieties which he has added to it.

The practical results, however, that Mr. Burbank has secured have been praised by the writers beyond reason.

Y

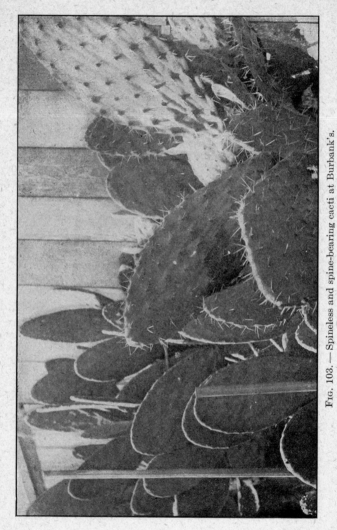

Fig. 103. — Spineless and spine-bearing cacti at Burbank's.

His place abounds in interesting and surprising things, just as would be expected of any man's place if conducted under similar conditions (Figs. 101–103), and many of the things will undoubtedly have great value. His work has been so much written about that it is not necessary to make any catalogue of the things that are under his hand. It is not too much to hope that some of his productions, as the plumcots, may be the starting-points of strong and noble lines of evolution. Some of those that have been much heralded are of doubtful economic value.

The value of Mr. Burbank's work lies above all merely economic considerations. He is a master worker in making plants to vary. Plants are plastic material in his hands. He is demonstrating what can be done. He is setting new ideals and novel problems. Heretofore, gardeners and other horticulturists have grown plants because they are useful or beautiful : Mr. Burbank grows them because he can make them take on new forms. This is a new kind of pleasure to be got from gardening, a new and captivating purpose in plant growing. It is a new reason for associating with plants.

APPENDIX A

GLOSSARY OF TECHNICAL PLANT–BREEDING TERMS

Allelomorph. — One of the pure unit-characters commonly existing singly or in pairs in the germ-cells of mendelian hybrids, and exhibited in varying proportion among the organisms themselves. Thus an *allelomorphic pair of characters* comprises the opposed units, one of which comes from each parent in a hybrid. For example, the roundness and wrinkledness found in two varieties of peas is an allelomorphic pair.

Biometry. — The application of statistical methods to biological problems.

Chromosome. — A term applied to certain minute bodies, in the nuclei of the animal and vegetable cells which appear at definite periods in the division of the cell; they are constant in number for each species of animal or plant, and are characterized by the fact that they stain very deeply with certain dyes. The chromosomes are supposed to be the bearers of heredity.

Dominant characters. — It often occurs, when two varieties or species are crossed, that the characters of one appear in the first generation hybrid to the exclusion of the other. These are called dominant characters.

Duplex. — The state of inheriting a character that is present in both parents.

Epistatic. — Used to describe a color factor which, in hybridization, covers up or hides other color factors in the first generation hybrid (opposed to hypostatic).

Factor hypothesis. — An assumption that organisms may contain various hereditary units which do not appear in their body cells. This is especially applied to color units. Very often these factors do not appear until the plant has been crossed with another plant containing a complementary factor.

F_1. — A symbol introduced by Bateson, to designate the first filial or hybrid generation.

F_2. — A symbol for the second generation.

F_3. — A symbol for the third hybrid generation. And so on.

Galton curve. — A curve, devised by Galton, when the values for all the individuals are recorded consecutively in an ascending series. The class values are plotted on the vertical axis.

Gamete. — A mature sex- or germ-cell, which will produce a new individual upon uniting with another such cell of the opposite sex.

Genetics. — A study of the phenomena of variability and heredity, or of the physiology of descent, as affecting individuals or races of plants, animals, or human beings.

Genotype. — A type represented by individuals of the same germinal constitution. The nature of such a type can be determined only by a breeding test, not by inspection.

Heterozygote. — An individual formed by the union of two germ-cells of unlike constitution.

Homozygote. — An individual which is of a pure type in regard to a certain character because both of its parents were of the same gametic constitution.

Hybrids. — The offspring of crosses between individuals of distinctly different natures.

Hypostatic. — Used to describe a color factor which is concealed by higher color factors. (See Epistatic.)

Mutation. — A sudden variation, differing from its parents in a distinct character or characters, and able to transmit its new characters in full degree to its offspring.

Nulliplex. — A condition of an individual when it does not possess a character because neither of its parents carried the possibilities for such a character in their germ-cells.

Phenotype. — The visible type of a group as expressed by external characteristics. Opposed to genotype. There may be several genotypes in a phenotype.

Plateation. — (From the Latin *platea*, meaning *place*.) A physiological variation caused by external influences such as locality, climate, soil, and so forth; sometimes called place-variation. It is what Darwin called "definite variation." This word was coined to express in one word the third of the three kinds of variation — fluctuation, mutation and plateation. (Here first defined. — *A. W. G.*)

Quetelet curve. — A curve which shows the relative frequency with which individuals of a given lot, or population, occur in certain classes. Class values are plotted on the horizontal line and frequencies on the vertical. The mode is the highest point of such a curve and represents the dominating type of the character studied.

Recessive characters. — (See Dominant characters.) The characters which are entirely covered up the first generation but reappear the second and subsequent generations.

Segregation. — The reappearance in definite ratios, in the second hybrid generation, of the characters of two forms crossed; and the first hybrid generation (when this differs from the dominant character).

Simplex. — The condition of an individual which has inherited a character from only one parent.

Somatic. — Of, or pertaining to, the body as opposed to the germ-cells.

Xenia. — The results of a cross-fertilization between different varieties of plants due to a double fertilization; found in such plants as corn, peas, etc.

Zygote. — The result of the union of two gametes. (See Gamete.)

APPENDIX B

PLANT-BREEDING BOOKS

Following is a brief list of books containing material more or less related to plant-breeding. This list is not intended to be complete, but is designed to give the reader an idea of the more important books on the subject. There are many books which are not listed upon the general subject of botany, others upon heredity and evolution in their broadest phases, and still others upon animal breeding which will contain much material which is related to the subject of plant improvement by breeding.

American Breeder's Association Reports. Washington, D.C. 1905–1912.

Bailey, L. H., *Cyclopedia of American Agriculture.* Vol. II, *Crops.* Macmillan Co. 1907.

Bailey, L. H., *Standard Cyclopedia of Horticulture.* 6 vols. (Continuing) Macmillan Co. 1914.

Bailey, L. H., *Sketch of Evolution of Our Native Fruits.* xiii + 472 pp., 125 figs. Macmillan Co. 3d edition. 1898.

Bailey, L. H., *The Survival of the Unlike.* 515 pp., illus. Macmillan Co. 1897.

Bateson, W., *Mendel's Principles of Heredity.* xiv + 396 pp., 9 pls., and 35 figs. Cambridge. 1909.

Baur, Dr. Erwin, *Einfuhrung in die experimentelle Vererbungs-lehre.* 293 pp., 80 figs. Berlin. Gebrüder Borntraeger. 1911.

CASTLE, W. E., COULTER, J. M., DAVENPORT, C. B., EAST, E. M., TOWER, W. L., *Heredity and Eugenics.* 315 pp., 98 figs. The Univ. of Chicago Press. 1912.

CASTLE, W. E., *Heredity, in Relation to Evolution and Animal Breeding.* 184 pp. N. Y. and London. D. Appleton Co. 1911.

CRAMPTON, HENRY EDW., *The Doctrine of Evolution; its Basis and its Scope.* ix + 311 pp. N. Y. Columbia Univ. Press. 1911.

DARBISHIRE, A. D., *Breeding and the Mendelian Discovery.* xii + 282 pp. Cassell & Co. London. 4 colored pls., 34 figs. 1911.

DAVENPORT, E., *Domesticated Animals and Plants.* xiv + 312 pp., 49 figs. Ginn & Co. 1910.

DAVENPORT, E., and RIETZ, H. L., *Principles of Breeding* (by E. DAVENPORT). Appendix: *Statistical Methods* (by H. L. RIETZ). A treatise on thremmatology, or the principles and practices involved in the economic improvement of domesticated animals and plants. xiii + 727 pp. Ginn & Co. Boston. 1907.

Fifty Years of Darwinism. v + 274 pp., 5 pls., 1 fig. N. Y. 1909.

FRUWIRTH, C., et al., *Die Züchtung der Landwirtschaftlichen Kulturpflanzen.* Vols. 1–5. 1904–1912.

JOHANNSEN, W., *Elemente der Exakten Erblichkeitslehre.* vi + 515 pp., 30 figs. Gustav Fischer. Jena. 1903.

JOHANNSEN, W., *Ueber Erblichkeit in Populationen und in reinen Linien.* 68 pp., 8 figs. Gustav Fischer. Jena. 1903.

KELLOGG, V. L., *Darwinism To-Day.* 403 pp. Henry Holt & Co. N. Y. 1907.

KNUTH, P., *Handbook of Flower Pollination.* Vol. I, xix + 382 pp. Oxford. Porter. 1906.

LANG, H., *Theorie und Praxis der Pflanzenzüchtung.* viii + 169 pp., 47 figs. 1910.

Löbner, M., *Leitfaden für Gärtnerische Pflanzenzüchtung* vii + 160 pp., 10 figs. Jena. 1909.

Lock, R. H., *Recent Progress in the Study of Variation, Heredity, and Evolution.* 2d ed., xiv + 334 pp. Murray. London. 4 pls., 45 figs., and 5 portraits. 1909.

Newman, L. H., *Plant Breeding in Scandinavia.* 193 pp., 63 figs. The Canadian Seed Growers' Association. Ottawa. 1912.

Punnett, R. C., *Mendelism.* 192 pp. N. Y. Macmillan Co. 5 pls., 35 figs. 1911.

Reid, G. A., *The Laws of Heredity.* 548 pp. Methuen & Co. London. 1910.

Rumker, von K., *Ueber Organisation der Pflanzenzüchtung.* 56 pp. Berlin. 1909.

Seward, A. C. (Editor), *Darwin and Modern Science.* xvii + 595 pp., fig. and pl. 1909.

Stevens, W. C., *Plant Anatomy from the Standpoint of the Development and Functions of the Tissues and Handbook of Micro-technic.* xii + 349 pp. Blakiston's Son & Co. Philadelphia. 136 illus. 1907.

Thomson, J. Arthur, *Heredity.* xvi + 605 pp., 49 figs. 2d ed. 1912.

Vernon, H. M., *Variation in Animals and Plants.* pp. ix + 415, 30 figs. Henry Holt & Co. 1902.

Vries, Hugo de, *Species and Varieties, their Origin by Mutation.* Edited by Daniel Trembly MacDougal. The Open Court Pub. Co. Chicago. 1904.

Vries, Hugo de, *Plant Breeding.* Comments on the experiments of Nilsson and Burbank. xiii + 360, figs. 114. 1907.

Vries, Hugo de, *The Mutation Theory.* Vol. I, "The Origin of Species by Mutation." English translation by Prof. J. B. Farmer and A. D. Darbishire. xvi + 582 pp. The Open Court Publishing Co. Chicago. 4 pls. and 119 figs. 1909.

VRIES, HUGO DE, *The Mutation Theory.* Vol. II, "The Origin of Varieties by Mutation." English translation by Prof. J. B. Farmer and A. D. Darbishire. viii + 683 pp. Chicago. The Open Court Publishing Co. 6 pls., 149 figs. 1911.

WALTER, HERBERT EUGENE, *Genetics.* An Introduction to the Study of Heredity. xiv + 264 pp. The Macmillan Co. N. Y. 72 figs. and Diagr. 1913.

WILSON, E. B., *The Cell in Development and Inheritance.* xxi + 483 pp., 194 figs. Macmillan Co. 1900.

Yearbooks U. S. Department of Agriculture. 1894–1913.

Hybrid Conference Report (First International Conference). London. Printed in Journal of the Royal Hort. Soc., April, 1900.

International Conference (Second) on Plant Breeding and Hybridization. Proceedings published as Memoir, Vol. I. Hort. Soc. of New York. 1902.

International Conference (Third) on Genetics. London. Report issued by Royal Hort. Soc. 1906.

International Conference (Fourth) on Genetics. Report published in Paris, 1911, under Editorship of Ph. de Vilmorin.

APPENDIX C

LIST OF PERIODICALS CONTAINING BREEDING LITERATURE

WE have attempted to include in this list such periodicals as are most likely to contain breeding articles that may be of interest to the general reader and the teacher and student of Genetics. This list is not intended to be complete, but to include the principal publications.

ABBREVIATIONS : semi-a = semi-annual ; q = quarterly ; semi-q = semi-quarterly ; m = monthly ; bi-m = bi-monthly ; semi-m = semi-monthly ; w = weekly : semi-w = semi-weekly ; i = irregular.

American Naturalist. New York. m.

American Philosophical Society. Proceedings. Philadelphia. 3 nos.

Annales de la science agronomique. Paris. m.

Annales des science naturelles. Botanique. Paris.

Annals of Applied Biology. London.

Annals of Botany. London. q.

Archiv für Rassen- und Gesellschafts-Biologie. Leipzig. bi-m.

Archives des sciences biologiques. St. Petersbourg.

Association internationale des botanistes. Progressus rei botanicæ. Jena. semi-a.

Biological Bulletin. m. Wood's Hole, Mass. Marine Biological Laboratory.

Biologisches Centralblatt. Erlangen, Leipzig. semi-m.

Biometrika. Cambridge, Eng. i.

Botanical Gazette.   Chicago.   m.

Botanische Zeitung.   Abt. 1 and 2.   Leipzig.   w.

Botanisches Centralblatt.   Jena.   w.

Botanisches Centralblatt-Beihefte., Abt. 1; 3 nos.   Anatomie,
   Histologie und Physiologie der Pflanzen.   Abt. 2; 3 nos.
   Systematik, Pflanzengeographie, Augewandte, Botanik, etc.
   Dresden.

Deutsche Botanische Gesellschaft.   Berichte.   Berlin.   m.

Deutsche Landwirtschafts-Gesellschaft.   Jahrbuch.   Berlin.   q.

Die Landwirtschaftlichen Versuch-Stationen.   Berlin.   semi-m.

Florists' Exchange.   New York.   w.

France — Institut national agronomique.   Annales.   Paris.   i.

Gardeners' Chronicle.   London.   w.

Jahrbücher für Wissenschaftliche Botanik (Pringsheim's).   12
   nos.   Leipzig.

Journal of Agricultural Research.   m.

Journal of Agricultural Science.   Eng.   q.

Journal de botanique.   Paris.   m.

Journal of Genetics.   Cambridge, Eng.   q.

Journal of Heredity.   Washington.   m.

La Cellule.   Lierre.   i.

La Science agronomique.   Paris.

Linnean Society :
   Journal, botany.   London.   m.
   Transactions, botany.   London.   i.

(The) Mendel Journal.   London.

New Phytologist.   London.   10 nos.

Physiological Researches.   Baltimore.   i.

Plant World.   Tucson, Ariz.   m.

Popular Science Monthly.   New York.   m.

Quarterly Journal of Microscopical Science.   London.   q.

Revue, générale agronomique.   Uccle lez-Bruxelles.   m.

Revue générale de botanique.   Paris.   m.

Royal Microscopical Society.   Journal.   bi-m.

Royal Society of London, Philosophical transactions.   i.

Science.   New York.   w.

Société de biologie, Comptes rendus.   Paris.   w.

Société botanique de France.   Bulletin.   Paris.   m.

Société des agriculteurs de France.   Bulletin.   Paris.   semi-m.

Société royale de botanique de Belgique.   Bulletin.   Bruxelles.

Torrey Botanical Club.   Bulletin.   New York.   m.

United States Dept. of Agriculture, Office of Experiment
Stations.   Experiment Station Record.   Washington.   16
nos.

Zeitschrift für Planzenzüchtung.   Wien.

Zentralblatt für Allgemeine und Experimentelle Biologie.   Leipzig.

APPENDIX D

BIBLIOGRAPHY

FOLLOWING is a list of miscellaneous references to writings on subjects related to plant-breeding. It is not intended to be either complete or comprehensive. This bibliography begins with the year 1905. References to earlier writings may be found in the fourth edition of this work.

For reference to the literature of cross-fertilization, the reader is directed to d'Arcy Thompson's list in Mueller's "Fertilization of Flowers," and an extensive bibliography to the rapidly growing literature upon the heredity of color can be found in a technical bulletin by the junior writer of this book. This bulletin will soon be published by the Agricultural Experiment Station of Cornell University.

1905. BALLS, W. L., *The Sexuality of Cotton.* Khed. **Agr.** Soc. Yearbook, 199–222.

1905. BIFFEN, R. H., *Mendel's Laws of Inheritance and Wheat Breeding.* Jour. Agr. Sci., Cambridge, 1 : 4–48, 1 pl.

1905. BIFFEN, R. H., *The Inheritance of Sterility in the Barleys (Hordeum sativum, etc.).* Jour. Agr. Sci. 1 : 250–257, 1 fig.

1905. BUTLER, E. J., *The Bearing of Mendelism on the Susceptibility of Wheat to Rust.* Jour. Agr. Sci. 1 : 361–363.

1905. CONKLIN, EDWIN G., *The Mutation Theory from the Standpoint of Cytology.* Science, n.s. 21 : 525–529.

1905. EASTMAN, C. R., *On the Spelling of "Clon."* Science, n.s. 22 : 206.

1905. Hurst, C. C., *Notes on the " Proceedings of the International Conference on Plant Breeding and Hybridisation, 1902."* Roy. Hort. Soc. Jour. 29 : 417–433.

1905. Jones, L. R., *Disease Resistance of Potatoes.* U. S. Dept. Agr. Bur. Plant Ind. Bull. 87 : (39 pp.).

1905. Jones, L. R., *Concerning Disease Resistance of Potatoes.* Vermont Agr. Exp. Sta. 18 : 264–267.

1905. Klinck, L. S., *Corn Breeding in the Corn Belt.* Can. Seed-Grow. Assoc. Rep. 2 : 56–61.

1905. Pearl, Raymond, *Investigation by Statistical Methods of Correlation in Variation.* Carnegie Inst. (Wash., D.C.), Yearbook (1905) (No. 4) : 285–286.

1905. Pearl, Raymond, *Note on Variation in the Ray Flowers of Rudbeckia.* Am. Nat. 39 : 87–88. 1 fig.

1905. Petrunkevitch, Alexander, *Natural and Artificial Parthenogenesis.* Am. Nat. 39 : 65–76. Bibliog.

1905. Pollard, Charles Louis, *On the Spelling of " Clon."* Science, n.s. 22 : 87–88.

1905. Pollard, Charles Louis, *" Clon " versus " Clone."* Science, n.s. 22 : 463.

1905. Shamel, A. D., *The Effect of Inbreeding in Plants.* U. S. Dept. Agr. Yearbook, 377–392. 3 pls., 1 fig.

1905. Shamel, A. D., *Tobacco Breeding Experiments in Conn.* Conn. (State) Agr. Exp. Sta. Ann. Rep. 331–343.

1905. Starnes, Hugh N., *Japan and Hybrid Plums.* Georgia Agr. Exp. Sta. 68 (see pp. 1–40).

1905. Vries, H. de, *Dauer der Mutationsperiode bei Œnothera Lamarckiana.* Deutsch. Bot. Gesell. Ber. 23 : 382–387.

1905. Vries, H. de, *The Mutation Theory.* Gard. Chron. 3d ser. 37 : 321–322.

1905. Webber, Herbert J., *The Science of Plant Breeding.* Can. Seed-Grow. Assoc. Rep. 2 : 79–92. Pl. II., fig. 1 & 2.

1905. Webber, Herbert J., *Pedigree or Grade Breeding.* Can. Seed-Grow. Assoc. Rep. 2 : 61–70. Pl., Photo., Fig.

1905. WIESNER, J., *Untersuchungen über den Lichtgenuss der Pflanzen im Yellowstone Gebiete und in, anderen Gegenden Nordamerikas. Photometrische Untersuchungen auf pflanzenphysiologischem Gebiete* (*V. Abhandlung*). Kais. kön. Akad. d. Wiss. in Wien, mathem. naturw. Klasse, Sitzungsber. 114: (Part 1). Rev. in Am. Nat. 40: 600–603.

1905. WILLIAMS, C. G., *Pedigreed Seed Corn.* Ohio Agr. Exp. Sta., Circ. 42: 1–11.

1906. ANDREWS, F. M., *Some Monstrosities in Trillium.* Ind. Acad. Sci. Proc. 187–188.

1906. BATESON, W., and SAUNDERS, MISS E. R., and PUNNETT, R. C., *Inheritance in Sweet Peas and Stocks.* Roy. Hort. Soc. (London) Proc. B. 77: 236–238.

1906. BATESON, W., *Coloured Tendrils of Sweet Peas.* Gard. Chron. 39: 333.

1906. BEAL, W. J., *Improving Wild Potatoes by Selection.* Soc. Prom. Agr. Sci. Proc. 27: 75.

1906. BIFFEN, R. H., *Experiments on the Hybridization of Barley.* Phil. Soc. Proc. (Cambridge), 13: 304–308.

1906. BLANCHARD, W. H., *A New Dwarf Blackberry.* Torreya 6: 235–237.

1906. BUCHANAN, J., *Some Effects in Varieties of Cereal Crops arising from Different Conditions of Growth.* Can. Seed-Grow. Assoc. Rep. 3: 74–77.

1906. CARD, F. W., BLAKE, M. A., and BARNES, H. L., *Raspberry Score Card.* Rhode Island Agr. Exp. Sta. 168–169.

1906. CARD, FRED W., *Apple Breeding.* Rhode Island Agr. Exp. Sta. 20: 250–252.

1906. CARD, FRED W., *Corn Selection.* Rhode Island Agr. Exp. Sta. Ann. Rept. 20: 216–220.

1906. CASTLE, W. E., *Inbreeding, Crossbreeding and Sterility in Drosophila.* Science, n.s. 23: 153.

1906. CROCKER, W., *Rôle of Seed Coats in Delayed Germination.* Bot. Gaz. 42: 265–291. Fig.

z

1906. DUVEL, J. W. T., *The Germination of Seed Corn.* U. S. Dept. Agr. Farmers' Bull. 253: (16 pp.), 4 figs. (Including: Value of a germination test. Average yield of corn to the acre. Testing individual ears. Selecting seed ears. Numbering the ears. The germination box. Results of tests.)

1906. GAGER, C. S., *De Vries and His Critics.* Science, n.s. 24: 81–89. Bibliog. in notes.

1906. GRAENICHER, S., *Some Notes on the Pollination of Flowers.* Wis. Nat. Hist. Soc. Bull. 4: 12–21.

1906. GRIFFON, E., *Le greffage des Solanées.* Acad. Sci. Compt. Rend. 143: 1249–1251.

1906. HAACKE, WILHELM, *Die Gesetze der Rassenmischung und die Konstitution des Keimplasmes.* Arch. f. Entwick'-mech. d. Org. 21: 1–93. 104 tab.

1906. HALSTED, B. D., *Breeding Sweet Corn — Coöperative Tests.* New Jersey Agr. Exp. Sta. Bull. 192: 1–30. Fig.

1906. HECKEL, E., *Variation in the Potato Tuber.* Gard. Chron. 3d ser. 39: 88.

1906. HENSLOW, G., *Evolution and Adaptation.* Roy. Hort. Soc. Jour. n.s. 31: 159–163.

1906. HENSLOW, G., *The True Meaning of " Natural Selection " and the "Survival of the Fittest " in Nature.* Roy. Hort. Soc. Jour. n.s. 31: 90–96.

1906. HENSLOW, G., *Species and Varieties; their Origin by Mutation.* Roy. Hort. Soc. Jour. n.s. 31: 164–168.

1906. HESKETH, R. T., *Apple Grafted on Hawthorn.* Gard. Chron. 3d ser. 39: 347.

1906. HURST, C. C., *Mendelian Laws of Inheritance.* Gard. Chron. 3d ser. 39: 187.

1906. LE CLERC, J. A., *The Effect of Climatic Conditions on the Composition of Durum Wheat.* U. S. Dept. Agr. Yearbook: 199–212, 2 pls. Same. Yearbook Separate, 417: 199–212, 2 pls.

1906. Lock, R. H., *Plant Breeding in the Tropics. III. Experiments with Maize.* Roy. Bot. Gard. Ann. 3 : 2 : 95–184.

1906. Macoun, W. T., *The Improvement of the Potato.* Can. Seed-Grow. Assoc. Rep. 3 : 77–84. Photo., Fig.

1906. Morgan, T. H., *Are the Germ-cells of Mendelian Hybrids "Pure"?* Biol. Centralbl. 26 : 289–296.

1906. Munson, W. M., *Plant-breeding in its Relation to American Pomology.* Maine Agr. Exp. Sta. Bull. 132 : 149–176.

1906. Ortmann, A. E., *The Mutation Theory Again.* Science, n.s. 24 : 314–317. Bibliog. in notes.

1906. Osterhout, W. J. V., *Experiments with Plants.* x + 493 pp. The Macmillan Co., N. Y. 252 figs. Rev. in Am. Nat. 40 : 146–148.

1906. Pearl, Raymond, *Variation in the Number of Seeds of the Lotus.* Am. Nat. 40 : 757–768. 4 figs. 5 tab.

1906. Raunkiaer, C., *Transmission par hérédité dans les espèces hétéromorphes.* Vid. Selsk. Overs. 31–39.

1906. Rivière, G., and Bailhache, G., *Influence du portegreffe sur le greffon.* Acad. Sci. Compt. Rend. 142 : 845–847.

1906. Rosenberg, O., *Embryobildung in der Gattung Hieracium.* Deutsch. Bot. Gesell. Ber. 24 : 157–161, 1 pl.

1906. Saame, O., *Kernverschnelzung bei der karyokinetischen Kernteilung im protoplasmatischen Wandeelag des Embryosacks von Fritillaria imperialis.* Deutsch. Bot. Gesell. Ber. 24 : 300–303, 1 pl.

1906. Scharf, E., *Keimkraft-Apparat.* Deutsch. landw. Presse 33 : 507–508, 514–516.

1906. Schulte, J. I., *Corn Breeding Work at the Experiment Stations.* U. S. Dept. Agr. Yearbook, 279–294.

1906. Solms(-Laubach), H. Graf zu, *Cruciferenstudien. IV. Die Varianten der Embroyolage.* Bot. Zeitung, 64 : 1 : 15–43, 1 pl.

1906. SPERLING, J., *Korrelation zwischen Kornfarbe und Aehren-
formen beim Roggen.* Fühlings landw. Zeitung, 55 : 93–99.

1906. STUART, W., *Disease Resistance of Potatoes.* Vermont
Agr. Exp. Sta. Bull. 122 : (see pp. 107–136). Abstr. in
Exp. Sta. Rec. 17 : 1078.

1906. VAN DEN HEEDE, A., *Variation chez les végétaux.* Soc.
Nantaise d'hort. Ann. 79 : 97–103.

1906. VRIES, H. DE, *Aelters und neuere Selektionsmethode.*
Biol. Centralbl. 26 : 385–395.

1906. VRIES, H. DE, *Die Svalöfer Methode zur Veredelung land-
wirtschaftlicher Kulturgewächse und ihre Bedeutung für
die Selektions-Theorie.* Arch. Rassenbiol. 3 : 325–358.

1906. VRIES, H. DE, *Species and Varieties; their Origin by
Mutation.* Second edition. xviii + 847 pp.

1906. WEBBER, H. J., *New Citrus and Pineapple Productions
of the Department of Agriculture.* U. S. Dept. Agr. Yearbook, 329–346. 8 pls., 1 fig. Same. Yearbook Separate,
427 : 329–346. 8 pls., 1 fig.

1906. WEISMANN, A., *The Evolution Theory.* Translated with
the author's coöperation by J. A. & Margaret R. Thomson.
2 vols. xvi + 416 pp. and 405 pp. E. Arnold. London.
Rev. in Am. Nat. 40 : 375–377.

1906. WIANCKO, A. T., *Corn Improvement.* Indiana (Purdue
Univ.) Agr. Exp. Sta. Bull. 110 : 79–120. 14 figs.

1906. WILBRINK, G., *Deuxième rapport sur les expériences de
sélection faites avec l'indigotier de Natal.* (In Dutch.)
Buitenzorg (1906), 1–20.

1906. WILSON, E. B., *Mendelian Inheritance and the Purity
of the Gametes.* Science, n.s. 23 : 112–113.

1906. WILSON, EDMUND B., *Studies on Chromosomes.* III. *The
Sexual Differences of the Chromosome-groups in Hemiptera,
with Some Considerations on the Determination and Heredity
of Sex.* Jour. Exp. Zoöl. 3 : (No. 1). Rev. in Arch. f.
Entwick'mech. d. Org. 21 : 357.

1906. WINKLER, H., *Morphologie und Biologie tropischer Blüten und Früchte.* Bot. Jahrb. 38 : 233–271.

1906. WINKLER, H., *Parthenogenesis bei Wikstroemis indica (L.), C. A. Mey, und ihre Bedeutung für die Lehre der Befruchtung.* Jard. Bot. Ann. n.s. 5 : 208–276, 4 pls.

1906. WITTMACK, L., *Berichte über die internationale Konferenz über Hybridisation und Pflanzenzucht in London vom 30. Juli bis 3. August 1906.* Gartenflora 55 : 481–486, 509–511.

1906. WITTMACK, L. *The Influence of the Graft on the Rooting of the Pear.* Gard. Chron. 3d ser. 40 : 150.

1906. WITTMACK, L. *Sports.* Gard. Chron. 3d ser. 40 : 223.

1907. BALLS, W. R., *Note on Mendelian Heredity in Cotton.* Jour. Agr. Soc. 2 : 216.

1907. BESSEY, C. E., *A Synopsis of the Plant Phyla.* Univ. Studies, Univ. of Nebraska, 7 : 275–373. 1–99.

1907. BIFFEN, R. H., *Studies in the Inheritance of Disease Resistance.* Jour. Agr. Sci. 2 : 109.

1907. BIFFEN, R. H., *The Hybridization of Barleys.* Jour. Agr. Sci. 2 : 183.

1907. BOULENGER, G. A., *On the Variations of the Evening Primrose, Œnothera biennis.* Jour. Bot. 45 : 353–363.

1907. BROWN, ARTHUR ERWIN, *Variation or Mutation.* Science, n.s. 25 : 107–108.

1907. BROWNLEE, JOHN, *Statistical Studies in Immunity.* A discussion of the means of estimating the severity of cases of acute diseases. Biometrika, 5 : 423–435. Tab., Diagr.

1907. BUTLER, E. J., *The Selection of Sugarcane Cuttings.* Agr. Jour. India, 2 : 193.

1907. CARD, FRED W., *Cherry Crosses.* Rhode Is. Agr. Exp. Sta. Rep. 258–259.

1907. CASTLE, W. E., *On a Case of Reversion Induced by Crossbreeding and its Fixation (guinea-pig).* Science, n.s. 25 : 151–153.

1907. COCKERELL, T. D. A., *Is there Determinate Variation?* Science, n.s. 25 : 34.

1907. COOK, O. F., *Mendelism and Other Methods of Descent.* Washington Acad. Sci. Proc. 9 : 189–240.

1907. CROSTHWAIT, G. A., *Indian Corn. Its Production and Improvement.* Idaho Agr. Exp. Sta. Bull. 57.

1907. DAVENPORT, C. B., *Heredity and Mendel's Law.* Washington Acad. Sci. Proc. 9 : 179–187.

1907. DAVENPORT, E., and RIETZ, H. L., *Type and Variability in Corn.* Illinois Agr. Exp. Sta. Bull. 119 : 1–29.

1907. DAVIDSON, A., *The Changes in our Weeds.* So. Calif. Acad. Sci. Bull. 6 : 11–12.

1907. EAST, E. M., *The Relation of Certain Biological Principles to Plant Breeding.* Connecticut Agr. Exp. Sta. Bull. 158 : 1–93. Fig.

1907. EAST, EDWARD M., *Some Essential Points in Potato Breeding.* Conn. (State) Agr. Exp. Sta. Ann. Rep. 429–448.

1907. EAST, EDWARD M., *Inbreeding in Corn.* Conn. (State) Agr. Exp. Sta. Ann. Rep. 419–429.

1907. EAST, EDWARD M., *Better Seed Corn in Conn.* Conn. (State) Agr. Exp. Sta. Ann. Rep. 397–406.

1907. EAST, EDWARD M., *Practical Use of Mendelism in Corn Breeding.* Conn. (State) Agr. Exp. Sta. Ann. Rep. 406–419.

1907. FLETCHER, S. W., and GREGG, O. I., *Pollination of Forced Tomatoes.* Mich. Agr. Exp. Sta. Spec. Bull. 39.

1907. FLETSCHER, F., *Mendelian Heredity in Cotton.* Jour. Agr. Sci. 281–282.

1907. GAGER, C. S., *An Occurrence of Glands in the Embryo of Zea Mays.* Torrey Bot. Club. Bull. 34 : 125–137.

1907. GALLARDO, A., *Estudios de Davenport sobre la herencia.* El Libro (Buenos Aires) 2 : 17–23.

1907. GATES, R. R., *Pollen Development in Hybrids of Œnothera lata × O. Lamarckiana, and its Relation to Mutation.* Bot. Gaz. 43 : 81–115, 3 pls. Rev. in Am. Nat. 41 : 403–404.

1907. GREGOIRE, V., *Les fondements cytologiques des theories courantes sur l'hérédité Mendelienne.* Soc. Roy. Zoöl. et Malacol. Belgique Ann. 42 : 267–320. 4 figs.

1907. GREGORY, E. S., *Pollen of Hybrid Violets.* Jour. Bot. 45 : 377.

1907. GREGORY, R. P., *On the Inheritance of Certain Characters in Primula sinensis.* British Assoc. Adv. Sci. Rep. 691–693.

1907. HATAI, S., *Studies on the Variation and Correlation of Skull Measurements in Both Sexes of Mature Albino Rats. (Mus norvegicus,* var. *Albus.)* Am. Jour. Anat. 7 : 423–441.

1907. HECKEL, E., *Sur l'origine de la pomme de terre cultivée et sur les mutations gemmaires culturales des Solanum tuberiferes sauvages.* Facult. d. Sciences Marseille Ann.

1907. HILL, A. W., *The Natural Hybrid between the Cowslip and Oxlip.* New Phytolog. 6 : 162.

1907. HURST, C. C., *Mendel's Law of Heredity.* Roy. Hort. Soc. Jour. 32 : 227.

1907. *International Conference on Plant Hardiness and Acclimatization.* Science, n.s. 26 : 356–357.

1907. JOHNSON, E. W., *Sage Brush and Cactus.* Am. Bot. 12 : 59–63.

1907. KAMMERER, PAUL, *Bastardierung von Flussbarsch (Perca fluviatilis* L.) *und Kaulbarsch (Acerina cernua* L).* Arch. f. Entwick'mech. d. Org. 23 : 511–551, 2 pls. & 1 fig. Bibliog.

1907. KLEBS, GEORG, *Studien über Variation.* Arch. f. Entwick'mech. d. Org. 24 : 29–113, 15 figs. 4 tab. Bibliog.

1907. LAMB, A. B., *A New Explanation of the Mechanics of Mitosis.* Jour. Exp. Zoöl. 5 : 27–33.

1907. LEVEILLE, H., *Un nouvel hybride de Juncus.* Soc. Botan. France Bull. 54 : 517–518.

1907. LOCK, R. H., *The Interpretation of Mendelian Phenomena.* Nature, 76 : 616, 77 : 32.

1907. Lock, R. H., *On the Inheritance of Certain Invisible Characters in Peas.* Roy. Soc. Proc. London B. 79 : 28 pp.

1907. Lutz, Anne M., *The Chromosomes of Œnothera Lamarckiana and One of its Mutants, O. gigas.* Science, n.s. 26 : 151–152. Fig.

1907. MacDougal, D. T., Vail, A. M., & Shull, G. H., *Mutations, Variations, and Relationships of the Œnotheras.* Carnegie Inst. Pub. no. 81. 1–92. pl. 1–22. & Fig. 1–73.

1907. MacDougal, D. T., *Hybrids among Wild Plants.* Plant World 10 : 25–37. Figs. 7–8.

1907. MacDougal, D. T., *Hybridization of Wild Plants.* Bot. Gaz. 43 : 45–58. Figs. 1–4.

1907. MacDougal, D. T., *Natural Hybrids.* Plant World, 10 : 138–139.

1907. Martinet, M., *Experiences sur la selection des cereales.* Annuaire Agr Suisse, 75.

1907. Mudge, G. P., *The Interpretation of Mendelian Phenomena.* Nature, 70 : 8.

1907. Noll, F. *Über eine Heegeri-ähnliche Form der Capsella bursa pastoris Mnch.* Niederrheinischen Gesell. f. Natur- u. Heilk. z. Bonn. Sitzungsber.

1907. Nusbaum, Jozef, *Kleiner Beitrag zur atavistischen Regeneration der Sch ren bei Flusskrebse.* Arch. f. Entwick'mech. d. Org. 24 : 124–130, 2 figs. Bibliog. in notes.

1907. O'Mara, P., *Sports.* Hort. Soc. N. Y. Jour. 1 : 39–43.

1907. Pearl, R., *Variation and Differentation in Ceratophyllum.* Carnegie Inst. Wash. Pub. 58 : (136 pp.), 2 pls., 126 figs.. Rev. in Am. Nat. 41 : 404–405.

1907. Reid, A. G., *The Interpretation of Mendelian Phenomena.* Nature, 7 : 566.

1907. Reitsma, J. F., *Correlative variabiliteit bij planten.* Dissert. 98 pp. Amsterdam.

1907. Rusby, H. H., *Some Little-known Edible Native Fruits of the United States.* N. Y. Bot. Gard. Jour. 8 : 175, 177–178.

1907. RUSBY, H. H., *The Wild Grains and Nuts of the United States.* Jour. N. Y. Bot. Gard. 7 : 269–273.

1907. SHAMEL, A. D., and COBEY, W. W., *Tobacco Breeding.* U. S. Dept. Agr. Bur. Plant Ind. Bull. 96 : 1–67, 10 pls. & 14 figs.

1907. SHAMEL, A. D., *The Art of Seed Selection and Breeding.* U. S. Dept. Agr. Yearbook, 221–236, 5 pls. Same. Year-book separate, 446 : 221–236 5 pls.

1907. SHEPARD, W. F., *The Calculation of the Moments of a Frequency Distribution.* Biometrika, 5 : 450–459. Rev. in Am. Nat. 42 : 418–422.

1907. SHULL, G. H., *Results of Crossing Bursa bursa-pastoris and Bursa Heegeri.* Intern. Zoöl. Congress, 7th Proc. (6 pp.) Boston. Cambridge, Mass. 1910.

1907. SPALDING, V. M., *The Artificial Production of Mutants.* Science, n.s. 26 : 349–350.

1907. SPILLMAN, W. J., *Standardizing Breed Characteristics.* Soc. for Prom. Agr. Sci. Proc. 28 : 116–120.

1907. STOLL, *Ein interessanter Bastard zwischen einem Emmer und Kolbenspelze.* Deutsche Landw. Presse, 100.

1907. VILMORIN, PH. DE, *Evolution et Sélection, theories an-ciennes et nouvelles.* Paris. Soc. Agr. de France.

1907. VRIES, H. DE, *Luther Burbank's Ideas on Scientific Horti-culture.* Century Mag. 73 : 674–681. Illus.

1907. VRIES, H. DE, *Evolution and Mutation.* The Monist, 17 : 6.

1907. VRIES, H. DE, *On Twin Hybrids.* Bot. Gaz. 44 : 401–407.

1907. WEBBER, H. J., and BOYKIN, F. B., *The Advantage of Planting Heavy Cotton Seed.* U. S. Dept. Agr. Farmers' Bull. 285 : (16 pp.), 6 figs.

1907. WIGHT, W. F., *The History of the Cowpea and its Intro-duction into America.* U. S. Dept. Agr. Bur. Pl. Ind. Bull. 1026 : 1–21. Pl. 1–3.

1907. WILSON, J. H., *The Hybridization of Cereals*. Jour. Agr. Sci. 2 : 68.

1907. WINKLER, H., *Über Pfropfbastarde und Üanzlichefl Chimären*. Deutsch. Bot. Gesell. Ber. 25 : 568. Rev. (Ger.) in Arch. f. Entwick'mech. d. Org. 28 : 163.

1907. YULE, U., *Mendelism and Biometry*. Nature, 76 : 152.

1908. BALLS, W. S., *Mendelian Studies of Egyptian Cotton*. Jour. Agr. Sci. 2 : 346–379.

1908. BEAL, W. J., *Mutations of Rudbeckia hirts*. Am. Ass'n Adv. Sci., Sec. Bot. Abstr. in Science, n.s. 27 : 207–208.

1908. BENNETT, B. L., *A Method of Breeding Early Cotton to Escape Boll-weevil Damage*. U. S. Dept. Agr. Farmers' Bull. 314 : (30 pp.), 16 figš. (Including: A description of the distinguishing characteristics of early cotton, instruction for seed selection, crossing one plant with another, treatment to insure a stand, experiments, etc.)

1908. BIFFEN, R. H., *On the Inheritance of Strength in Wheat*. Jour. Agr. Sci. 3 : 86–101. 1 fig.

1908. BOLLEY, HENRY L., *Observations regarding the Constancy of Mutants and Questions regarding the Origin of Disease Resistance in Plants*. Am. Nat. 42 : 171–183. Bibliog. in notes.

1908. BRIEM, H., *Natürliche Bastardierungen zwischen Zuckerrüben und Futterrüben*. Oester.-rung. Zeitsch. f. Zuckerindustrie u. Landw.: (4 pp.).

1908. BRIEM, H., *Mitteilungen und Bemerkungen zu de Vries, züchtersichen Ansichten*. Blätter f. Zuckerrübenbau, 15 : 309–312.

1908. BRISTOL, C. L., *Otter Sheep*. (Note.) Am. Nat. 42 : 282.

1908. BULL, C. P , *Corn Breeding in Minnesota*. Minnesota Agr. Exp. Sta. Bull. 173–266.

1908. BURTT-DAVY, J., *How to Secure Good Seed-maize*. Transvaal Agr. Jour. 6 : 441–453. 5 pls.

1908. CANNON, W. A., *A Redwood Sport*. Plant World, 11 : 232–234.

1908. CLARK, CHARLES C., *Wheat Crops of the United States, 1866–1906.* U. S. Dept. Agr. Bur. Statistics Bull. 57: (39 pp.) (revised).

1908. CLUTE, W. N., *The Boston Fern and its Sports.* Fern Bull. 15: 73–74.

1908. CLUTE, W. N., *A Remarkable Change of Color in Trillium.* Am. Bot. 14: 33–35. Illus.

1908. COBB, J. A., *The Effect of Errors of Observation upon the Correlation Coefficient.* Biometrika, 6: 109.

1908. COCKERELL, T. D. A., *Variation in Helianthus.* Bot. Gaz. 45: 338.

1908. COOK, O. F., *The Mendelian Inheritance of Mutations.* Science, n.s. 28: 86–88.

1908. COOK, O. F., *Reappearance of a Primitive Character in Cotton Hybrids.* U. S. Dept. Agr. Bur. Plant Ind. Circ. 18: (11 pp.).

1908. CORRENS, C., *Die Bestimmung und Vererbung des Deschlechtes nach neuen Versuchen mit hoheren Pflanzen.* Abstract presented before a recent meeting of the Medico-Biological Journal Club of the University of Virginia, by H. E. Jordan, adjunct professor of anatomy. Rev. in Am. Nat. 42: 811.

1908. CORRENS, C., *Weitere Untersuchungen über die Geschlechtsformen polygamer Blütenpflanze.* Jahr. f. Wiss. Botan. 45: 661–700.

1908. COTTON, J. S., *The Improvement of Mountain Meadows.* U. S. Dept. Agr. Bur. Plant Ind. Bull. 127: (29 pp.), 4 pls.

1908. CRAMER, P. J. S., *Mutaties bij Coffea robusta.* Teysmannia (Batavia), 19: 531–537.

1908. CRAMER, P. J. S., *De variaties van Coffea liberica in Liberia.* Teysmannia, 19: 667–683.

1908. CUENOT, L., *"Les Idées Nouvelles sur l'Origine des Espèces par Mutation."* Abstr. in Science, n.s. 30: 768–769. Trans. from Rev. gen. Sci. pures et appliq. 19: (No. 21).

1908. CUENOT, L., and MERCIER, L., *Études sur le cancer des Souris. Y a-t-il un rapport entre les differentes mutations connues chez les souris et la receptivite à la greffe?* Acad. Sci. Paris Compt. Rend. 147 : 1003–1005.

1908. CUNNINGHAM, J. T., *The Inheritance of Acquired Characters.* Nature, 77 : 367.

1908. DACHNOWSKI, A., *Type and Variability in the Annual Wood-increment of Acer rubrum L.* Ohio Nat. 8 : 343–349. Fig. 1.

1908. DANFORTH, C. H., *Notes on Numerical Variation in the Daisy.* Bot. Gaz. 46 : 349–356.

1908. DARBISHIRE, A. D., *On the Result of Crossing Round with Wrinkled Peas, with Especial Reference to their Starch-grains.* Roy. Soc. London Proc. B. 80 : 122–135.

1908. DAVENPORT, C. B., *The American Breeder's Association.* Science, n.s. 27 : 413–417.

1908. DAVENPORT, C. B., *Determination of Dominance in Mendelian Inheritance.* Amer. Phil. Soc. Proc. 47 : 59–63.

1908. DAVENPORT, C. B., *Recessive Characters.* Science, n.s. 28 : 729.

1908. DAVIS, C. A., *Some Interesting Variations of Common Plants.* Michigan Acad. Sci. Rep. 10 : 37–38.

1908. DEAN, BASHFORD, *The Lamarck Manuscript in Harvard.* Am. Nat. 42 : 145–153. Illus.

1908. DIX, W., *Über die Entstehung eines Squarehead bei Triticum turgidum Weizen.* Ill. Landw. Zeitg. 837–838. 2 figs.

1908. DRUERY, C. T., *Natural Selection.* Roy. Hortic. Soc. Jour. 33 : 114–118.

1908. DRUERY, D. T., *The Origin of the Potato.* Nature, 79 : 305.

1908. EAST, E. M., *Suggestions concerning Certain Bud Variations.* Plant World, 11 : 77–83.

1908. FIORI, A., *Un nuovo ibrido di Carduus (C. simplicifolius × nutans Nol).* Soc. Bot. Ital. Bull. 155–156.

1908. FYSON, P. F., *Some Experiments in the Hybridising of Indian Cottons.* India Dept. Agr. Mem. Bot. Ser. (29 pp.).

1908. GAIN, E., *Étude biometrique sur un hybride de primeveres, Primula flagellicaulis Pax.* Assoc. Franc. Avanc. Sci. Compt. Rend. 36 : 490.

1908. GALLARDO, A., *Sur l'epreuve statistique de la loi de Mendel.* Acad. Sci. Compt. Rend. 146 : 367–372.

1908. GATES, R. R., *The Chromosomes of Œnothera.* Science, n.s. 27 : 193–195. Bibliog. in notes.

1908. GATES, R. R., *A Preliminary Account of Studies in the Variability of a Unit Character in Œnothera.* Am. Ass'n Adv. Sci., Sec. Bot. ; Abstr. in Science, n.s. 27 : 209.

1908. GEERTS, J. M., *Über die Zahl der Chromosomen von Œnothera Lamarckiana.* Deut. Bot. Gesell. Ber. 25 : 191.

1908. HANSEN, N. E., *New Hybrid Fruits.* South Dakota Agr. Exp. Sta. Bull. 108 : (14 pp.), 9 pl. (Plums.)

1908. HARDY, G. H., *Mendelian Proportions, in a Mixed Population.* Science, n.s. 28 : 49–50.

1908. HARRIS, D. F., *The Functional Inertia of Living Matter.* A contribution to the physiological theory of life. 136 pp. London.

1908. HENSLOW, G., *The History of the Cabbage Tribe.* Roy. Hort. Soc. Jour. 34 : 15–23.

1908. HILDEBRAND, F., *Über Sämlinge von Cytisus Adamii.* Deutsch. Bot. Gesell. Ber. 26a : 590–595.

1908. HILL, E. J., *A Red Fruited Huckleberry.* Torreya, 8 : 30–31 pp.

1908. ILTIS, H., *Johann Gregor Mendel als Forscher und Mensch.* 20 pp. Brünn.

1908. JACKSON, H. S., *Development of Disease-resistant Varieties of Plants.* Mass. Hort. Soc. Trans. 123–136.

1908. JENNINGS, H. S., *Heredity, Variation and Evolution in Protozoa II.* *Heredity and Variation of Size and Form in*

Paramœcium, with Studies of Growth, Environmental Action and Selection. Am. Philos. Soc. Proc. 47 : 393–546.

1908. KORIBA, K., *Variation in the Ray-flowers of Some Compositæ.* Bot. Mag. Tokyo, 22 : 109–112, 121–128.

1908. KRIBS, H. G., *Note on the Relative Variability of the Sexes in Carabus auratus, L.* Biometrika, 6 : 103–105. Tab.

1908. LEAKE, H. M., *Studies in Experimental Breeding of the Indian Cottons; and introductory note.* Asiat. Soc. Bengal Jour. 13–20.

1908. LEFEVRE, J., *Contribution à l'histoire des theories proposées sur la variation des types vegetaux.* Assoc. Franc. Avanc. Sci. Compt. Rend. 36 : 426.

1908. LOCHHEAD, W., *The Problem of Breeding Disease-resistant Plants.* Can. Seed-Grow. Assoc. Rep. 4 : 64–70. 2 tabs.

1908. LOCK, R. H., *The Present State of Knowledge of Heredity in Pisum.* Roy. Bot. Gard. Peradeniya Ann. 4 : 93–111.

1908. LOLLI, A., *Osservazioni su una varieta di Mais ramificato.* Staz. Sper. Agr. Ital. 41 : 761–767. 1 pl.

1908. MACDOUGAL, D. T., *First Crosses Breeding True.* Plant World, 11 : 42.

1908. MCALPINE, D., *The Improvement of Cereals by Selection and Crossing.* Dept. Agr. Victoria Jour. 6 : 282.

1908. MEYER, P., *Les croisements et l'hérédité des caracteres (la loi de Mendel).* Rev. Gen. des Sci. pures et appliquées, 27–31.

1908. MINKIEWICZ, R., *L'etendue des changements possibles de couleur de Hippolyte varians.* Compt. Rend. Acad. Sci. 147 : 943–944.

1908. MOORE, E., *Abnormalities in the Radish, Clover, and Ash.* Torreya, 8 : 220 pp.

1908. O'FARELL, H. H., *The Interpretation of Mendelian Phenomena.* Nature, 77 : 271.

1908. ORTMANN, A. E., *The Inheritance of Fluctuating Variation.* Science, n.s. 27 : 545–546.

1908. ORPHAL, K., *Untersuchungen über Korrelation-ser-scheinungen bei mehreren.* Sorten der Vicia Faba. Jena. 75 pp.

1908. ORTON, W. A., *The Development of Farm Crops Resistant to Disease.* U. S. Dept. Agr. Yearbook, 453–464. 2 pls. Same. Yearbook separate, 494 : 453–464. 2 pls.

1908. PAULIN, G., *No Struggle for Existence, no Natural Selection.* Critical examination of the fundamental principles of the Darwinian theory. 284 pp. London.

1908. PEARL, RAYMOND (Reviewer), *Biometrics.* Recent contributions to theory. (Review.) Am. Nat. 42 : 418–422. Bibliog. in notes.

1908. PRICE, H. L., and DRINKARD, A. W., *Inheritance in Tomato Hybrids.* Virginia Agr. Exp. Sta. Bull. 177 : 15–54. Pl. Fig.

1908. PUNNETT, R. C., *Mendelism in Relation to Disease.* Roy. Soc. of Med. Proc. Epidemiol. Sect. 1 : 83–168.

1908. REID, G. A., *Mendelism and Sex.* Nature, 77 : 236–237.

1908. REID, G. A., *The Inheritance of "Acquired" Characters.* Nature, 77 : 442.

1908. ROBBINS, W. W., *Variation in Flower-heads of Gaillardia aristate.* Biometrika, 6 : 106–108. Fig. Diagr.

1908. ROLFE, R. A., and HURST, C. C., *The Orchid Stud-book.* Enumeration of hybrid orchids of artificial origin, with their parents, raisers, rate of first flowering, etc. xlvi + 325 pp. Kew. 121 figs.

1908. ROSENAU, J., and ANDERSON, J. F., *Further Studies upon Hypersusceptibility and Immunity.* Jour. of Med. Research, Vol. 16, pp. 381–418. Rev. in Am. Nat. 42 : 135.

1908. SEAVER, F. J., *Color Variation in some of the Fungi.* Torrey Bot. Club Bull. 35 : 307–314.

1908. SHIMEK, B., *A Hybrid Oak.* Iowa Acad. Sci. Proc. 15 : 77–83, pls. 1–2.

1908. SHULL, G. H., *Dr. Baur on Variegation.* Plant World, 11 : 147–151.

1908. SHULL, G. H., *The Pedigree Culture, its Aims and Methods.* Plant World, 11 : 21.

1908. SHULL, G. H., *Some New Cases of Mendelian Inheritance.* Am. Ass'n Adv. Sci., Sec. Bot.; Abstr. in Science, n.s. 27 : 206.

1908. SHULL, G. H., *Some New Cases of Mendelian Inheritance.* Bot. Gaz. 45 : 103–116, figs. 1–4.

1908. SHULL, G. H., *A New Mendelian Ratio and Several Types of Latency.* Am. Nat. 42 : 433–451. Bibliog. in notes.

1908. SUTTON, ARTHUR W., *Brassica Crosses.* Linnean Soc. Bot. Jour. 38 : 337–349. 12 pls. Rev. in Zeitsch. f. ind. Abs. u. Vererb. 2 : 140.

1908. TERRY, W. A., *A New Variety of the Ostrich Fern.* Fern Bull. 16 : 3–4.

1908. TRAIL, J. W. H., *Floral Variation in the Genus Veronica.* Scottish Nat. Hist. Soc. Ann. 68 : 158–259.

1908. TSCHERMAK, E. VON, *Die Mendelschen Vererburgegesetze.* Schr. zur Verbr. Naturwiss. Kennt. (Wien.) 48 : 145–164.

1908. TSCHERMAK, E. VON, *Der Moderne Stand des Vererbungs-problems.* Arch. f. Rassen- und Ges.-Biol. 5 : 305–326.

1908. VRIES, H. DE, *Especes et varietes; leur naissance par mutation.* Trad. de l'angl. p. L. Blaringhem. Paris.

1908. VRIES, H. DE, *Über die Zwillingsbastarde von Œnothera nanella.* Deutsch. Bot. Gesells. Ber. 26a : 667–676.

1908. WEBBER, H. J., *Plant Breeding for Farmers.* Cornell Univ. Agr. Exp. Sta. Bull. 251 : 282–332.

1908. WEBBER, H. J., *Improving Corn by Seed Selection.* Cornell Univ. Farmers' Reading Course Bull. 42 : 5. Figs.

1908. WERNER, F., *Nochmals Mimikry und Schutzfärbung.* Biol. Centralbl. 28 : 567–576, 588–601.

1908. WHITE, C. A., *Aggregate Mutation of Gossypium.* Science, n.s. 27 : 193.

1908. WICKSON, E. J., *Luther Burbank and his New Environment.* Sunset Mag. 27 : 151–162.

1908. WILLISTON, S. W., *What is a Species?* Am. Nat. 42 : 184–194.

1908. WINKLER, HANS, *Über Parthenogenesis und Apogamie im Pflanzenreiche.* Prog. Rei. Bot. 2 : 293–454. Fig. Bibliog.

1908. WINKLER, H., *Solanum tubingense, ein echter Pfropf-bastard zwischen Tomate und Nachtschatten.* Deutsch. Bot. Gesell. Ber. 26a : 595–608. 2 illus.

1908. WINKLER, H., *Parthenogenesis und Apogamie im Pflan-zenreich* (— in the plant kingdom), 166 pp. Reprint from Prog. Rei. Bot. 2; Rev. (Ger.) in Arch. f. Entwick'-mech. d. Org. 26 : 696.

1908. ZAVITZ, C. A., *The Work of Plant Improvement at Home and Abroad.* Can. Seed-Grow. Assoc. Rep. 4 : 42–46. Tab.

1909. AARONSOHN, A., *Contribution à l'histoire des cereales. Le ble, l'orge et le seigle à l'état sauvage.* Soc. Bot. France Bull. 56 : 196–203, 56 : 237–245, 56 : 251–258.

1909. AIKMAN, P. J. A., *On Some Hybrid Tuberous Solanums.* Roy. Hort. Soc. Jour. 35 : 53–55.

1909. BACO, F., *Sur des variations de vignes greffées.* Acad. Sci. Paris, Compt. Rend. 148 : 429–431.

1909. BALLS, LAWRENCE, *Some Cytological Aspects of Cotton Breeding.* A. B. A. Rep. 5 : 16–29.

1909. BATESON, W., SAUNDERS, MISS E. R., PUNNETT, R. C., *Experimental Studies in the Physiology of Heredity.* Roy. Soc. London Evol. Com. Rep. 4 : (60 pp.). Rev. in Zeitsch. f. ind. Abs.- u. Vererb. 2 : 17–19.

1909. BATESON, W., *Mendel's Principles of Heredity.* 396 pp. G. P. Putnam's Sons, N. Y. Cambridge (England) Univ. Press. 6 pls., 35 figs., 3 plates. Rev. in Science, n.s. 30 : 481–483.

1909. BAUR, E., *Die Aurea-Sippen von Antirrhinum majus.*

2 A

Zeitsch. f. indukt. Abst.- u. Vererb. 1 : 124–125. Bibliog.
in notes.

1909. BAUER, E., *Pfropfbastarde. Periklinalchimären und
Hyperchimären.* Deutsch. Bot. Gesell. Ber. 27 : 603–605.

1909. BEACH, S. A., *The Present Status of Apple Breeding in
America.* A. B. A. Rep. 5 : 28–36.

1909. BELLAIR, G., *L'hybridation en horticulture.* 350 pp.
Paris, 123 figs.

1909. BENEDICT, R. C., *New Hybrids in Dryopteria.* Torrey
Bot. Club Bull. 36 : 41–49. Includes *D. Cintoniana* ×
spinuloss, D. cristata × *Goldiana, D. Goldiana* × *spinulos*
and *D. intermedia* × *marginalis* hybb. nov.

1909. BLARINGHEM, L., *Sur les hybrides d'orges et la loi de
Mendel.* Acad. Sci. Paris, Compt. Rend. 148 : 854–857.

1909. BOAS, FRANZ, *Determination of the Coefficient of Correlation.* Science, n.s. 29 : 823–824.

1909. BROOMALL, C. M., *Flower Pigments.* Delaware County
Inst. Sci. Proc. 4 : 81–84.

1909. BROWN, HARRY R., *Selection of Seed Potatoes.* Can.
Seed-Grow. Assoc. Rep. 5 : 103–105.

1909. BROZEK, A., *Variabilität bei Palæmonetes varians.*
Böhm Ges. Wiss. Prag. S. B. 1–11.

1909. BURTT-DAVY, J., *Mendelism in Maize.* Transvaal Agr.
Jour. 7 : 461–462.

1909. BYBOWSKI, J., *Regeneration des plantations de cafeiers
par l'introduction d'une espece nouvelle.* Acad. Sci.
Paris, Compt. Rend. 148 : 232–235.

1909. CANNON, W. A., *Studies in Heredity as Illustrated by the
Trichomes of Species and Hybrids of Juglans, Œnothera,
Papaver and Solanum.* Carnegie Inst. Wash. Pub. 117.
Washington, D.C., pls. 1–10, and figs. 1–21.

1909. CARLETON, M. A., *Field Methods in Wheat Breeding.*
A. B. A. Rep. 5 : 185–207.

1909. CASTLE, W. E., *The Behavior of Unit Characters in Heredity.*

In Fifty Years of Darwinism. pp. 143–159. Bibliograph. in notes.

1909. CHAMBERS, ROBERT, *Einfluss der Eigrosse und der Temperatur auf das Wachsthum und die Grosse des Frosches und dessen Zellen.* Arch. für Mikroskopische Anatomie und Entwicklungsgeschichte? Vol. 72, pt. 3, pp. 607–661. Rev. in Am. Nat. 43 : 57.

1909. CHAMBLISE, CHARLES E., *A Note on Rice Breeding.* A. B. A. Rep. 5 : 182–185.

1909. CLOTHIER, GEO. L., *Practical Possibilities of Grafting and Building Forest and Nut Trees.* A. B. A. Rep. 5 : 262–265.

1909. COLLINS, G. N., *The Importance of Broad Breeding in Corn.* Dept. Agr. Bur. Plant Ind. 141 (pt. 4) : 33–44.

1909. COOK, O. F., McLACHLAN, ARGYLE, and MEADE, ROWLAND M., *A Study of Diversity in Egyptian Cotton.* U. S. Dept. Agr. Bur. Plant Ind. Bull. 156 : (60 pp.), 6 pls.

1909. COOK, O. F., *Pure Strains as Artifacts of Breeding.* Am. Nat. 43 : 241–242.

1909. COOK, O. F., *Suppressed and Intensified Characters in Cotton Hybrids.* U. S. Dept. Agr. Bur. Plant Ind. Bull. 147 : (27 pp.).

1909. COOK, O. F., *The Superiority of Line Breeding over Narrow Breeding.* U. S. Dept. Agr. Bur. Plant Ind. Bull. 146 : (45 pp.).

1909. CRIDDLE, N., *The So-called White Wild Oats and What they Are.* Ottawa Nat. 23 : 127–128.

1909. DARBISHIRE, A. D., *An Experimental Estimation of the Theory of Ancestral Contributions in Heredity.* Roy. Soc. London Proc. 81 : 61–79.

1909. DARBISHIRE, A. D., *Recent Advances in the Study of Heredity.* III. New Phytolog. 7 : 157–181 ; 7 : 237–248.

1909. DAVENPORT, CHARLES B., *Mutation.* In Fifty Years of Darwinism, pp. 160–181.

1909. DE LOACH, R. J. H., *The Problem of Fixation in Cotton Hybrids.* A. B. A. Rep. 5 : 130–138.

1909. DEMOLL, R., and STROHL, J., *L'influence de la température sur le développement des organismes et la durée de la vie.* Soc. Biol. Compt. Rend. 66 : 855–857.

1909. DOW, GEORGE, *Some Results Obtained through the Careful Selection of Seeds.* Can. Seed-Grow. Assoc. Rep. 5 : 109–111.

1909. EAST, E. M., *A Study of the Factors Influencing the Improvement of the Potato.* III. Exp. Sta. Bull. 127 : Rev. in Zeitsch. f. ind. Abs.- u. Vererb. 2 : 142–143.

1909. EAST, E. M., *Note concerning Inheritance in Sweet Corn.* Science, n.s. 29 : 465–467.

1909. EAST, EDWARD M., *The Distinction between Development and Heredity in Inbreeding.* Am. Nat. 43 : 173–181. Bibliog. in notes.

1909–10. EAST, E. M., *The Transmission of Variations in the Potato in Asexual Reproduction.* (Contr. from the Laboratory of Genetics, Bussey Institution of Harvard University, No. 3.) Conn. Exp. Sta. Rep. 120–160, 5 pls.

1909. EMERSON, R. A., *Factors for Mottling in Beans.* A. B. A. Rep. 5 : 368–376.

1909. EMERSON, R. A., *Inheritance of Color in the Seeds of the Common Bean, Phaseolus vulgaris.* Nebraska Agr. Exp. Sta. Rep. 22 : 65–101.

1909. FORBES, F. E., *A New Hybrid Violet.* Rhodora, 11 : 15–15. *V. Brittoniana* × *lanceolata.*

1909. GARNER, W. W., *Breeding Tobacco for High and Low Nicotine Content.* A. B. A. Rep. 5 : 299–303.

1909. GATES, R. R., *A Litter of Hybrid Dogs.* Science, n.s. 29 : 744–747. Tab.

1909. GATES, R. R., *The Behavior of the Chromosomes in Œnothera lata* × *O. gigas.* Bot. Gaz. 48 : 179–199, pls. 12–14.

1909. GATES, R. R., *The Stature and Chromosomes of Œnothera gigas De Vries.* Archiv Zellforsch. 3 : 525–552. Pls. 29–30.

1909. GATIN, M. C. L., *La morphologie de la germination et ses rapports avec la phylogenie.* Rev. Gen. Bot. 21 : 147–158.

1909. GEERTS, J. M., *Beiträge zur Kenntnis der Cytologie und der partiellen Sterilität von Œnothera Lamarckiana.* Rec. Trav. Bot. Neerlandais, 5 : 1–114, 28 pls.

1909. GRIFFON, E., *Recherches sur la xenie chez les Solanées.* Soc. Bot. France Bull. 55 : 714–720.

1909. GUTHRIE, C. C., *Guinea Pig Graft-hybrids.* Science, n.s. 30 : 724–725. Bibliog. in notes.

1909. HAGEDOORN, AREND L., *Mendelian Inheritance of Sex.* Arch. f. Entwick'mech. d. Org. 28 : 1–34, 3 figs.

1909. HANSEN, N. E., *The Wild Alfalfas and Clovers of Siberia, with a Prospective View of the Alfalfas of the world.* U. S. Dept. Agr. Bur. Plant Ind. Bull. 150 : (31 pp.), 1 pl.

1909. HARRIS, J. A., *Variation in the Number of Seeds per Pod in the Broom, Cytisus scoparius.* Am. Nat. 43 : 350–355, 2 tab. Diag. Bibliog. in notes.

1909. HARRIS, J. A., *A Short Method of Calculating the Coefficient of Correlation in the Case of Integral Variates.* Biometrika, 7 : 214–218.

1909. HARRIS, J. A., *Note on Variation in Adoxa.* Biometrika, 7 : 218–222.

1909. HARRIS, J. A., *The Correlation between Length of Flowering Stalk and Number of Flowers per Inflorescence in Nothoscordum and Allium.* Missouri Bot. Gard. Rep. 20 : 105–115.

1909. HARRIS, J. A., *Variation and Correlation in the Flowers of Lagerstrœmia indica.* Missouri Bot. Gard. Rep. 20 : 97–104.

1909. HARSHBERGER, J. W., *The Biologist's Part in Practical Plant and Animal Breeding.* Amer. Vet. Rev. 35 : 254–265.

1909. HECKEL, M., *Fixation de la mutation gemmaire culturale du Solanum maglia*. Soc. Nation. d'Agr. Bull. 69 : 874–877.

1909. HOLDEFLEISS, P., *Bastardierungsversuche mit Mais*. Landwirtsch. Inst. Halle a. S. Ber. 19 : 178–198, 1 pl.

1909. HOLMES, S. J., *The Categories of Variation*. Am. Nat. 43 : 257–285.

1909. HOWARD, A., and HOWARD, G. L. C., *The Varietal Characters of Indian Wheats*. India Dept. Agr. Mem. Bot., Series 2 : (66 pp.).

1909. HY, F., *Sur une forme sterile de Cardamine hirsuta*. Soc. Bot. France Bull. 56 : 210–213.

1909. JENNINGS, S. H., *Heredity and Variation in the Simplest Organism*. Am. Nat. 43 : 321–337. Bibliog. in notes.

1909. JEPSON, WILLIS L., *Spontaneous Hybrids of Native Californian Trees*. A. B. A. Rep. 5 : 259–262.

1909. JOHANNSEN, W., *Über Knospenmutation bei Phaseolus*. Zeitsch. f. indukt. Abst.- u. Vererb. 1 : 1–10, 2 figs. Bibliog. $\frac{1}{3}$ p.

1909. JOHNSON, R. H., *Variation in Syndesmon and Hepatica*. Ohio Nat. 9 : 431–436.

1909. JORDON, D. S., and KELLOGG, V. L., *The Scientific Aspects of Luther Burbank's Work*. xiv + 115 pp. San Francisco.

1909. KNUTH, R., *Über Bastardbildung in der Gattung Pelargonium*. Bot. Jahrb. f. Systematik usw. (Engler) 44 : 1–35. 4 figs.

1909. LEAKE, H. M., *Studies in the Experimental Breeding of Indian Cottons 2. On Buds and Branching*. Asiat. Soc. Bengal Jour., n.s. 5 : 23–30.

1909. LEAVITT, R. G., *A Vegetative Mutant and the Principle of Homœosis in Plants*. Bot. Gaz. 47 : 30–68, figs. 1–19.

1909. LEE, F. E., *Report of Wheat Improvement Committee*. Dept. Agr. Victoria Jour. 7 : 239–254.

1909. LOCK, R. H., *A Preliminary Survey of Species Crossing*

in the Genus Nicotiana from the Mendelian Standpoint.
Roy. Bot. Gard., Peradeniya Annals, 4 : 195–227, 12 pls. &
1 fig.

1909. LOVE, HARRY H., *Influence of Food Supply on Variation.*
A. B. A. Rep. 5 : 357–365.

1909. MACALLUM, A. B., *On the Origin of the Life on the Globe.*
Canadian Inst. Trans. 8 : 423–441.

1909. MACDOUGAL, D. T., *The Direct Influence of Environment.*
In Fifty Years of Darwinism, pp. 114–142, 2 pls. Bibliography in notes.

1909. MCALPINE, D., and DE CASTELLA, F., *Bud-variation in
Corinth Currant Vine.* Victoria Dept. Agr. Jour. 7 : 145–
149.

1909. MCCALLUM, W. B., *The Reciprocal Influence of Scion
and Stock.* Plant World, 12 : 281–286.

1909. MARRYAT, (MISS) DOROTHEA C. E., *Hybridisation Experiments with Mirabilis Jalapa.* Roy. Soc. London Evol.
Comm. Rep. 5 : 32–50, 2 pls. Tables.

1909. MARTIUS, FR., *Das pathogenetische Vererbungsproblem. 4.
(letztes) Heft der "Pathogenese innerer Krankheiten."* Nach
Vorlesungen für Studierende und Ärzte. pp. 323–467.
Leipzig und Wien.

1909. MAYNARD, G. D., *Variability in Shirley Poppies from
Pretoria.* Biometrika, 7 : 227–230. Fig.

1909. MEISENHEIMER, JOHANNES, *Experimentelle Studien zur
Soma und Geschlechts-Differenzierung.* Erster Beitrag.
Jena, Gustav Fischer. Rev. in Am. Nat. 44 : 316.

1909. MERZBACHER, L., *Gesetzmassigkeiten in der Vererbung
und Verbreitung verschiedener hereditärfamiliärer Erkran-
kungen.* Archiv f. Rassen- u. Gesell.-Biologie, 6 : 172–198,
2 pls., 19 figs.

1909. NEWMAN, L. H., *Certain Biological Principles and their
Practical Application in the Improvement of the Field Crops
of Canada.* Ottawa Nat. 23 : 85–91; 23 : 105–110.

1909. PATON, J. AIKMAN, *Notes on Some Hybrid Tuberous Solanums.* Roy. Hort. Soc. Jour. 35 : 53–55.

1909. PEARL, RAYMOND, *A Note on the Degree of Accuracy of Biometric Constants.* Am. Nat. 43 : 238–240.

1909. PEARL, RAYMOND, and SURFACE, FRANK M., *Selection Index Numbers and their Use in Breeding.* Am. Nat. 43 : 385–400.

1909. PEARL, RAYMOND, and SURFACE, FRANK M., *Data on the Inheritance of Fecundity obtained from the Records of Egg Production of the Daughters of "200-egg" Hens.* Maine Agr. Exp. Sta. Bull. 166 : (34 pp.), 13 figs.

1909. PEARSON, KARL, *Determination of the Coefficient of Correlation.* Science, n.s. 30 : 23–25.

1909. PEARSON, K., *On the Ancestral Gametic Correlations of a Mendelian Population Mating at Random.* Roy. Soc. London Proc. 81 : 225–229.

1909. PERRIRAZ, J., *Étude biologique et biometrique sur Narcissus angustifolius.* Soc. Vaud. Sci. Nat. Bull. 45 : 153–176.

1909. PIPER, C. V., *Alfalfa and its Improvement by Breeding.* A. B. A. Rep. 5 : 94–115.

1909. PLATE, L., *Darwinismus u. Landwirtschaft.* 24 pp. Parey, Berlin.

1909. POWERS, H. J., *Are Species Realities or Concepts Only?* Am. Nat. 43 : 598–610.

1909. PRICE, H. L., and DRINKARD, W., *Inheritance in Tomato Hybrids.* Plant World, 12 : 10–18, figs. 1–2.

1909. PRICE, H. L., and DRINKARD, A. W., *Inheritance in Tomato Hybrids.* Virginia Agr. Exp. Sta. Bull. 177 : 17–53, 10 pls. Rev. (English) in Zeitsch. f. indukt. Abst.- u. Vererb. 1 : 402–403.

1909. RITTER, G., *Über discontinuierliche Variation im Organismenreiche.* Bot. Centralbl. Beih. 251 : 1–29.

1909. RITTER, W. E., *The Hypothesis of "Presence and Ab-*

sence" in Mendelian Inheritance. Science, n.s. 30 : 367–368.

1909. ROSENBERG, O., *Über die Chromosomenzahlen bei Taraxacum und Rosa.* Svensk Bot. Tidskr. 3 : 150–162.

1909. ROUX, G., *Les problemes de l'heredite.* La Revue (Oct. 1) : 375–383.

1909. RUSSEL, E. S., *The Transmission of Acquired Characters.* Rivista di Scienza, 5 : 192–203.

1909. SANDSTEN, E. P., *Improvement of Wisconsin Tobacco through Seed-selection.* Wisconsin Agr. Exp. Sta. Bull. 176.

1909. SAUER, L. W., *Quercus Leana; a Hybrid Oak.* Plant World, 12 : 198–201, figs. 1–2.

1909. SAXTON, W. T., *Parthenogenesis in Pinus Pinaster.* Bot. Gaz. 47 : 406–409, figs. 1–7.

1909. SEYOT, P. M., *Étude biometrique des pepins d'un Vitis vinifera franc de pied et greffe.* Acad. Sci. (Paris) Compt. Rend. 149 : 53–56.

1909. SHOEMAKER, D. N., *Report of the Committee on Breeding Cotton.* A. B. A. Rep. 5 : 115–116.

1909. SHULL, G. H., *A Simple Chemical Device to Illustrate Mendelian Inheritance.* Plant World, 12 : 145–152. Illus.

1909. SMITH, J. RUSSELL, *Elimination of the Gullied Hillside through Tree Breeding.* A. B. A. Rep. 5 : 265–269.

1909. SPILLMAN, W. J. (Reviewer), *The Nature of "Unit" Characters.* (Review.) Am. Nat. 43 : 243–248. Bibliog. in notes.

1909. SPILLMAN, W. J., *The Effect of Different Methods of Selection on the Fixation of Hybrids.* A. B. A. Rep. 5 : 341–347.

1909. STEVENS, F. L., and HALL, J. G., *Variation of Fungi Due to Environment.* Bot. Gaz. 48 : 1–30, figs. 1–37.

1909. STRAUGIN, M. N., and CHURCH, C. G., *The Influence of Environment on the Composition of Sweet Corn, 1905–1908.* U. S. Dept. Agr. Bur. Chemistry Bull. 127 : (69 pp.), 11 figs.

1909. SUDWORTH, GEO. B., *Prelim. Rep. Chairman Committee on Breeding Nut and Forest Trees.* A. B. A. Rep. 5 : 255–259.

1909. TEDIN, H., *Redogörelse för arbetena pa Svalof med korn, ärter och vicker under ar.* Sveriges Utsadesfor. Tidskr. 20 : 245–255. 1910.

1909. TRABUT, *Contribution à l'étude de l'origine des avoines cultivées.* Acad. Sci. Paris Compt. Rend. 149 : 227–229.

1909. TRACY, J. E. W., *Work conducted by the United States Department of Agriculture in breeding Highgrade Strains of Sugar Beet Seed and testing Important Varieties.* A. B. A. Rep. 5 : 284–285.

1909. TROW, A. H., *Forms of Senecio vulgaris.* Jour. of Bot. 47 : 304–306.

1909. TSCHERMAK, E. V., *Der Moderne Stand der Kreuzungszüchtung der landwirtschaftlichen Kulturpflanzen.* Vortrag gehalten in der Ökonomischen Gesellschaft in Königreich Sachsen zu Dresden am 5. Feb. 19 pp.

1909. TSCHERMAK, E. V., *Über Correlationen.* Landw. Umschau, 1 : (2 pp.).

1909. VAN FLEET, W., *Report of the Committee on Breeding Roses.* A. B. A. Rep. 5 : 14–15.

1909. VOGT, O., *Studien über das Artproblem.* 1. Mitt. *Über das Variieren der Hummeln.* 1. Teil. Ges. Naturf. Freunde Berlin Sitzungsber. 28–83, 1 pl. & fig.

1909. VOLLMANN, F., *Die Bedeutung der Bastardierung für die Entstehung von Arten und Formen in der Gattung Hieracium.* Bayer Bot. Gesell. Ber. 12 : 29–37.

1909. VRIES, H. DE, *Fertilization and Hybridization.* Monist, 19 : 514–555.

1909. VRIES, H. DE, *On Triple Hybrids.* Bot. Gaz. 47 : 1–8.

1909. VRIES, H. DE, *Transformisme et mutation.* Rev. du Mois. (Sept.), 269–302.

1909. WAGNER, A., *Die drei Elemente der Lamarckschen Lehre.* Zeitsch. Ausbau Entw. Lehre, 3 : 44–60.

1909. WARBURTON, C. W., *Improvement of the Oat Crop.* U. S. Dept. Agr. Bur. Plant Ind. Circ. 30: (10 pp.).

1909. WAUGH and SHAW, *Variation in Peas.* Mass. (State) Agr. Exp. Sta. Ann. Rep. 167–173.

1909. WEBBER, H. J., *Improving Corn by Seed Selection.* Cornell Univ. Reading-Course for Farmers, 42.

1909. WEBBER, H. J., *Methods of Breeding and Improving the Potato Crop.* Cornell Univ. Farmers' Reading-Course Bull. 43: 3 figs.

1909. WEBBER, H. J., *Clonal or Bud Variation.* A. B. A. Rep. 5: 347–357.

1909. WEISMANN, AUGUST, *The Selection Theory.* Darwin and Mod. Sci. pp. 18–65, pl., fig. Bibliog. in notes.

1909. WESTGATE, J. M., *Methods of Breeding Alfalfa by Selection.* A. B. A. Rep. 5: 144–166.

1909. WESTGATE, J. M., *Another Explanation of the Hardiness of Grimm Alfalfa.* Science, n.s. 30: 184–186.

1909. WHELDALE, (MISS) M., *The Colours and Pigments of Flowers, with Special Reference to Genetics.* Roy. Soc. London Proc. 81: 44–60.

1909. WHELDALE, (MISS) M., *Further Observations upon the Inheritance of Flower-colour in Antirrhinum majus.* Roy. Soc. London Evol. Comm. Rep. 5: 1–26. Tables. Bibliog. in notes.

1909. WILSON, EDMUND B., *Studies on Chromosomes V. The Chromosomes of Metapodius. A Contribution to the Hypothesis of the Genetic Continuity of Chromosomes.* Jour. Exp. Zoöl. 6: 147–205, 1 pl. & 13 figs.

1909. WILSON, EDMUND B., *The Cell in Relation to Heredity and Evolution.* In Fifty Years of Darwinism, pp. 92–113.

1909. WOODHEAD, J. W., and DRIERLEY, M. M., *Development of the Climbing Habit in Antirrhinum majus.* New Phytologist, 8: 284–298, 3 pls. & 5 figs.

1909. WOODRUFFE-PEACOCK, E. A., *Heredity of Acquired Characters*. Jour. of Bot. 47 : 320–321.

1909. WRIGHT, R. P., *Potatoes, Effect of Planting Sprouted Tubers on Yield*. West. Scot. Agr. Coll. Ann. Rep. 9 : 101. Roy. Hort. Soc. Abs. in Jour. 35 : 557.

1909. ZAVITZ, Z. A., *Foundation Stock on Plant Breeding*. A. B. A. Rep. 5 : 167–171.

1909. ZIMMERMANN, W., *Orchis coriophora × morio*. Allg. Bot. Zeitsch. 15 : 150–151.

1910. ANDREWS, F. M., *Twin Hybrids (læta and velutina) and their Anatomical Distinctions*. Bot. Gaz. 50 : 193–201.

1910. BABCOCK, ERNEST B., *Walnut-Oak Hybrid Experiments*. Am. Breed. Mag. 1 : 200–202. Tab.

1910. BALL, CARLETON R., *The Breeding of Grain Sorghums*. Am. Breed. Mag. 1 : 283–293.

1910. BALLS, W. L., *Some Complications in Mendelian Cotton Breeding*. Inst. Égyptien Bull. 3 : 120–127.

1910. BALTZER, F., *Über die Beziehungenzwischen dem Chromatin und der Entwickelung und Vererbungs-richtung bei Echinodermenbastarden*. Arch. Zellforschung, 5 : 497–621. 5 pls. & 19 figs.

1910. BARUS, C., *Variations Graphically*. Science, n.s. 31 : 867–868.

1910. BATAILLON, E., *Contribution à l'analyse experimentale des phenomènes karyocinetiques chez Ascaris megalocephala*. Arch. f. Entwick'mech. d. Org. 30 : 1 : 24–44, 1 pl. Bibliog. $1\frac{1}{4}$ pp.

1910. BAUR, E., *Pfropfbastards*. Biol. Centralbl. 30 : 497–514. 7 figs.

1910. BENEDIKT, MORIZ, *Biomechanische Grundfragen. Offenes Sendschreiben an Herrn Hofrat Ernst Ludwig*. Arch. f. Entwick'mech. d. Org. 31 : 164–174.

1910. BERNARD, NÖEL, *L'origine de la pomme de terre*. 19 pp. Soc. Franc. d'Impr. et de Librairie, Poitiers. Reprint from Soc. Acad. d'Agric., Belleslettres, Sci. et Arts de Poitiers Bull.

1910. BERTHAULT, P., *À propos de l'origine de la pomme de terre.* Rev. Gén. Bot. 22 : 345–353.

1910. BERTHAULT, P., *Sur les types sauvages de la pomme de terre cultivée.* Acad. Sci. Paris, Compt. Rend. 150 : 47–50.

1910. BESSEY, E. A., *Air Drainage as Affecting the Acclimatization of Plants.* N. Y. Hort. Soc. Mem. 2 : 25–28.

1910. BLANCHARD, HENRY F., *Improvement of the Wheat Crop in California.* U. S. Dept. Agr. Bur. Plant Ind. Bull. 178 : (37 pp.), 10 figs.

1910. BORDAGE, E., *À propos de l'hérédité des caractères acquis.* Bull. Scient. France et Belgique 44 : (Heft 1).

1910. BORNET, E., and GARD, M., *Recherches sur les hybrides artificiels de Cistes obtenus par M. Ed. Bornet. I. Notes inedites et resultats experimentaux.* Ann. des Sci. Naturelles (Botanique) 12 : 71–116.

1910. BRAND, CHARLES J., *The Utilization of Crop Plants in Paper Making.* U. S. Dept. Agr. Yearbook, 329–340. Same. Yearbook Separate, 541 : 329–340.

1910. BRUCE, A. B., *The Mendelian Theory of Heredity and the Augmentation of Vigor.* Science, n.s. 32 : 627–628.

1910. BRUCE, A. B., *Self-fertilization and Loss of Vigour.* Nature. March 3.

1910. BUDER, J., *Pfropfbastarde und Chimaeren.* Zeitsch. f. allg. Physiol. 11 : 15–31.

1910. BUDER, J., *Studien an Laburnum Adami.* Deutsch. Bot. Gesell. Ber. 28 : 188–192.

1910. BURTT-DAVY, J., *A Note on the Correlation of Characters in Maize Breeding.* Transvaal Agr. Jour. 8 : 453–455.

1910. BURTT-DAVY, J., *An Experiment in Breeding a New Type of Maize.* Transvaal Agr. Jour. 8 : 450–453.

1910. CHEVALIER, J., *Influence de la culture sur la teneur en alcaloides de quelques Solanées.* Acad. Sci. Paris Compt. Rend. 150 : 344–347.

1910. CLARK, CHAS. F., *Variation and Correlation in Timothy.* Cornell Univ. Agr. Exp. Sta. Bull. 279 : 421–469, 40 figs.

1910. CLEMENTS, F. E., *The Real Factors in Acclimatization.* N. Y. Hort. Soc. Mem. 2 : 37–40.

1910. CLOTHIER, GEO. L., *Breeding to Improve Physical Qualities of Timber.* Am. Breed. Mag. 1 : 261–263.

1910. COCKERELL, T. D. A., *A New Variety of the Sunflower.* Science, n.s. 32 : 384.

1910. COIT, J. E., *The Relation of Asexual or Bud Mutation to the Decadence of California Citrus or Deads.* Fruit Growers' Cons. (Cal.) Proc. 37 : 31–39.

1910. COLLINS, G. N., *Increased Fields of Corn from Hybrid Seed.* U. S. Dept. Agr. Yearbook, 319–328. Same. Yearbook Separate, 540 : 319–328.

1910. COLLINS, G. N., *The Value of First-Generation Hybrids in Corn.* U. S. Dept. Agr. Bur. Plant Ind. Bull. 191 : (45 pp.).

1910. COTTE, J., and COTTE, C., *Sur l'indigenat du ble en Palestine.* Soc. Bot. France Bull. 56 : 538–540.

1910. COUPIN, H., *Sur la vegetation de quelques moisissures dans l'huile.* Acad. Sci. Paris Compt. Rend. 150 : 1192–1193.

1910. CROSBY, DICK J., and HOWE, F. W., *School Lessons on Corn.* U. S. Dept. Agr. Farmers' Bull. 409 : (29 pp.), 12 figs. (This bulletin contains outlines for class studies and exercises on the growth and structure of the corn plant, selection and testing of seed corn, and the cultivation and breeding of corn, with list of publications on the subject.)

1910. CROSBY, DICK J., *School Exercises in Plant Production.* U. S. Dept. Agr. Farmers' Bull. 408 : (48 pp.), 39 figs. (This bulletin describes the material needed for laboratory exercises in plant production, and contains outlines of lessons in the structure and growth of plants, methods of propagation, seed testing, etc., and a list of publications on agriculture, of special interest to teachers.)

1910. DACHNOWSKI, A., *Physiologically Arid Habitats and Drought Resistance in Plants.* Bot. Gaz. 49 : 325–339.

1910. DERR, H. B., *A New Awnless Barley.* Science, n.s. 32 : 473–474.

1910. DILLMAN, ARTHUR C., *Breeding Drought-Resistant Forage Plants for the Great Plains Area.* U. S. Dept. Agr. Bur. Plant Ind. Bull. 196 : (40 pp.), 4 pls.

1910. Dow, GEO., *The Status of the "False" Wild Oats.* Can. Seed-Grow. Assoc. Rep. 6 : 105–107.

1910. DRZEWINA, A., *La transmission des caractères hérédi-taires chez les hybrides.* Revue des Idées, 7 : 372–376.

1910. EAST, EDWARD M., *A Mendelian Interpretation of Varia-tion that is apparently Continuous.* Am. Nat. 44 : 65–82. 7 tab. Bibliog. in notes.

1910. EAST, EDWARD M., *Inheritance in Potatoes.* Am. Nat. 44 : 424–430. Bibliog. in notes.

1910. EAST, E. M., *Notes on an Experiment concerning the Nature of Unit Characters.* Science, n.s. 32 : 93–95.

1910. EAST, E. M., *The Rôle of Hybridization in Plant Breeding.* Pop. Sci. Mo. 77 : 342–355, figs. 1–11.

1910. EAST, E. M., *The Transmission of Variations in the Potato in Asexual Reproduction.* Conn. Agr. Exp. Sta. Rep. 119–160, 5 pls. Rev. in Zeitsch. f. indukt. Abst.-u. Vererb. 4 : 375–376.

1910. EMERSON, R. A., *The Inheritance of Sizes and Shapes in Plants.* Amer. Nat. 44 : 739–746. Rev. in Zeitsch. f. indukt. Abst.- u. Vererb. 5 : 193.

1910. FLETCHER, S. W., *Varieties of Fruit Originated in Mich.* Mich. Agr. Exp. Sta. Spec. Bull. 44.

1910. FROST, H. B., *Variation as related to the Temperature Environment.* A. B. A. Rep. 6 : 384–396.

1910. FRYE, T. C., *Height and Dominance of the Douglas Fir.*
Forest Quart. 8 : 465–470.

1910. GASSNER, G., *Über Solanum Commersonii und S. "Commersonii violet" in Uruguay.* Landw. Jahrb. 1011–1020,
1 pl.

1910. GATES, R. R., *Abnormalities in Œnothera.* Missouri
Bot. Gard. Ann. Rep. 21 : 175–184, pls. 29–31.

1910. GATES, R. R., *The Earliest Description of Œnothera
Lamarckiana.* Science, n.s. 31 : 425–426.

1910. GATES, R. R., *The Material Basis of Mendelian Phenomena.* Am. Nat. 44 : 203–213. Bibliog., 1 p.

1910. GAUSS, ROBERT, *Acclimatization in Breeding Droughtresistant Cereals.* Am. Breed. Mag. 1 : 209–217.

1910. GRIFFON, E., *Sur la variation dans le greffage et l'hybridation asexuelle.* Acad. Sci., Paris, Comp. Rend. 150 :
629–632.

1910. GRIFFON, E., *Variations avec ou sans greffage chez les
Solanées et les Composées.* Soc. Bot. de France Bull. 57 :
517–535, 2 pl.

1910. GROFF, H. H., *Hybridizing the Gladiolus. Are its Lessons
Possible of General Application?* Can. Seed-Grow. Assoc.
Rep. 6 : 52–58.

1910. GUTHRIE, C. C., *On Graft Hybrids.* A. B. A. Rep. 6 :
356–373.

1910. HAECKER, VALENTIN, *Die Radiolarien in der Variationsund Vererbungslehre.* Zeitsch. f. indukt. Abs.- u. Vererb.
2 : 1–17. Rev. in Arch. f. Entwick'mech. d. Org. 29 : 573.

1910. HANSEN, N. E., *Is Acclimatization an Impossibility?*
N. Y. Hort. Soc. Mem. 2 : 69–74.

1910. HARPER, J. N., *Experiments with Hybrid Cottons.* South
Carolina Agr. Exp. Sta. Bull. 148 : (17 pp.).

1910. HARTLEY, C. P., *Seed Corn.* U. S. Dept. Agr. Farmers'
Bull. 415 : (12 pp.), 3 figs. (This bulletin contains directions for the growing, selection, and care of seed corn,

the destruction of weevils or grain moths, the testing, grading, and shelling of the corn to be planted, with suggestions to the corn grower as to the importance and requirements of good seed, and adaptability of any variety to his locality.)

1910. HENRY, A., *On Elm Seedlings Showing Mendelian Results.* Linn. Soc. Bot. Jour. 39 : 290–300.

1910. HENSLOW, G., *The Origin and History of our Garden Vegetables and their Dietetic Values — II.* Royal Hort. Soc. Jour. 36 : 345–357, figs. 120–125. Roots and tubers.

1910. HENSLOW, G., *The Origin and History of our Garden Vegetables.* Roy. Hort. Soc. Jour. 36 : 115–127.

1910. HERRE, A. C., *Suggestions as to the Origin of California's Lichen Flora.* Plant World, 13 : 215–220.

1910. HEUER, W., *Pfropfbastarde.* Gartenflora, 59 : 434–438.

1910. HIMMELBAUR, W., *Der Gegenwärtige Stand der Pfropfhybridenfrage.* Natw. Ver. Univ. Wien Mitt. 8 : 105–127.

1910. HINDLE, EDWARD, *A Cytological Study of Artificial Parthenogenesis in Strongylocentrotus Purpuratus.* Arch. f. Entwick'mech. d. Org. 31 : 145–163, 1 pl. Bibliog. 1½ pp.

1910. HOWARD, ALBERT, and HOWARD, GABRIELLE, *Wheat in India. Its Production, Varieties, and Improvement.* Calcutta. 288 pp., 7 maps, 4 figs., 7 pls. Rev. in Zeitsch. f. indukt. Abst.- u. Vererb. 4 : 153–154.

1910. HUMPHREYS, E. W., *Variation among Non-lobed Sassafras Leaves.* Torreya, 10 : 101–108, figs. 1–8.

1910. HURD, WM. D., *Corn Selection for Seed and for Show.* Mass. State Board of Agr. Ann. Rep. 58.

1910. HURST, C. C., *Mendel's Law of Heredity and its Application to Horticulture.* Roy. Hort. Soc. Jour. 36 : 22–52.

1910. IKENO, J., *Sind Alle Arten der Gattung Taraxacum Parthenogenetisch?* Deutsch. Bot. Gesell. Ber. 28 : 394–397.

1910. JAVILLIER, M., *Sur la migration des alcaloides dans les greffes de Solanées sur Solonées.* Inst. Pasteur Annales, 24 : 569–576.

1910. KEARNEY, THOMAS H., *Breeding New Types of Egyptian Cotton.* U. S. Dept. Agr. Bur. Plant Ind. Bull. 200 : (39 pp.) 4 pl.

1910. KEEBLE, FREDERICK, and (MISS) PELLEW, C., *The Mode of Inheritance of Stature and of Time of Flowering in Peas. Pisum sativum.* Jour. of Gen. 1 : 47–56.

1910. KEEBLE, FREDERICK, and (MISS) PELLEW, C., *White Flowered Varieties of Primula sinensis.* Jour. of Gen. 1 : 1–5.

1910. KEEBLE, F., PELLEW, C., and JONES, W. N., *The Inheritance of Peloria and Flower Colour in Foxgloves (Digitalis purpurea).* New Phytolog. 9 : 68–77, 1 fig.

1910. KROLL, H. G., *Über Polygamie bei Polygonatum officinale.* Bot. Ver. Brandenb. Verh. 52 : 98–101.

1910. LÉCAILLON, A., *La parthénogénèse naturelle rudimentaire.* Bull. Scientif. de France et Belgique, 7th ser. 44 : 235–272.

1910. LOVE, HARRY H., *Are Fluctuations Inherited?* Am. Nat. 44 : 412–423, 9 figs. & 4 tab. Bibliog. in notes.

1910. MACDOUGAL, D. T., VAIL, A. M., and SHULL, G. H., *Mutations, Variations, and Relationships of the Œnotheras.* Carnegie Inst. Wash. Publ. 81 : (92 pp.) 1907. Rev. in Zeitsch. f. indukt. Abst.- u. Vererb. 3 : 226–228.

1910. MAIGRE, E. F., *L'hérédité Mendélienne.* Rev. des Idées, 234–242.

1910. MOOREHOUSE, L. A., *Improvements of Bermuda Grass.* Am. Breed. Mag. 1 : 95–98, fig.

1910. MORGAN, T. H., *Chromosomes and Heredity.* Am. Nat. 44 : 449–496, 3 tab. Illus.

1910. NAKANO, H., *Variation and Correlation in Rays and Disk of Aster fastigiatus.* Bot. Gaz. 49 : 371–378, figs. 1–4.

1910. NASH, G. V., *Observations on Hardiness of Plants culti-*

vated at the New York Botanical Garden. N. Y. Hort. Soc. Mem. 2 : 130–143.

1910. NĚMEC, B., *Das Problem der. Befruchtungavorgänge.* 526 pp. Borntraeger, Berlin. 5 pls. & 119 figs.

1910. NEWMAN, L. H., *The Correlation of Characters in Plants and its Economic Importance to the Plant Breeders.* Ottawa Nat. 23 : 220–224.

1910. NIENBURG, W., *Die Jüngsten Ergebnisse der Pfropf-bastardforschung.* Gartenflora, 59 : 479–495.

1910. NILSSON-EHLE, H., *Kreuzungsuntersuchungen an Hafer und Weizen.* Lunds Universitats Areskirft. N. F. Afd. 2. 5 : 1–122. Rev. in Zeitsch. f. indukt. Abst.- u. Vererb. 3 : 290–291.

1910. NILSSON-EHLE, H., *Svalöfs Pudelhvete.* Sveriges Utsädes-för. Tidskr. 20 : 69–87.

1910. OLIVER, GEORGE W., *New Methods of Plant Breeding.* Fig. Am. Breed. Mag. 1 : 21–30.

1910. ORCHARD, HAROLD, *Potato Breeding in Manitoba and Some Results Obtained.* Can. Seed-Grow. Assoc. Rep. 6 : 103–104.

1910. OSTENFELD, C. H., *Further Studies on Apogamy and Hybridization of Hieracium.* Zeitsch. f. Indukt. Abst. 3 : (Heft 4). Rev. in Am. Nat. 44 : 750–762. Bibliog. in notes.

1910. PATON, ALKMAN, *Notes on Some Hybrid Tuberous Solanums.* Roy. Hort. Soc. Jour. 36 : 127–133.

1910. PEARL, RAYMOND, and SURFACE, F. M., *Experiments in Breeding Sweet Corn.* Maine Agr. Exp. Sta. Bull. 183 : (66 pp.).

1910. PEARSON, KARL, *Darwinism, Biometry and Some Recent Biology, I.* Biometrika, 7 : 368–385. Tab.

1910. PEARSON, KARL, *On a New Method of Determining Cor-relation when one Variable is given by Alternative and the Other by Multiple Categories.* Biometrika, 7 : 248–257. Tab.

1910. PLANCHON, *Mutation gemmaire du Solanum Commersonii.* Soc. Nation. d'Agr. Bull. 70 : 373–375.

1910. REHDER, A., *A New Hybrid Cornus (Cornus rugosa × stolonifera).* Rhodora, 12 : 121–124. *C. Slavinii Rehder.*

1910. RICHTER, O., *Pfropfungen, Pfropfbastarde und Pflanzenchimaeren.* Lotos, 58 : 1–22.

1910. RIETZ, H. L., *Correlation in Corn.* Ill. Agr. Exp. Sta. Bull. 148 : (25 pp.).

1910. SALAMAN, R. N., *The Inheritance of Colour and Other Characters in the Potato.* Jour. of Gen. 1 : 7–46, 29 pl. Rev. in Zeitsch. f. indukt. Abst.- u. Vererb. 5 : 192–193.

1910. SAUNDERS, E. R., *Studies in the Inheritance of Doubleness in Flowers.* I. *Petunia.* Jour. of Gen. Fig. 1 : 57.

1910. SCHRIBAUX, *Sur le Solanum Commersonii.* Soc. Nation. d'Agr. Bull. 70 : 798–801.

1910. SHEPPERD, J. H., *Report of Committee on Breeding Fiber Crops.* Am. Breed. Mag. 1 : 197–199.

1910. SHOEMAKER, D. N., *Report of Committee on Breeding Cotton.* Am. Breed. Mag. 1 : 293–294.

1910. SHULL, GEORGE HARRISON, *Color Inheritance in Lychnis dioica L.* Am. Nat. 44 : 83–91, 3 tab. Bibliog.

1910. SHULL, A. FRANKLIN, *The Artificial Production of the Parthenogenetic and Sexual Phases of the Life Cycle of Hydatina senta.* Am. Nat. 44 : 146–150, 5 tab.

1910. SHULL, GEORGE HARRISON, *Hybridization Methods in Corn Breeding.* Am. Breed. Mag. 1 : 98–107. Bibliog.

1910. SMITH, LOUIE H., *Increasing Protein and Fat in Corn.* Am. Breed. Mag. 1 : 15–21. Tab.

1910. SMITH, J. RUSSELL, *Breeding and Use of Tree Crops.* Am. Breed. Mag. 1 : 86–91.

1910. SPILLMAN, W. J., *A Theory of Mendelian Phenomena.* Am. Breed. Mag. 1 : 113–125. Diagr.

1910. SPILLMAN, W. J., *Effect of Recent Discoveries on the Art of Breeding.* Am. Breed. Mag. 1 : 69–70.

1910. SPILLMAN, W. J., *Mendelian Phenomena without de Vriesian Theory.* Am. Nat. 44 : 214–228, 4 tab. Bibliog. in notes.

1910. SPILLMAN, W. J. (Reviewer), *Heredity.* (Rev.) Am. Nat. 44 : 504–512. Bibliog. in notes.

1910. SPILLMAN, W. J., *The Nature of "Unit" Characters.* The American Naturalist, 43 : 243–248. Rev. in Zeitsch. f. indukt. Abst.- u. Vererb. 3 : 110.

1910. STEVENS, R. L., and HALL, J. G., *Variation of Fungi Due to Environment.* Bot. Gaz. 48 : 1–30, fig. 37. Rev. in Zeitsch. f. indukt. Abst.- u. Vererb. 3 : 343–344.

1910. SUDWORTH, GEORGE S., *Report of Committee on Breeding Nut and Forest Trees.* Am. Breed. Mag. 1 : 185–193. Tab.

1910. TAYLOR, GEORGE M., *The Cross Fertilization of the Potato.* Gard. Chron. 3d ser. 48 : 279.

1910. TISCHLER, G., *Untersuchungen über die Entwicklung des Bananen-Pollens.* Arch. f. Zellforschung, 5 : 622–670, 2 pls. & 4 figs.

1910. TRABUT, L., *Sur une mutation inerme du Cynana Cardunculus.* Soc. Bot. de France Bull. 57 : 350–354, 2 pls.

1910. TRACY, W. W., *Breeding and Raising Garden Seeds.* Mass. State Board of Agr. Ann. Rep. 58.

1910. TRACY, W. W., *Report of Committee on Breeding Vegetables.* Am. Breed. Mag. 1 : 110–113.

1910. TUTTLE, A. H., *Mitosis in Œdogonium.* Jour. Exp. Zoöl. 9 : 143–157, 18 figs.

1910. VILMORIN, PHILIPPE DE, *Recherches sur l'hérédité mendélienne.* Acad. Sci., Paris, Compt. Rend. 151 : 548–551.

1910. VRIES, H. DE, *The Production of Horticultural Varieties.* Roy. Hort. Soc. Jour. 35 : 321–326.

1910. WALDRON, L. R., *A Suggestion regarding Heavy and Light Seed Grain.* Am. Nat. 44 : 48–56.

1910. WALDRON, L. R., *Heredity in Populations and in Pure Lines.* Plant World, 13 : 1–12, figs. 1–5.

1910. WESTGATE, J. M., *Variegated Alfalfa.* U. S. Dept. Agr. Bur. Plant Ind. Bull. 169 : (63 pp.), 9 pls. & 5 figs.

1910. WHEELER, SEAGER, *Plant Breeding of the Farm.* Can. Seed-Grow. Assoc. Rep. 6 : 107–109.

1910. WHELDALE, M., *Plant Oxydases and the Chemical Inter-relationships of Colour-varieties.* Prog. Rei. Bot. Vol. 3 : 457–473. Bibliog. in notes.

1910. WILSON, E. B., *Studies on Chromosomes.* Jour. Exp. Zoöl. 9 : 53–79.

1910. WINKLER, H., *Über das Wesender Pfropfbastarde. (Vorläufige Mitteilung.)* Deutsch. Bot. Gesell. Ber. 28 : 116–118.

1910. WINKLER, H., *Uber die Nachkommenschaft der Solanus-Pfropfbastarde und die Chromosomes zahlen ihre Keimzellen.* Zeitschr. für Botanik. 2 : 1–33. Rev. in Zeitsch. f. indukt. Abst.- u. Vererb. 3 : 223–224.

1910. WINKLER, HANS, *Weiters Mitteilungen über Pfropfbastarde.* Zschr. f. Botanik. 1 : 315–345, 1 pl., 4 figs. Rev. in Zeitsch. f. indukt. Abst.- u. Vererb. 3 : 111–113.

1910. WINKLER, HANS, *Zur Kritik der Ansichten von der Entstegung der Angiospermenbluten.* Schles. Ges. Vaterl. Kult. Bteslau. Jahresber. 87 : 22–28.

1910. WINSLOW, E. J., *A New Hybrid Fern.* Am. Fern Jour. 1 : 22–23, figs. 1–4.

1910. WITTE, H., *Vallväxtförädlingen pa Svalöf, dess nödvändighet och behafver af utsträckt inhemsk fröodling.* Sveriges Utsädesför. Tidskr. 20 : 317–331.

1910. ZAVITZ, C. A., *Heredity in Plants and its Bearing on Agricultural Problems.* Can. Seed-Grow. Assoc. 6th Ann. Meeting Rep. 49–52.

1910. ZEIJLSTRA, H. H., *On the Cause of Dimorphism in Œnothera nanella.* Kon. Akad. Wetensch. Amsterdam Proc. 13 : 660, 1 pl.

1911. AGEE, HAMILTON P., *Propagation of Seedlings of Sugar Cane in Louisiana.* A. B. A. Rep. 6 : 178–183.

1911. ATKINSON, ALFRED, *Grain Investigations with Different Varieties of Wheat, Oats, and Barley.* (Types and variety tests.) Montana Agr. Exp. Sta. Bull. 84 : 24 pp.

1911. BABCOCK, ERNEST B., *Walnut-Oak Hybrid Experiments.* A. B. A. Rep. 6 : 138–141.

1911. BALLS, W. LAWRENCE, *The Inheritance of Measurable Characters in Hybrids between Reputed Species of Cotton.* IV Inter. Conf. Genetique, Paris, 429–440, fig. 9.

1911. BALLY, W., *Cytologische Studein an Chytridineen.* Jahrb. wissensch. Bot. 50 : 95–156, 5 pls. & 8 figs.

1911. BARRUS, M. F., *Variation of Varieties of Beans in their Susceptibility to Anthracnose.* Phytopathology, 1 : 190–195, 1 pl.

1911. BATESON, W., and PUNNETT, R. C., *Reduplication of Terms in Series of Gametes.* IV Inter. Conf. Genet. Paris, 99–100.

1911. BEMBOWER, W., *Pollination Notes from the Cedar Point Region.* Ohio Nat. 11 : 378–383.

1911. BENEDICT, RALPH C., *Do Ferns Hybridize ?* Science, n.s. 33 : 254–255.

1911. BRINGHAM, E. S., *A Year's Work in Potato Breeding.* R. N. Y. 70 : 559.

1911. BLARINGHEM, L., *L'état present de la theorie de la mutation.* Soc. Bot. de France Bull. 58 : 644–652.

1911. BLARINGHEM, L., *Sur l'hérédité en Mosaique.* IV Inter. Conf. Genet. Paris, 101–151.

1911. BRAEM, F., *Die Varoation bei den Statoblasten von Pectinatella magnifica.* Arch. f. Entwick'mech. d. Org. 32 : 314–348, 8 figs., 2 tab. Bibliog. $\frac{1}{4}$ p.

1911. BUFFUM, B. C., *Effect of Environment on Plant Breeding.* A. B. A. Rep. 6 : 212–225.

1911. CAMPBELL, DOUGLAS HOUGHTON, *The Nature of Graft-Hybrids.* Am. Nat. 45 : 41–53, 1 fig. Bibliog. in notes.

1911. CHUBBUCK, LEVI, *A Variety of Corn for Elevated Regions.* Am. Breed. Mag. 2 : 235, fig.

1911. CLEMENTS, FREDERICK B., *Proposals for a System of Tree Breeding.* A. B. A. Rep. 6 : 275–282.

1911. CLOTHIER, GEO. T., *Breeding to Improve Physical Qualities of Timber.* A. B. A. Rep. 6 : 170–172.

1911. CLUTE, W. N., and FERRISS, J. H., *A New Species of Phlox.* Am. Bot. 17 : 74–76. *Phlox argillacea* sp. nov.

1911. COLLINS, G. N., and KEMPTON, J. H., *Inheritance of Waxy Endosperm in Hybrids of Chinese Maize.* IV Inter. Conf. Genet. Paris, 347–357. Tab. X.

1911. COLLINS, G. N., *Increased Yields of Corn from Hybrid Seed.* U. S. Dept. Agr. Yearbook, 319–328.

1911. COOK, O. F., *Hindi Cotton in Egypt.* U. S. Dept. Agr. Plant Ind. Bull. 210 : 1–58, pls. 1–6.

1911. COOK, O. F., and MEADE, R. M., *Arrangement of Parts in the Cotton Plant.* U. S. Dept. Agr. Plant Ind. Bull. 222 : 26, figs. 1–9.

1911. COUPIN, H., *Sur la localisation des pigments dans le tegument des graines de haricots.* Acad. Sci. Compt. Rend. 153 : 1489–1492.

1911. CREED, RICHARD, *The Growing of Turnip Seed in the Maritime Provinces.* Can. Seed-Grow. Assoc. Rep. 7 : 49–50.

1911. DALLIMORE, W., *Notes on Trees suitable for Experimental Forestry.* Kew Bull. Misc. Inf. 1911 : 211–223.

1911. DANIEL, L., *Étude biometrique de la descendance de Haricots greffes et de Haricots francs de pied.* Acad. Sci. Compt. Rend. 152 : 1018–1020.

1911. DANIEL, L., *Recherches biometrique sur un hybride de greffe entre poirier et Cognassier.* Acad. Sci. Compt. Rend. 152 : 1186–1188.

1911. DAVENPORT, E., *"Domesticated Animals and Plants."* Science, n.s. 34 : 715.

1911. DAVIS, BRADLEY MOORE, *Genetical Studies on Œnothera. II. Some Hybrids of Œnothera biennis and O. grandiflora that resemble O. Lamarckiana.* Am. Nat. 45 : 193–233, 18 figs. Bibliog. $\frac{3}{4}$ p.

1911. DECKER, H., *Mendel's Law as Related to Heredity and Breeding.* I–V. Horticulture, 13 : 635 ; 13 : 669 ; 13 : 705–706 ; 13 : 741–742 ; 13 : 780. Illus. Translated from Cosmos by G. Thommen.

1911. DELACROIX, G., *Maladies des plantes cultivees dans les pays chauds, publie par A. Maublanc,* vol. 1., 605 pp. Challamel. Paris.

1911. EMERSON, R. A., *Genetic Correlation and Spurious Allelomorphism in Maize.* Neb. Agr. Exp. Sta. Ann. Rep. 24 : 59–90, 9 figs.

1911. EMERSON, R. A., *Latent Colors in Corn.* A. B. A. Rep. 6 : 233–237.

1911. EMERSON, R. A., *Production of a White Bean Lacking the Factor for Total Pigmentation. A Prophecy Fulfilled.* A. B. A. Rep. 6 : 396–397.

1911. EVANS, G. W., *Wheats and Wheat Breeding.* Agr. Jour. of Brit. East Africa, 3 : 348–356.

1911. EWING, E. C., *Correlation of Characters in Corn.* Cornell Univ. Agr. Exp. Sta. Bull. 287 : 67–100, 14 tab., 2 figs.

1911. FAIRCHILD, DAVID, *Plant Introduction for the Plant Breeder.* U. S. Dept. Agr. Yearbook, 411–422, 6 pls. & 1 fig. Same. Yearbook Separate, 580 : 411–422, 6 pls.

1911. FOOTE, E. H., *A Study of the Supposed Hybrid of the Black and Shingle Oaks.* Sci. Lab. Denison Univ. Bull. 16 : 315–338, pls. 11–14.

1911. FREEMAN, E. M., *Resistance and Immunity in Plant Diseases.* Phytopathology, 1 : 109–115. (Also published in Publ. Bot. Soc. Am. 50 : 17–26.)

1911. FREEMAN, G. F., and JONES, D. F., *Plant Breeding.* Univ. Arizona Agr. Exp. Sta. Ann. Rep. 541–546.

1911. GATES, R. R., *Mutation in Œnothera.* Am. Nat. 45 : 577–606. Bibliog.

1911. GATES, R. R., *Studies on the Variability and Heritability of Pigmentation in Œnothera.* Zeitsch. f. indukt. Abst.- u. Vererb. 4 : 337–372, pl. & 5 figs. Bibliog. ½ p.

1911. GAUSS, ROBERT, *Acclimatization in Breeding Drought-Resistant Cereals.* A. B. A. Rep. 6 : 147–156.

1911. GAUSS, ROBERT, *The Plant Breeding Problem.* Am. Breed. Mag. 2 : 259–263.

1911. GAUTIER, ARMAND, *Sur le Principe de la coalescence des plasmus vivants et l'origine des races et des especes.* IV International Conf. Genetique, Paris, 79–90.

1911. GENTY, C., *Note sur deux Carduus hybrides.* Monde des Plantes, 14 : 26.

1911. GILBERT, ARTHUR W., *Suggestions for an Undergraduate Course in Plant Breeding.* A. B. A Rep. 6 : 352–356.

1911. GILBERT, ARTHUR W., *Suggestive Laboratory Exercises for a Course in Plant Breeding.* Am. Breed. Mag. 2 : 196–212, fig. Tab. Bibliog. in notes.

1911. GRANIER, J., and BOULE, L., *Sur le phenomene de conjugaison des chromosomes à le prophase de la premiere cinese reductrice (microsporogenese chez Endymion nutans Dum).* Acad. Sci. Compt. Rend. 152 : 393–396.

1911. GREGORY, R. P., *Experiments with Primula sinensis.* Jour. of Gen. 1 : 73. Illus.

1911. GREGORY, R. P., *On Gametic Coupling and Repulsion in Primula sinensis.* Roy. Soc. London Proc. 84 : 12–15.

1911. GRIFFON, E., *Greffage et Hybridation Asexuelle.* IV Internat. Conf. Genetique, Paris, 164–196, figs. 24.

1911. GRIFFON, E., *Observations et recherches experimentales sur la variation chez le mais.* Soc. Bot. France Bull. 57 : 604–615.

1911. GROTH, H. A., *The F_1 Heredity of Size, Shape, and Number in Tomato Leaves. I. Seedlings.* N. J. Agr. Exp. Sta. Bull. 238 : 3–38, 5 figs. & 1 pl.

1911. GROTH, H. A., *The F_1 Heredity of Size, Shape, Number* *in Tomato Leaves.* Part II. *Mature plants.* New Jersey Exp. Sta. Bull. 239 : 3–12, pl. 1- 9.

1911. HAGEDOORN, A. L., *Facteurs Genetiques et Facteurs du Milieu dans l'amelioration et l'obtentian des races.* IV Internat. Conf. Genetique, Paris, 132–135.

1911. HALSTEAD, B. D., *Geometrical Figures in Plant Breeding.* Am. Breed. Mag. 2 : 217–220, fig.

1911. HANSEN, N. E., *Some New Fruits.* So. Dak. Agr. Exp. Sta. Bull. 130 : 163–200, 1 fig.

1911. HARRIS, J. ARTHUR, *On the Formation of Correlation and Contingency Tables when the Number of Combinations is Large.* Am. Nat. 45 : 566–571, 2 tab. Bibliog. in notes.

1911. HARRIS, J. ARTHUR, *The Biometric Proof of the Pure Line Theory.* Am. Nat. 45 : 346–363. Bibliog. in notes.

1911. HARRIS, J. ARTHUR, *The Measurement of Natural Selection.* Pop. Sci. Mo. 78 : 521–538, figs. 1–7.

1911. HARTLEY, C. P., *The Corn Breeder's Problems.* Am. Breed. Mag. 2 : 212–217. Diagr.

1911. HATAI, SHINKISHI, *The Mendelian Ratio and Blended Inheritance.* Am. Nat. 45 : 99–106. Bibliog.

1911. HAYES, H. K., and EAST, E. M., *Improvement in Corn.* Conn. Agr. Exp. Sta. Bull. 168 : 21, 4 pls.

1911. HAYES, H. K., *Inheritance in Corn.* Conn. (State) Agr. Exp. Sta. Ann. Rep. 407–427.

1911. HECKEL, E., *Sur les mutations gemmaires culturales du Solanum Maglia et sur les premiers resultats culturaux de ces mutations.* Acad. Sci., Paris, Compt. Rend. 153 : 417–420.

1911. HENRY, J. L., *Results obtained through the Use of Hand Selected Seed.* Can. Seed-Grow. Assoc. Rep. 7 : 79–80.

1911. HILL, E. J., *Œnothera Lamarckiana: its Early Cultivation and Description.* Bot. Gaz. 51 : 136–140.

1911. HILLMAN, F. H., *Testing Farm Seeds in the Home and in the Rural School.* U. S. Dept. Agr. Farmers' Bull. 428 :

(47 pp.), 32 figs. (This bulletin describes the seed-trade condition, the seed used as adulterants, methods and apparatus used in making tests, etc.)

1911. HONING, J. A., *Die Doppelnatur der Œnothera Lamarckiana.* Zeitsch. f. indukt. Abst.- u. Vererb. 4 : 227–278, 10 figs. Bibliog. in notes.

1911. HOPKINS, L. S., *A New Variety of the Cinnamon Fern.* Am. Fern Jour. 1 : 100–101. *Osmunda cinnamomea auriculata* var. nov. described and illustrated.

1911. HUMBERT, E. P., *A Quantitative Study of Variation. Natural and Induced, in Pure Lines of Silene noctiflora,* Zeitsch. f. indukt. Abst.- u. Vererb. 4 : 161–226, 12 figs. Bibliog. in notes.

1911. HURST, C. C., *The Application of the Principles of Genetics to Some Practical Problems.* IV Internat. Conf. Genetique, Paris, 210–221.

1911. HUS, H., and MURDOCK, A. W., *Inheritance of Fasciation in Zea Mays.* Plant World, 14 : 88–96, 1 fig.

1911. JANSONIUS, H. H., and MOLL, J. W., *Der anatomische Bau des Holzes der Pfropfhybrids Cytisus Adami und ihrer Compomenten.* Rec. Trav. Bot. Neerland. 8 : 333–368.

1911. JENNINGS, H. S., *Computation of the Coefficient of Correlation.* Am. Nat. 45 : 413.

1911. JENNINGS, H. S., *Pure Lines in the Study of Genetics in Lower Organism.* Am. Nat. 45 : 79–89. Diagr.

1911. JESENKA, F., *Sur un hybride fertile entre Triticum sativum (Ble Mold-Squarehead) and Secale Cereale. (Seigle de Petkus.)* IV Inter. Conf. Genetique, Paris, 501–511.

1911. JOHANNSEN, W., *Mutations dans des lignees pures de haricots et discussion au subject de le mutation en general.* IV Internat. Conf. Genetique, Paris, 160–163.

1911. KASTLE, J. H., and HADEN, R. L., *Color Changes in Blue Flowers of Wild Chicory (Cichorium intybus).* Amer. Chem. Jour. 46 : 315–325.

1911. KEEBLE, F., and PELLEW, C., *The Mode of Inheritance of Stature and of Time of Flowering in Peas (Pisum sativum).* Jour. of Gen. 1 : 47–56. Rev. in Zeitsch. f. indukt. Abst.- u. Vererb. 5 : 331.

1911. KÖCK, G., *Eine Mutation der Kartoffelsorte Up to Date.* Monatsh. f. Landw. 4 : 108–109.

1911. KROEMER, K., *Über das "Mendeln" und seine Bedeutung für die gärtnerische Pflanzenzüchtung.* Möllers Deutsche Gärtner-Zeitung, 26 : 50–52.

1911. LACKE, M., and PARR, A. E., *The Problem of the Improvement of Cotton in the United Provinces of Agra and Oudh.* Agr. Jour. India, 6 : 1–13, 5 pl.

1911. LANG, H., *Technisches aus dem Gebiete der Futterpflanzenzüchtung.* Illus. Landw. Zeitung, 704.

1911. LEAKE, H. M., *Studies in Indian Cotton.* Jour. of Gen. 1 : 205–272. Illus.

1911. LEIDIGH, A. H., *Methods for the Improvement of Sorghum.* Am. Breed. Mag. 2 : 294–296. Port.

1911. LOTSY, J. P., *Hybrids entre especes d'antirrhinum.* IV Inter. Conf. Genetique, Paris, 416–428, figs. 9.

1911. LOVE, HARRY H., *Studies of Variation in Plants.* Cornell Univ. Agr. Exp. Sta. Bull. 297 : 593–677, 70 figs., 48 tab.

1911. MACDOUGAL, D. T., *Climatic Selection in a Hybrid Progeny Oak.* Plant World, 14 : 129–131, 1 fig.

1911. MASON, SILAS C., *Drought Resistance of the Olive in the Southwestern States.* U. S. Dept. Agr. Bur. Plant Ind. Bull. 192 : (60 pp.), 6 pls. & 20 figs.

1911. MAYER, A., *Bemerkungen zu G. Lewitsky: Über die Chondriosomen in pflanzlichen Zellen.* Deutsch. Bot. Gesell. Ber. 29 : 158–160.

1911. MENDEL, G., *Versuche über Pflanzenhybriden.* Herausgegeben von E. v. Tachermak. Ostwalds Klassiker der exakten Wissenschaften, No. 121, 2d ed. Leipzig, Engelmann. Rev. in Zeitsch. f. indukt. Abst.- u. Vererb. 6 : 182.

1911. MONTGOMERY, E. G., *Correlation Studies in Corn.* Nebraska Agr. Exp. Sta. Ann. Rept. 24 : 109–158.

1911. MONTGOMERY, E. G., *Note regarding Maize Flowers.* Science, n.s. 33 : 435.

1911. MONTGOMERY, E. G., *Perfect Flowers in Maize.* Pop. Sci. Mo. 79 : 346–349, figs. 1–6.

1911. MOREHOUSE, L. A., *Improvement of Bermuda Grass.* Figs. A. B. A. Rep. 6 : 60–63.

1911. MÜLLER, R., *Mutationen bei Typhus- und Ruhrbacterian. Mutation als spezifischee Kulturmerkmal.* Centralbl. f. Bacteriologie, 58 : 1 : 97–106, 2 pls.

1911. MUNDY, H. S., *Maize Breeding and Seed Selection.* Rhodesia Agr. Jour. 8 : 385–390.

1911. MUNSON, T. V., *Single Character vs. Tout Ensemble Breeding in Grapes.* A. B. A. Rep. 6 : 183–189.

1911. NEWMAN, H. H., *Reply to E. Godlewski's "Bemerkungen zu der Arbeit von H. H. Newman: 'Further Studies of the Process of Heredity in Fundulus Hybrids.'"* Arch. f. Entwick'mech. d. Org. 32 : 472–476. Bibliog. in notes.

1911. NEWMAN, L. H., *Plant Breeding in Sweden.* Can. Seed-Grow. Assoc. Rep. 7 : 89–99, 4 tab.

1911. NILSSON-EHLE, H., *Mendelisme et Acclimatation.* IV Internat. Conf. Genetique, Paris, 136–157.

1911. NILSSON-EHLE, H., *Svalöfs Solhvete, Ny sort för södra Sverige. Sveriges Utsädesför.* Tidskr. 21 : 123–126, 1 pl.

1911. NOMBLOT, A., *Recherches de varietes fruitieres nouvelles.* IV Inter. Conf. Genetique, Paris, 464–468.

1911. OLIVER, GEORGE W., *New Methods of Plant Breeding.* A. B. A. Rep. 6 : 11–20. Figs.

1911. ORTON, W. A., *Disease Resistance in Varieties of Potatoes.* Indiana Acad. Sci. Proc. 219–221.

1911. ORTON, W. A., *The Development of Disease Resistance Varieties of Plants.* IV Internat. Conf. Genetique, Paris, 247 : 265, figs. 9.

1911. OWEN, E. J., *Inheritance Studies with Beans*. N. J. Agr. Exp. Sta. Bot. Dept. Rep. 277–281, 1 pl.

1911. PARDE, L., *Enquete sur l'acclimation des essences exotiques en France*. Soc. Dendr. France Bull. 19 : 5–12. Illus.

1911. PEARL, RAYMOND, *Biometrics*. Am. Nat. 45 : 319–320.

1911. PEARL, RAYMOND, *Biometric Arguments regarding the Genotype Concept*. Am. Nat. 45 : 561–566. Bibliog. in notes.

1911. PEARL, RAYMOND (Reviewer), *Some Recent Studies on Variation and Correlation in Agricultural Plants*. (Review.) Am. Nat. 45 : 415–425. Bibliog. 1 p.

1911. PEARL, R., *The Personal Equation in Breeding Experiments involving Certain Characters of Maize*. Biol. Bull. 21 : 339–366.

1911. PEARSON, KARL, *On a Correction to be made to the Correlation Ration*. Biometrika, 8 : 254–256, pl.

1911. POLE-EVANS, J. B., *South African Cereal Rusts with Observations on the Problem of Breeding Rust-resistant Wheats*. Jour. Agr. Sci. 4 : 95–104.

1911. REDFIELD, R. L., *Acquired Characters Defined*. Am. Nat. 45 : 571–573.

1911. ROBERTS, F. B., *A Method of Corn Pollination*. Am. Breed. Mag. 2 : 54–60. Fig.

1911. ROBERTS, HERBERT F., *Breeding for Type of Kernel in Wheat*. A. B. A. Rep. 6 : 142–147. Figs.

1911. RUDOLPH, J., *L'Aster cordifolius et ses varietes*. Rev. Hort. 83 : 326–327.

1911. RUGG-GUNN, A., *Sociological and Other Aspects of the Unit-Character Conception*. IV Inter. Conf. Genet., Paris, 204–208.

1911. SALAMAN, R. N., *Studies in Potato Breeding*. IV Inter. Conf. Genetique, Paris, 373–376.

1911. SAUNDERS, EDITH R., *The Breeding of Double Flowers*. IV Inter. Conf. Genetique, Paris, 397–405.

1911. SAUNDERS, CHARLES E., *Production de varietes de ble de haute valeur boulougere.* IV Inter. Conf. Genet., Paris, 290–300.

1911. SAUNDERS, E. R., *On Inheritance of a Mutation in the Common Foxglove (Digitalis purpurea).* New Phytologist, 10 : 49–63, 1 pl. & 12 figs.

1911. SCUDDER, H., *Similarity of Color in Bud and in Leaf.* Rhodora, 13 : 86–87.

1911. SHAMEL, A. D., *A Study of the Improvement of Citrus Fruits through Bud Selection.* U. S. Dept. Agr. Plant Ind. Circ. 77 : 1–19, 5 figs.

1911. SHERFF, E. E., *Tragopogon pratensis × porrifolius.* Torreya, 11 : 14–15.

1911. SHULL, G. H., *A Pure-Line Method in Corn Breeding.* Amer. Breeders' Assoc. Rep. 5 : 51–59. Rev. in Zeitsch. f. indukt. Abst.- u. Vererb. 5 : 331–332.

1911. SHULL, G. H., *Defective Inheritance-Ratios in Bursa Hybrids.* Naturf. Vereins Brünn Verh. 49 : (12 pp.), 6 pls.

1911. SHULL, G. H., *Hybridization Methods in Corn Breeding.* A. B. A. Rep. 6 : 63–72, figs.

1911. SHULL, G. H., *Reversible Sex-Mutants in Lychnis dioica.* Bot. Gaz. 52 : 329–368, 15 figs.

1911. SMITH, LOUIE H., *Increasing Protein and Fat in Corn.* A. B. A. Rep. 6 : 5–11.

1911. SMITH, RUSSELL J., *Breeding and Use of Tree Crops.* A. B. A. Rep. 6 : 51–56.

1911. SPILLMAN, W. J., *Heredity.* Am. Nat. 45 : 60–64.

1911. STRAMPELLI, N., *De l'étude des characteres anormaux presentes par les plantules pour la recherche des varietes nouvelles.* IV Internat. Conf. Genetique, Paris, 237–246, figs. 11.

1911. STYAN, K. E., *Pollen Grains.* Rev. in Am. Bot. 17 : 41–44. Originally published in Selbourne Magazine.

1911. SUTTON, W., *Compte Rendu. D'esperiences de Croisements faites entre le pois sauvage de Palestine and les pois de commerce dans le but de decouvris entre eux quelque trace d'identite specifique.* IV Inter. Conf. Genetique, Paris, 558–567, figs. 4.

1911. TAYLOR, G. M., *Disease Resisting Potatoes.* Gard. Chron., 3d ser. 49 : 181.

1911. TEDIN, H., *Ar skalhalten hos arter en sortegenskap?* (With German résumé.) Sveriges Utsadesfor. Tidskr, 21 : 72–77.

1911. *The Sugar-Beet Industry is based on Breeding.* Am. Breed. Mag. 2 : 234.

1911. THODAY, M. G., and THODAY, O., *On the Inheritance of the Yellow Tinge in Sweet Pea Colouring.* Cambridge Phil. Soc. Proc. 16 : 71–84.

1911. THOMAS, ROSE HAIG, *Nicotiana Crosses.* IV Inter. Conf. Genetique, Paris, 453–461, figs. 6.

1911. TOWER, W. L., *The Determination of Dominance and the Modification of Behavior in Alternative (Mendelian) Inheritance, by Conditions Surrounding or Incident upon the Germ-Cells at the Time of Fertilization.* Biol. Bull. 18 : (No. 6). Rev. (Ger.) in Arch. f. Entwick'mech. d. Org. 31 : 345–348.

1911. TRACY, W. W., *Report of Committee on Breeding Vegetables.* A. B. A. Rep. 6 : 75–78.

1911. TSCHERMAK, PROF. ERICH VON, *Examen de le theorie des facteurs par le recroisement methodique des hybrids.* IV Internat. Conf. Genetique, Paris : 91–95. Tab. VIIIc.

1911. VILMORIN, P. DE, and BATESON, W., *A Case of Gametic Coupling in Pisum.* Roy. Soc. London Proc. B. 84 : 9–11.

1911. VILMORIN, PHILIPPE DE, *Fixite des races de Froment.* IV Inter. Conf. Genetique, Paris, 512–516. Tab. 3.

1911. VILMORIN, PH. DE, *Recherches sur l'hérédité mendelienne.* Acad. Sci. Compt. Rend., 548–551.

2 c

1911. Vogler, *Die Variationen der Blattspreite bei Cybisulaburnum L.* Bot. Zentralbl. Beih. 27 : 337–390.

1911. Vries, Hugo de, *Intracellular Pangenesis.* Translated into English by C. Stuart Gager, Chicago. Open Court Publ. Compt. Rev. in Zeitsch. f. indukt. Abst.-u. Vererb. 5 : 90.

1911. Vries, H. de, *Über doppeltreziproke Bastarde von Œnothera biennis L. und O. muricata L.* Biol. Centralbl. 31 : 97–104.

1911. Waldron, L. R., *Variegation of European Alfalfas.* Science, n.s. 33 : 310–312.

1911. Wheldale, M., *On the Formation of Anthocyanin.* Jour. of Gen. 1 : 133.

1911. Wheldale, M., *The Chemical Differentiation of Species.* Biochemical Jour. 5 : 445–456.

1911. Wittmack, L., *Botanische Fragen in Beziehung zur Kartoffelzüchtung.* Illus. Landw. Zeitung, 51 : 289.

1911. Woodruff, Chas. E., *Breeding for Color Adjustment, under Certain Climates.* Am. Breed. Mag. 2 : 313–000.

1911. Zavitz, C. A., *Report of Committee on Breeding Cereals.* A. B. A. Rep. 6 : 141–142.

1911. Zeijlstra, H. H., *Œnothera nanella de Vries, eine krankhafte Pflanzenart.* Biol. Centralbl. 31 : 129–138.

1912. Acloque, A., *La genealogie du chrysantheme.* Monde des Plantes, 14 : 27–28.

1912. Ball, Carleton R., and Hastings, Stephen H., *Grain-Sorghum Production in the San Antonio Region of Texas.* U. S. Dept. Agr. Bur. Plant Ind. Bull. 237 : (30 pp.), 4 figs.

1912. Batchelor, Leon D., *Carnation Breeding.* A. B. A. Rep. 7 : 199–205.

1912. Baur, Erwin, *Vererbungs- und Bastardierungeversuche mit Antirrhinum. II. Faktorenkoppelung.* Zeitsch. f. indukt. Abst.- u. Vererb. 6 : 201–216, 3 tab. Bibliog. in notes.

1912. BEACH, S. A., and MANEY, T. J., *Mendelian Inheritance in Prunus Hybrids.* A. B. A. Rep. 7 : 214–227, fig.

1912. BEACH, S. A., *Report of the Committee on Breeding Tree and Vine Fruits.* A. B. A. Rep. 7 : 213.

1912. BELLING, JOHN, *Breeding Experiments with Forage Plants in Florida.* A. B. A. Rep. 8 : 438–440.

1912. BELLING, JOHN, *Selection in Pure Lines.* Am. Breed. Mag. 3 : 311–312.

1912. BLARINGHEM, L., *Les problemes de biologie appliquée examines dans la quatrieme conference internationale de genetique.* Revue Scientifique, 50 : 50 : 265–269.

1912. BRAINERD, E., *Violet Hybrids between Species of the Palmata Group.* Torrey Bot. Club Bull. 39 : 85–97, 3 pls.

1912. BURTT-DAVY, J., *Observations on the Inheritance of Characters in Zea Mays.* Roy. Soc. South Africa Trans. 2 : 261–270.

1912. CASTLE, W. E., *The Inconstancy of Unit-Characters.* Am. Nat. 46 : 352–362.

1912. CHRISTIE, W., *Untersuchungen über alte norwegische Hafersorten.* Fühlings landw. Zeitung : 297.

1912. COCKERELL, T. D. A., *The Red Sunflower.* Pop. Sci. Mo. 80 : 373–382. Illus.

1912. COCKERELL, T. D. A., *The Word Genotype.* Science, n.s. 35 : 304.

1912. COLLINS, G. N., and KEMPTON, J. H., *An Improved Method of Artificial Pollination in Corn.* U. S. Dept. Agr. Bur. Plant Ind. Circ. 89 : (7 pp.), 2 figs.

1912. COLLINS, G. N., *Improvements in Technique of Corn Breeding.* A. B. A. Rep. 8 : 349–353.

1912. COOK, O. F., *Results of Cotton Experiments in 1911.* U. S. Dept. Agr. Bur. Plant Ind. Circ. 96 : (21 pp.).

1912. DAVIS, BRADLEY MOORE, *Genetical Studies on Œnothera. III. Further Hybrids of Œnothera biennis and O. grandiflora that resemble Q. Lamarckiana.* Am. Nat. 46 : 377–427, 15 figs. Bibliog. ½ p.

1912. DEAN, A., *The Potato and Floral Sterility.* Gard. Chron. 3d ser. 51 : 13.

1912. DERR, H. B., *The Breeding of Winter Barleys.* Am. Breed. Mag. 3 : 103–113.

1912. DILLMAN, A. C., *Breeding Alfalfa as a Dry-land Crop.* A. B. A. Rep. 8 : 414–424.

1912. DONCASTER, L., *Sex-limited Inheritance in Cats.* Science, n.s. 36 : 144.

1912. DORSEY, M. J., *Variation in the Floral Structures of Vitis.* Torrey Bot. Club Bull. 39 : 37–52, 3 pl.

1912. DORSEY, M. J., *Variation Studies of the Venation Angles and Leaf Dimensions in Vitis.* A. B. A. Rep. 7 : 227–250, fig.

1912. EAST, E. M., *A Study of Hybrids between Nicotiana Bigelovii and N. quadrivalvis.* Bot. Gaz. 53 : 243–248, 4 figs.

1912. EAST, E. M., and HAYS, H. K., *Inheritance in Maize.* Conn. Agr. Exp. Sta. Bull. 167 : (137 pp.), 25 pls. Rev. in Zeitsch. f. indukt. Abst.- u. Vererb. 6 : 193–196.

1912. EAST, E. M., *Inheritance of Color in the Aleurone Cells of Maize.* Am. Nat. 46 : 363–365.

1912. EAST, E. M., *The Application of Biological Principles to Plant Breeding.* In Heredity and Eugenics, pp. 113–138, fig.

1912. EAST, E. M., *The Mendelian Notation as a Description of Physiological Facts.* Am. Nat. 46 : 633–655, 1 tab.

1912. FINLOW, R. S., and BURKILL, J. H., *The Inheritance of Red Colour and the Regularity of Self-fertilization in Corchorus capsularis L., the Common Jute-plant.* India Dept. Agr. Bot. Ser. Mem. 4 : 73–92.

1912. FROST, H. B., *The Origin of an Early Variety of Matthiola by Mutation.* A. B. A. Rep. 8 : 536–545.

1912. Funk, Eugene D., *Ten Years of Corn Breeding.* Am. Breed. Mag. 3 : 295–302, 4 figs.

1912. Gates, R. R., *Early Historico-botanical Records of the Œnotheras.* Iowa Acad. Sci. Proc. 85–124, 6 pls. Rev. in Zeitsch. f. indukt. Abst.- u. Vererb. 6 : 285–287.

1912. Gerner, W. W., *Some Observations on Tobacco Breeding.* A. B. A. Rep. 8 : 458–468, fig.

1912. Gernert, Walter B., *A New Subspecies of Zea Mays L.* Am. Nat. 46 : 616–622, 3 figs.

1912. Gernert, Walter B., *Methods in the Artificial Pollination of Corn.* A. B. A. Rep. 8 : 353–367.

1912. Gilbert, A. W., *A Mendelian Study of Tomatoes.* A. B. A. Rep. 7 : 169–188.

1912. Gilbert, A. W., and Upton, G. B., *An Algebra of Mendelism and its Application to a Mixed Hybrid Population.* A. B. A. Rep. 7 : 312.

1912. Gilbert, A. W., *Present Status of Plant-breeding Instruction in the United States.* A. B. A. Rep. 7 : 7–11.

1912. Glawe, M., *Timotheezüchtung in Amerika.* Deutsch. Landwirtsch. Gesell. Mitt. 146.

1912. Groth, B. H. A., *The F_2 Heredity of Size, Shape, and Number in Tomato Fruits.* N. J. Agr. Exp. Sta. Bull. 242 : 3–39, 3 pl.

1912. Hartley, C. P., Brown, E. B., Kyle, C. H., and Zook, L. L., *Cross-breeding Corn.* U. S. Dept. Agr. Bur. Plant Ind. Bull. 218 : (72 pp.), 1 fig.

1912. Hartley, C. P., Brown, E. B., Kyle, C. H., and Zook, L. L., *Cross-breeding Corn.* U. S. Dept. Agr. Plant Ind. Bull. 218 : 5–72.

1912. Hartley, C. P., *Productivity of Seed Corn as Influenced by Factors Other than Heredity.* A. B. A. Rep. 8 : 335–338.

1912. Hartley, C. P., *The Seed-Corn Situation.* U. S. Dept. Agr. Bur. Plant Ind. Circ. 95 : (13 pp.), 2 figs.

1912. Hauman-Merck, L., *Observations sur la pollination*

d'une Malpighiacee du genre Stigmaphyllon. Rec. Inst. Bot. Leo Errera, 9 : 21–28, 1 fig.

1912. HAYES, H. K., *Methods of Corn Breeding.* Am. Breed. Mag. 3 : 99–108, pl. Tab. Bibliog.

1912. HAYES, H. K., *Correlation and Inheritance in Nicotiana Tabacum.* Connecticut Agr. Exp. Sta. Bull. 171 : 3–45, 5 pls.

1912. HEDRICK, U. P., and WELLINGTON, R., *An Experiment in Breeding Apples.* N. Y. (Geneva) Agr. Exp. Sta. Bull. 350. Rev. in Zeitsch. f. indukt. Abst.- u. Vererb. 8 : 347.

1912. HILL, ARTHUR W., *The History of Primula obconica, Hance, under Cultivation, with Some Remarks on the History of Primula sinensis Sab.* Jour. of Gen. 2 : 1–20, 2 pls. Bibliog. in notes.

1912. HOUSER, TRUE, *Certain Results in Ohio Tobacco Breeding.* A. B. A Rep. 8 : 468–479.

1912. HUNT, B. W., *Fig Breeding.* Univ. Georgia Bull. 12 : 107–110.

1912. JOHNSON, ROSWELL H., *The Malthusian Principle and Natural Selection.* Am. Nat. 46 : 372–376.

1912. JONES, W. NEILSON, *Species Hybrids of Digitalis.* Jour. of Gen. 2 : 71–88, 3 pls., 45 figs. Bibliog. in notes.

1912. KAJANUS, BIRGER, *Genetische Studien an Beta.* Zeitsch. f. indukt. Abst.- u. Vererb. 6 : 137–139. (Correction : p. 268), 9 pls., 2 figs., 5 tab.

1912. KELLOGG, VERNON LYMAN, *The Animals and Man.* An elementary text-book of zoölogy and human physiology. 495 pp. Henry Holt & Co., N. Y. Rev. in Science, n.s. 35 : 270–272.

1912. LEAKE, H. M., and PEYSHAD, R., *Observations on Certain Extra-Indian Asiatic Cottons.* India Dept. Agr. Mem. 4 : 93–112, 7 pls.

1912. LEIGHTY, CLYDE E., *Correlation of Characters in Oats with Special Reference to Breeding.* A. B. A. Rep. 7 : 50–61.

1912. Lewis, C. I., *The Teaching of Genetics.* A. B. A. Rep. 8 : 327–329.

1912. Lock, R. H., *Notes on Color Inheritance in Maize.* Royal Bot. Gard. Peradeniya Abbls. 5 : (part IV). Rev. in Zeitsch. f. indukt. Abst.- u. Vererb. 8 : 347–348.

1912. Love, H. H., *A Study of the Large and Small Grain Question.* A. B. A. Rep. 7 : 109–118.

1912. Love, H. H., *Relation of Certain Ear Characters to Yield in Corn.* A. B. A. Rep. 7 : 29–40.

1912. Love, H. H., *The Relation of Seed Ear Characters to Earliness in Corn.* A. B. A. Rep. 8 : 330–335.

1912. Lutz, A. M., *Triploid Mutants in Œnothera.* Biol. Centralb. 32 : 385–435, 7 figs.

1912. Macoun, W. T., *Apple Breeding in Canada.* A. B. A. Rep. 8 : 479–488.

1912. McLendon, C. A., *Mendelian Inheritance in Cotton Hybrids.* Georgia Exp. Sta. Bull. 99 : 143–228, 20 figs.

1912. Montgomery, E. G., *Wheat Breeding Experiments.* Nebraska Agr. Exp. Sta. Bull. 125 : 5–16, 7 pl.

1912. Moore, A. R., *On Mendelian Dominance.* Arch. f. Entwick'mech. d. Org. 34 : 168–175, 9 figs. Bibliog. in notes.

1912. Muller, R., *Bakterienmutationen.* Zeitsch. f. indukt. Abst.-u. Vererb. 8 : 305–324. Bibliog. ½ p.

1912. Munson, T. V., *Problems in Breeding Tree and Vine Fruits.* A. B. A. Rep. 7 : 13–214.

1912. Myers, Clyde H., *Effect of Fertility upon Variation and Correlation in Wheat.* A. B. A. Rep. 7 : 61–74.

1912. Newman, L. H., *Principles Recognized in the Breeding of Cereal Plants at Svalöf, Sweden.* A. B. A. Rep. 8 : 502–508.

1912. Norton, J. B., *Asparagus Breeding.* A. B. A. Rep. 8 : 440–444.

1912. Park, J. B., and Smith, L. H., *Experiment on the Methods of Conducting Plot Tests.* A. B. A. Rep. 8 : 525–528.

1912. PLANCHON, L., *Solanum Commersonii et Solanum tubero-sum*. Soc. Bot. de France Bull. 59 : 70–77.

1912. RAMALEY, FRANCIS, *Mendelian Proportions and the In-crease of Recessives*. Am. Nat. 46 : 344–351, 4 tab. Bibliog. in notes.

1912. ROBERTS, H. F., *Variation and Correlation in Wheat*. A. B. A. Rep. 7 : 80–109, figs.

1912. SHAMEL, A. D., *Bud Selection as a Means of Improving Citrus and Other Fruits*. A. B. A. Rep. 8 : 497–502.

1912. SHULL, G. H., *Defective Inheritance-ratios in Bursa Hybrids*. Naturf. Vereines in Brünn. Verhandl. 49 : (12 pp.), 6 pls. Rev. in Zeitsch. f. indukt. Abst.- u. Vererb. 6 : 281–282.

1912. SHULL, G. H., *"Genotypes," "Biotypes," "Pure Lines," and "Clones."* Science, n.s. 35 : 27–29. Bibliog. in notes.

1912. SHULL, G. H., *Hermaphrodite Females in Lychnis dioica*. Science, n.s. 36 : 482–483.

1912. SHULL, G. H., *"Phenotype" and "Clone."* Science, n.s. 35 : 182–183.

1912. SHULL, G. H., *Reversible Sex-Mutants in Lychnis dioica*. Bot. Gaz. 52 : (No. 5). Rev. in Zeitsch. f. indukt. Abst.- u. Vererb. 6 : 282–283.

1912. SMITH, F. W., *The Application of Mendelian Principles to Sugar-cane Breeding*. West Ind. Bull. 12 : 365–377.

1912. SMITH, L. H., *Occurrence of Natural Hybrids in Wheat*. A. B. A. Rep. 8 : 412–414.

1912. SNOW, E. C., *The Application of the Correlation Coefficient to Mendelian Distributions*. Biometrika, 8 : 420–424. Tab.

1912. SPILLMAN, W. J., *Chromosomes in Wheat and Rye*. Science, n. s. 35 : 104.

1912. STOCKBERGER, W. W., *A Study of Individual Performance in Hops*. A. B. A. Rep. 8 : 452–458.

1912. SUDWORTH, GEO. B., *Annual Report of Committee on Breeding Nut and Forest Trees*. A. B. A. Rep. 7 : 250.

1912. VRIES, HUGO DE, and BARTLETT, H. H., *The Evening Primroses of Dixie Landing, Alabama.* Science, n.s. 36: 599–601.

1912. WALDRON, L. R., *Breeding Certain Field-crop Plants in the Cold Northwest.* A. B. A. Rep. 8: 429–438.

1912. WALDRON, L. R., *Hardiness in Successive Alfalfa Generations.* Am. Nat. 46: 463–469, 2 tab.

1912. WALDRON, L. R., *Influence of Variegation in Alfalfa upon Hardiness.* A. B. A. Rep. 8: 424–429.

1912. WALDRON, L. R., *Value of Continuous Selection and its Bearing upon Hardiness in Winter Wheat.* A. B. A. Rep. 7: 74–80.

1912. WATTS, FRANCIS, *Work with Seedling Sugar-canes in the British W. I. and British Guiana.* A. B. A. Rep. 7: 167–169.

1912. WEBBER, H. J., *Preliminary Notes on Pepper Hybrids.* A. B. A. Rep. 7: 188–199, fig.

1912. WEBBER, H. J., *The Cornell Experiments in Breeding Timothy.* Am. Breed. Mag. 3: 85–99, tab., 4 pls.

1912. WEBBER, H. J., *The Effect of Research in Genetics on the Art of Breeding.* Science, n.s. 35: 597–609.

1912. WEBBER, H. J., *The Production of New and Improved Varieties of Timothy.* Cornell Univ. Agr. Exp. Sta. Bull. 313: 339–381, 10 pl.

1912. WELLINGTON, R., *Influence of Crossing in Increasing the Yield of the Tomato.* N. Y. (Geneva) Agr. Exp. Sta. Bull. 346: 57–76.

1912. WILLIAMS, C. G., *Variation in Pure Lines of Wheat.* A. B. A. Rep. 8: 409–412.

1912. WINKLER, HANS, *Untersuchungen über Pfropfbastarde.* Erster Teil: *Die unmittelbare, gegenseitige Beeinflussung der Pfropfsymbionten.* 186 p. Jena, Gustav Fischer. 2 Illus. Rev. in Zeitch. f. indukt. Abst.- u. Vererb. 7: 77–80.

1912. ZOOK, L. I., *Tests with First Generation Corn Crosses.* A. B. A. Rep. 8: 338–343.

APPENDIX E

LABORATORY EXERCISES

THE following laboratory exercises are intended to serve merely as suggestions. It is impossible and inadvisable to attempt to outline a rigid set of exercises for instructors to follow. It is the hope that these may serve as hints or type exercises, capable of all sorts of modification to suit conditions. An attempt has been made to avoid elaborate laboratory equipment which is expensive and unnecessary. The instructor should always aim to arrange laboratory practicums so that the student's inquisitive curiosity may be aroused and he may be induced to find out things for himself from the material with which he has to work. These exercises are not arranged with any particular order or sequence. The sequence will depend on the time of the year, material at hand, and so forth. The first group of exercises is of a general nature, and the exercises on corn, potatoes, and the cereals are grouped more or less together.

We wish to acknowledge the assistance of Professor E. E. Barker in the preparation of these exercises, most of which have been successfully used by him with large classes. A few new ones have been added.

EXERCISE 1

Field Study of Variations by making an Herbarium of Variations

Have each student collect, press, and mount fifty variations of plants. This is an excellent exercise, because it calls the

394

Fig. 104. — A specimen herbarium sheet, showing variation in the leaves of the mulberry.

Fig. 105. — A specimen herbarium sheet, showing differences between two leaves of the horse-radish.

student's attention very effectively to the vast extent of variation in wild and cultivated plants. Since variation is the basis of artificial selection as well as evolution in nature, it is highly important that considerable time and attention should be given to this study.

Material. — A botanical collecting case, 20 blotters, 12 × 18 inches; 50 mounting sheets, 12 × 18 inches; 50 labels, and glue.

The accompanying photographs represent specimens treated as above (Figs. 104 to 107). The following directions may be given to each student : —

Directions for collecting, pressing, and mounting an herbarium of variations

1. Search for fluctuations, plateations, mutations, and bud-variations of plant characters which have been discussed in the lectures.

2. Collect as nearly the whole plant as practicable. The size of the mounting sheets is 12 × 18 inches. When you collect your specimens plan upon this size of sheet, and arrange them accordingly when you are putting them into the blotters.

3. Do not mount large, woody branches showing different degrees of thorniness, etc., upon the mounting sheets, but preserve them in bundles properly labeled.

4. If you wish to show variations of berries, such as thorn-apples, etc., dry the fruits and fasten them to the mounting sheets by threads.

5. Leave specimens in the blotters until they are thoroughly dry. If you do not have enough blotters, take out the specimens which have been in the blotters for a week or more, and put them between pieces of newspapers, under pressure, until they become thoroughly dry. Then dry your blotters near a radiator and put in the fresh material.

6. After the specimens have become thoroughly dry, stick them to the mounting sheets, preferably with glue. Put a small

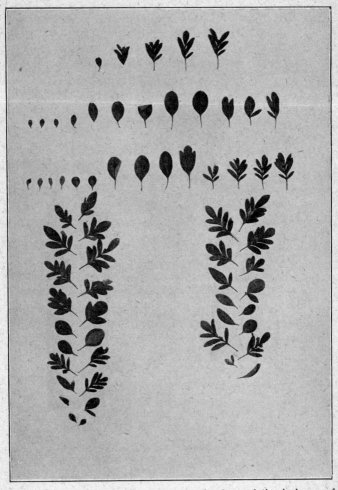

FIG. 106. — A specimen herbarium sheet, showing variation in leaves of the Persian lilac.

band of adhesive tissue over the larger stems. Arrange the specimens, if possible, so that you have at least one variation on a sheet.

7. Put the label on the lower right-hand corner, leaving a small margin. Attach the label to the mounting sheet with glue or paste, putting it only on the left edge of the label, that is, do not cover the back of the label with paste or glue.

SAMPLE OF LABEL

HERBARIUM OF VARIATIONS
DEPARTMENT OF PLANT-BREEDING. NEW YORK STATE COLLEGE OF AGRICULTURE

Name . . . .
Locality . . . . Date . . . .
Habitat . . . .
Description of variation . . . .

Class of variation . . . .
Collector . . . . No. . . . .

8. Before the specimen is handed in, fill in as many of the blank spaces on the label as possible. Place your name after the word "Collector." Fill in both the scientific and common names.

9. Absolute neatness is essential.

EXERCISE 2

The Statistical Study of Type and Variability

Making measurements. — The value and uses of the statistical method of studying variation are explained in Chapter IV. In dealing statistically with a group of organisms, or parts of them, the first step in the procedure is, of course, to collect data. These

FIG. 107. — A specimen herbarium sheet, showing variations in leaves
of the blackberry.

will consist of quantitative measurements of characters to be studied. These data are later analyzed, certain constants are derived therefrom, and, lastly, the constants are interpreted. The conclusions of the breeder or the investigator are based on his interpretations of these constants. The meaning of the various constants is explained in Chapter IV.

In collecting data, it is important that as large a proportion as possible of the entire population should be measured. Failing this, the sample should be fairly representative of the whole. The time or season during which measurements are taken is important where populations are to be compared. It would obviously be unfair to collect data one year on fully matured plants and another year on immatured plants. It is not always easy to avoid a selection, conscious or unconscious, but the collector should try to take his data with absolute impartiality. He should collect at random until he has obtained a representative sample. Much time and labor will be saved if he can conveniently limit the number of individuals measured to a number whose square root is an integer.

The frequency distribution. — Having measured a representative sample of the entire population, the next step is to sort the data. All individuals of the same or nearly the same size are grouped together in one order of magnitude. In order to give a clear understanding of what follows, let us take, for example, the data collected by a class of students on 500 bean plants. The individual lengths range from 5 cm. to 95 cm. This is known as the *range of variability* and the way in which the individuals are distributed along the successive equal intervals in this range is spoken of as the *frequency distribution* of the varying character. For convenience, these lengths may be grouped into classes, thus: 5–14; 15–24; 25–34 . . . 85–94.

It is desirable that the number of classes be limited to not more than about a dozen, and thus the size of the class will depend upon the nature of the material. For example, bean

2 D

plants may vary in height from 5 cm. to 95 cm.; to make the classes differ by only 1 cm. would give us 90 classes, which would be very inconvenient to handle mathematically.

The class limits should be given in all cases, not the mid-point of the class. The magnitude of a class is its *value* and is designated by the symbol V. In calculations the mid-point of a class is used as the class value. The number of individuals falling into each class is termed its *frequency* and is symbolized by the letter f. The accompanying table shows how the various bean lengths are distributed throughout the range: —

V	f
5–14	4
15–24	72
25–34	169
35–44	125
45–54	64
55–64	38
65–74	11
75–84	11
85–94	6
	500

The graph or frequency polygon. — It is often desirable to present the data in a graphic way so that the eye can take in at a glance such information as would otherwise require an extended and careful study of quantities of figures. For this purpose the frequency polygon is used. Such a simple diagram or chart presents a picture embodying the chief characteristics of the given population. Its significance is apparent to the student at once. The frequency polygon is made, as explained in Chapter IV, by plotting the class range along the base-line or axis of abscissas. On the vertical axis, or axis of ordinates, are plotted the class frequencies.

When all the frequencies have been plotted in their proper places on the chart they may be connected by a continuous line. This will form the *frequency* or *distribution curve*, known also as the "probability curve." It will take the form of a *Quetelet curve* rising from the lowest class value at the left end of the base-line to an apex at the class of greatest frequency, then dropping to the right end at the highest class value. Such a curve shows at once four things about our data: (1) The extreme values, or the extent of the range, (2) the way in which the individuals are distributed throughout this range, (3) the prevailing type, or class of greatest frequency, and (4) whether the curve is symmetrical, following the normal probability curve or not. If the classes are arranged along the base-line in the sequence of their values instead of their frequencies, the curve will ascend constantly from the lowest value on the left end toward the highest value at the right end. This forms a *Galton curve*. The Galton type of curve shows merely a different method of exhibiting the frequency distribution of a population that is under study.

Mode. — The class of greatest frequency, the most "popular" or "modish" class, so to speak, is known as the *mode* or *modal class*. In our problem, the modal class is 25–34, or the mode is 29.5, the mid-value of this class. This is one way, and an excellent one, of expressing type. A typical bean plant of this population, we can say, is 29.5 cm. long.

Modal coefficient. — It is desirable to know what proportion of the population conforms to this type, or falls into this modal class. This proportion, which is expressed as a percentage designated as the *modal coefficient*, is found by dividing the number of individuals in the modal class by the total number of individuals measured. In our example, it would be $\frac{169}{500} = .338 = 33.8\%$, which is the percentage of the population in the class of greatest frequency, hence, the modal coefficient.

Mean. — If one desires to know what an average individual in the population is worth, the *mean*, symbolized by the letter M, will show it. The mean shows the average value of the population, hence it is only another method of expressing type. It is found by multiplying the mid-value of each class (V) by the number of individuals in that class (f), then summing the products and dividing this sum by the total number of individuals. The formula for this operation is $\frac{\Sigma Vf}{n}$.[1] Thus: —

V		f		Vf
9.5	×	4	=	38.0
19.5	×	72	=	1404.0
29.5	×	169	=	4985.5
39.5	×	125	=	4937.5
49.5	×	64	=	3168.0
59.5	×	38	=	2261.0
69.5	×	11	=	764.5
79.5	×	11	=	874.5
89.5	×	6	=	537.0
		500		18970.0

$$\frac{18970.0}{500} = 37.94 \text{ cm.}$$

We would get exactly the same result if we arranged the bean plants, in order of size, in a single line, placing them end to end, and then divided the total length of this line by 500, the number of individuals in it.

Average deviation. — One way of expressing variability is to find out by how much, on the average, any individual in the population deviates from the mean, the constant thus secured being termed the *average deviation*. This is ascertained as follows: the amount by which each class differs from the mean, or in other words, the deviation from the mean (designated by D) is multiplied by the frequency of the corresponding class, and then the sum of these products is divided by the total

---

[1] The Greek letter capital "sigma" (Σ) indicates that the sum of a series of values is to be taken.

The total number of individuals measured is designated by n.

number of individuals. The formula for the operation is $\frac{\Sigma Df}{n}$.
Thus in our problem it would be found as shown in the table : —

V		f	D	Df
9.5	×	4	28.44	113.76
19.5	×	72	18.44	1327.68
29.5	×	169	8.44	1426.36
39.5	×	125	1.56	195.00
49.5	×	64	11.56	739.84
59.5	×	38	21.56	819.28
69.5	×	11	31.56	347.16
79.5	×	11	41.56	457.16
89.5	×	6	51.56	309.36
				5735.60

$$\frac{5735.60}{500} = 11.4712 \text{ cm.}$$

Of course, the deviations below the mean (28.44, 18.44, 8.44) are negative quantities, those above (1.56, 11.56, 21.56, 31.56, 41.56, 51.56) positive, but inasmuch as we are here concerned only with *deviation* from type, we are correct in neglecting these signs, and using the arithmetic sum, and not the algebraic.

We would secure the same result if we went along our line of bean plants spoken of above with an average or mean individual as a measure, added up the lengths by which each one missed of being an average individual, and then divided this total by 500, the number of individuals measured. Clearly this would give the amount by which, on the average, each individual missed of being the mean or the average individual.

Standard deviation. — Another constant expressing departure from type, and one which is preferred by biometricians on mathematical grounds, is *standard deviation*, designated by the Greek letter small "sigma" (σ). It is found by squaring the deviations from the mean before multiplying by the frequencies, dividing the summation of these products by the number of individuals, and then extracting the square root of the quotient. The formula is: —

$$\sigma = \sqrt{\frac{D^2 f}{n}}.$$

V	f	Vf	D	Df	D²	D²f
5–14	4	38.0	28.44	113.76	808.8336	3235.3344
15–24	72	1404.0	18.44	1327.68	340.0336	24482.4192
25–34	169	4985.5	8.44	1426.36	71.2336	12038.4784
35–44	125	4937.5	1.56	195.00	2.4336	304.2000
45–54	64	3168.0	11.56	739.84	133.6336	8552.5504
55–64	38	2261.0	21.56	819.28	464.8336	17663.6768
65–74	11	764.5	31.56	347.16	996.0336	10956.3696
75–84	11	874.5	41.56	457.16	1727.2336	18999.5696
85–94	6	537.0	51.56	309.36	2658.4336	15950.6016
	500	18970.0		5735.60		112183.2000

$M = 37.94$ cm.

Av. Dev. $= 11.4712$ cm.

$\sigma = 14.9789$ cm.

Performing the operations indicated by this formula, we find the standard deviation in our problem to be

$$\sqrt{\frac{112183.2000}{500}} = 14.9789 \text{ cm.}$$

The squaring of the deviations has the effect of exaggerating the departures of the extremes, and thus the standard deviation is always greater than the average deviation, so that the two are not comparable. For the practical breeder the one is just as good as the other and whether he employs the average deviation or the standard deviation is of little practical importance so long as he is consistent in the use of one to the total exclusion of the other in the same piece of work.

Finding the mean and the standard deviation by the " short method." — Where large numbers are used, the derivation of the mean and the standard deviation by the method presented above is a long and laborious process, in which the liability to error is great. A much shorter, simpler, and at the same time more accurate method has been devised. This consists in making a guess at the mean (designated by G), and indicating the difference between each class value and this guess in a column marked $(V-G)$. Each of these differences is then multiplied by the corresponding frequency and the algebraic sum of the total negative differences and the total positive differences is found. This is the total amount by which our guess missed the mean for the whole population, and hence we should divide this quantity by n to find the average amount by which we missed our guess. If this amount, which is called the "correction," is *positive*, then our guess has been *too low* by that amount, and it is to be added to the guess. On the other hand, if it is negative, then our guess has been *too high*, and it is to be *diminished* by this amount. The formula for this procedure is:—

$$\text{correction } (c) = \text{(Algebraic)} \frac{\Sigma f(V-G)}{n}$$

$$M = G \pm c.$$

LENGTH OF PLANTS (SHORT METHOD)

V	f	$(V-G)$	$f(V-G)$		$f(V-G)^2$
5–14	4	−30	− 120		3600
15–24	72	−20	−1440		28800
25–34	169	−10	−1690	−3250	16900
35–44	125	0	0		0
45–54	64	10	640		6400
55–64	38	20	760		15200
65–74	11	30	330		9900
75–84	11	40	440		17600
85–94	6	50	300	2470	15000
	500		Sum	= − 780	113400

$$c = \frac{-780}{500} = -1.56 \qquad\qquad c^2 = 2.4336$$

$$M = 39.5 - 1.56 = 37.94 \text{ cm.}$$

$$\sigma = \sqrt{\frac{113400}{500} - 2.4336} = \sqrt{224.3664} = 14.9789 \text{ cm.}$$

$$C = \frac{14.9785}{37.94} = 39.48 \text{ \%.}$$

In our problem, the mean as determined by this method, as shown in the accompanying table, is exactly the same as was found by the long method, 37.94 cm.

We would have secured the same result if, after a casual inspection of the line of bean plants spoken of above, we guessed that the mean was 39.5, and taking an individual of this length as a measure, we found the total amount which the short ones lack of being equal in length to the assumed mean, or the guess, and likewise the total amount which the long ones exceed the guess. The algebraic sum of these two amounts would be the total amount by which our guess missed of being the true mean, and since 500 individuals were measured, the average amount by which we missed on each individual would be found by dividing this sum by 500. Our assumed length would then be corrected by this amount, just as above. If we had guessed that the mean was 37.94, and went through the same process, then the sum of the negative differences would have exactly counterbalanced the sum of the positive differences, since our guess in this case coincides with the true mean.

It would have made no difference whatever had we made our guess at 9.5. Indeed, this would have the advantage that minus signs would be eliminated and thus a frequent source of error removed, since students are prone to forget the algebraic signs. On the other hand, larger numbers would be involved.

In finding the standard deviation by the short method, the elements of the (V–G) column are squared before multiplying by the corresponding class frequencies. The sum of these prod-ducts is then divided by n, just as in the long method. In find-ing the mean a certain correction was applied to the guess. Now, since we are here dealing with squares, we must apply as a correction the square of the correction found previously; but unlike the previous procedure, this square of the correction is always subtracted from the quotient found as stated above. (All this has been proven mathematically correct, but the proof is beyond the scope of this study.) The square root is then found as before. The formula for deriving the standard deviation by this method is: —

$$\sigma = \sqrt{\frac{\Sigma f(V - G)^2}{n} - c^2}.$$

Using this method, we find the standard deviation to be exactly the same as before, as shown in the table above and the following calculations: —

$$\sigma = \sqrt{\frac{113400}{500} - (-1.56)^2} = 14.9789 \text{ cm.}$$

A further considerable shortening of the short method can be employed when the class values differ by amounts other than unity or a simple multiple of it, such as 10. In such a case the class differences are to be treated as unity and a correction made at the end of the calculation. The modified formulæ are: —

$$M = G \pm (c \times \text{True Difference between Classes}).$$

$$\sigma = \left[\sqrt{\frac{\Sigma f(V - G)^2}{n} - c^2} \right] \times \text{True Difference.}$$

The short method, because of its simplicity and its labor-saving features, recommends itself for general use. It is also slightly more accurate than the long method because no deci-mals are dropped until the very end of the calculation.

Coefficient of variability. — Standard deviation, as a measure of variability, allows of comparison only between similar organisms or parts, between such characters as are measured in the same denomination, as tubers with tubers, or height measured in inches with height in inches. This is because it is not an absolute, or abstract constant, but really represents a certain number of feet, pounds, centimeters, or what not. And just as we cannot compare 5 pounds with 5 inches mathematically, so we cannot compare standard deviation in inches with that in pounds.

An undenominational abstract constant that will allow of comparing diverse variabilities, let us say, height with thickness, or pounds with inches, is designated as the *coefficient of variability*. It is found by dividing the standard deviation by the mean. The formula is $\frac{\sigma}{M} \times 100$ and it is symbolized by C. It is really only the standard deviation measured in terms of the mean. For our beans the coefficient of variability for length is .3948 or since it is usually read as percentage, 39.48 %. This constant is now comparable with any other coefficient of variability for whatever character or in whatever denomination it may have been measured. Thus we can compare the variability in the length of beans in millimeters with their variability in breadth measured in millimeters or inches, or with height in men or sugar content in beets, if we wish.

Probable error. — Probable error does not mean the amount of error that an investigator is likely to make in his experiments or measurements. It means that if he would measure another random sample of a population similar in size and character to the sample he had measured before, the chances are even that the mean for the new sample would lie somewhere between the limits denoted by the probable error. Thus, the mean as to length of plants for our beans is 37.94 cm. with a probable error of ± .4518. This means that the mean for the new population would not be greater than 37.9400 + .4518 = 38.3918 cm., or less than $37.94 - .4518 = 37.4882$ cm., but would fall some-where in between these two limiting values. It is symbolized by E with the initial of the constant to which it belongs attached in smaller case type. Thus, the symbol for the probable error of the standard deviation is E_σ; of the mean, E_M; of the co-efficient of variability, E_C.

The probable errors are based upon certain relations between the standard deviation and the number of individuals. The greater the number of individuals, the smaller will be the prob-able error. In short, the probable error will indicate how much confidence we can place in our constant, and should always accompany the latter. It is really a part of the constant.

In finding the probable errors the constant .6745 is used. This has been derived mathematically and is used by all biom-etricians in the same way.

The following formulæ will show how the various probable errors can be found : —

$$E_M = \pm .6745 \frac{\sigma}{\sqrt{n}}.$$

$$E_\sigma = \pm .6745 \frac{\sigma}{\sqrt{2\,n}}.$$

$$E_C = \begin{cases} \pm .6745 \dfrac{C}{\sqrt{2\,n}}, \text{ where } C \text{ is } 10\% \text{ or less.[1]} \\ \pm .6745 \dfrac{C}{\sqrt{2\,n}} \sqrt{1 + 2\left(\dfrac{C}{100}\right)^2}, \text{ where } C \text{ is greater than } 10\%.[1] \end{cases}$$

Our completed constants for length of bean plants are then as follows : —

$$M = 37.9400 \pm .4518 \text{ cm.}$$
$$\sigma = 14.9789 \pm .3195 \text{ cm.}$$
$$C = 39.48 \quad \pm .96\%.$$

[1] In these equations the value of C in per cent is to be used. The prob-able error will come out as a percentage.

In the accompanying table the constants for the number of pods borne on these plants are likewise determined by the short method. Note that the column $(V-G)^2$ is entirely omitted, a short cut which is another considerable time saver. Instead, the elements of column $f(V-G)$ are simply multiplied by the corresponding elements of the $(V-G)$ column since $f(V-G)$ times $(V-G)$ equals $f(V-G)^2$.

Number of Pods (Short Method)

V	f	$(V-G)$	$f(V-G)$		$f(V-G)^2$
5–14	16	−20	− 320		6400
15–24	140	−10	−1400	−1720	14000
25–34	169	0			0
35–44	115	10	1150		11500
45–54	40	20	800		16000
55–64	12	30	360		10800
65–74	5	40	200		8000
75–84	3	50	150	+ 2660	7500
	500		Sum	= 940	74200

$$c = \frac{940}{500} = 1.88 \qquad\qquad c^2 = 3.5344$$

Mode = 29.5 $\qquad\qquad$ Modal Coefficient = 38.36 %

$$M = 29.5 + 1.88 = 31.38 \pm .3631 \text{ (pods)}.$$

$$\sigma = \sqrt{\frac{74200}{500} - 3.5344} = 12.0360 \pm .2568 \text{ (pods)}.$$

$$C = \frac{12.0360}{31.38} = .3836 = 38.36 \pm .93 \%.$$

Exercise 3

Correlation

Certain characters in organisms tend to appear together and the inference is that they are causally connected, that is, one is the cause of the other or else both are dependent upon the same cause.

Two phenomena are causally connected if any one of the following four cases is true: —

(1) If, when the first is present, the second is invariably present also.

(2) If, when the first increases in amount, the second also invariably increases a proportional amount.

(3) If, when the first is absent, the second is invariably absent also.

(4) If, when the first decreases in amount, the second also invariably decreases a proportional amount.

Because a fixed or absolute relationship exists in each of the four cases the correlation between the two phenomena is said to be perfect, but in the first two cases it is positive in nature, in the second two negative in nature. If absolutely no relation existed between the two phenomena, the correlation would be zero.

Now, in the bean problem used in the preceding exercise, it might be asked, "Is there any fixed relation between the length of plant and its number of pods?" Suppose, for example, that if on selecting a plant from the whole lot, it was found to be a long one, could we then say, on this information only, that it will be found to bear a great number of pods? If so, we are assuming that some relation exists between the two characters.

Let us, for the sake of illustration, suppose that each bean plant bears one pod for every centimeter in length. Because in this case there exists a fixed or absolute relationship, the correlation is said to be perfect, and is expressed by 100 %, or more usually simply by unity (1).

Now, suppose, however, that on selecting 300 plants averaging 80 cm. in length, we find the first 100 plants to bear an average of 50 pods per plant, the second 25 pods, and the third 10, it is clear that if we select one more plant at random and measure it to be 80 cm. also, we could no more predict the number of pods it bears than if we had not measured it at all. Here, then, we say there is no relationship whatever between length of plant and number of pods, or, in other words, the correlation is 0.

Now suppose a third case, in which we find that invariably the longest plant bears the fewest pods, and the shortest the most. Here we could say the relationship is fixed or absolute too, but in an opposite, or negative manner, and accordingly, the correlation would be expressed by -1.

But now turning back to the first supposition, where it was assumed that one pod was borne for each centimeter length, suppose that the relationship were not so definite. Suppose that one pod occurs not for every centimeter, but sometimes for a little more than a centimeter, sometimes for a little less; then the relationship, though not absolute, is high, and the degree to which this relationship approaches the perfect 100 % relationship will express the correlation between the two characters. The correlation coefficient, in other words, would fall between 0 and $+1$.

We rarely find characters or organs in an organism to be absolutely related; usually they are associated in a more or less intermediate degree, somewhere between 0 and $+1$, or 0 and -1. The degree to which they are associated, or correlated, if it can be determined in an exact manner and expressed by a mathematical constant, should be an index of the degree for which one is the cause of the other, or the probability of finding the other when we know the first is present. This may be of importance sometimes to the breeder because some easily seen character may be responsible for, or indicative of, the presence of a desired, but unseen character. Thus a certain shaped kernel of corn (one with a large germ) is known to run high in oil content, one with large endosperm high in starch. To select kernels with large germs is much easier than to analyze many ears by chemical methods. Or if, after a relation had been established, we could safely choose the longest or tallest bean plants right in the field and know that they will bear the greatest number of pods, it would be of great advantage to the breeder.

Now, an exact determination of the degree of correlation can be obtained by the biometrical method. Let us follow the process step by step, using our bean data.

First of all, we take our data for the two characters for which we wish to find the correlation, length of plant, and number of pods.

Our original observations will be somewhat as follows : —

No. of Observation (or Plant)	Length of Plant in Cm.	No. of Pods
1	27	32
2	46	27
3	18	45
etc.	*etc.*	*etc.*

In finding the constants — mean, standard deviation, etc., for each of these characters, the observations for length and those for number of pods were distributed in separate tables. Now, however, we distribute both sets of observations on *one* table, in what are known as *arrays* of a correlation table. (See Table 1.) For example, the first observation tabulated above would fall in the vertical array 25–34, as regards length, and in the 25–34 horizontal array, as regards number of pods. The second observation would fall in the 5th column (vertical array 45–54) and in the third row (horizontal array 25–34).

Thus each vertical array would be a frequency distribution of length of plant with respect to number of pods, and each horizontal array would be a distribution of number of pods with respect to length of plant. But if we add up all the frequencies along each horizontal array, we will get the frequency distribution with respect to the number of pods and it will be exactly the same as that found in the preceding exercise (see table on p. 404); likewise, if we add up the frequencies in the vertical arrays, we will get the frequency distribution with respect to length of plants.

The various steps by means of which the constants for length of plant and those for number of pods were obtained were given in the preceding exercise and need no repetition. They are here secured by the "short method" and are given in the correlation table. We are here concerned with the finding of the constant which will express the degree of correlation between these two characters.

The only new feature of this correlation table, aside from the method in which the observations are distributed, is the column marked ΣP. *Each element of this column represents the total deviation* (from the assumed mean, or guess) *of the individuals in each array with respect to both length of plant and number of pods*. Thus, taking the first horizontal array, the 5–14 class as regards number of pods, we wish to find how much the individuals in this class deviate from the assumed mean for length of plants. It is found as follows: —

3 individuals each deviated by $- 30 = -\ \ 90$
9 individuals each deviated by $- 20 = - 180$
3 individuals each deviated by $- 10 = -\ \ 30 - 300$
1 individual deviated by $\ \ \ \ + 20 = \ \ \ \underline{20 + 20}$
　　　　　　　　　　Algebraic Sum $= - 280$

All the individuals in this array deviate from the assumed mean for length of plants by the algebraic sum of the total minus deviations and the total plus deviations, which is $- 280$, as indicated. But each individual in this array with respect to length deviated by − 20 from the assumed mean with respect to number of pods, and hence we must multiply − 280 by − 20 to find the total deviation from both assumed means and this gives us + 5600.

All the elements in the **Σ***P* column are secured in exactly the same way. The third element is zero, since the deviation from the assumed mean for number of pods is zero in this case. The fourth element comes out a minus quantity according to the following calculation:—

$$
\begin{array}{rcl}
1 \times -30 &=& -30 \\
11 \times -20 &=& -220 \\
42 \times -10 &=& -420 \\
33 \times 0 &=& 0 \\
\hline
&& -670
\end{array}
\qquad
\begin{array}{rcl}
18 \times 10 &=& 180 \\
5 \times 20 &=& 100 \\
2 \times 30 &=& 60 \\
1 \times 40 &=& 40 \\
2 \times 50 &=& 100 \\
\hline
&& 480
\end{array}
$$

$$ -670 + 480 = -190 \times 10 = -1900. $$

The algebraic signs for each quantity must be carefully observed throughout the calculations.

Finally, the *algebraic* sum of all the elements in the **Σ***P* column is determined.[1] This will give us the grand total deviation from both assumed means for all the individuals, and hence to find the deviation for each individual we must divide by 500. Performing the operation we get $\dfrac{33100}{500} = 66.20$.

Now all along we have been working from an assumed mean, or guess, and we must apply a correction, which, mathematicians tell us, must be the product of the correction for length by that

---

[1] The elements of the **Σ***P* column can be obtained by finding the total deviation of each vertical array with respect to number of pods and multiplying by the deviation of that array with respect to length, instead of *vice versa*. The elements will be different, but their sum will be exactly the same by either method.

2 E

TABLE I
Correlation Length of Plant × Number of Pods

Length of Plant in cm. $G = 29.5$ cm.

V	5–14	15–24	25–34	35–44	45–54	55–64	65–74	75–84	85–94	f	V–G	f(V–G)	f(V–G)²	ΣP
5–14	3	9	3							16	–20	–320	6400	5600
15–24		37	54	30						140	–10	–1400	14000	10000
25–34		14	59	45	12	1				169	0	0	0	0
35–44	1	11	42	33	26	6				115	10	1150	11500	–1900
45–54		1	10	13	18	14	7			40	20	800	16000	5000
55–64			1	3	5	5	2	1	2	12	30	360	10800	6600
65–74				1	1	5	1	4	1	5	40	200	8000	4800
75–84					2	3	1	3	2	3	50	150	7500	3000
f	4	72	169	125	64	38	11	11	6	500		940	74200	33100
V–G	–30	–20	–10	0	10	20	30	40	50					
f(V–G)	–120	–1440	–1690	0	640	760	330	440	300					
			–3250					+2470		–780				
f(V–G)²	3600	28800	16900	0	6400	15200	9900	17600	15000	113400				

f(V–G) subtotals: –1720, 2660

G = 39.5   Number of Pods

	Length	No. Pods
C	$= -1.56$	1.88
C^2	$= 2.4336$	3.5344
M	$= 37.94 \pm .4518$ cm.	$31.38 \pm .3631$ pods
σ	$= 14.9787 \pm .3195$ cm.	$12.0360 \pm .2568$ pods
C	$= 39.48 \pm .96\%$	$38.36 \pm .93\%$

$$r = \frac{\dfrac{33100}{500} - [(1.88)\,(-1.56)]}{(14.9789)\,(12.0360)}$$

$$= .3835 \pm .0257$$

for number of pods. This product is *always subtracted* from the quotient of $\frac{\Sigma P}{n}$.

$$66.20 - (1.88 \times - 1.56) = 69.1328.$$

Now this corrected deviation must be secured in terms of the standard deviations for each character, and hence this quantity 69.1328 is to be divided by the product of both standard deviations : —

$$\frac{69.1328}{14.9789 \times 12.0360} = .3835.$$

We have now finally arrived at our correlation coefficient, designated universally by the letter r, the formula for the determination of which is as follows : —

$$\text{Correlation Coefficient } (r) = \frac{\frac{\Sigma P}{n} - c_1 \, c_2}{\sigma_1 \, \sigma_2}.$$

Like all other constants the correlation coefficient must be accompanied by its probable error, the formula for the finding of which is as follows : —

$$E = \pm \frac{.6745 \, (1 - r^2)}{\sqrt{n}}.$$

Solving this for our correlation coefficient, we find the probable error to be $\pm .0257$.

The amount of confidence which can be placed in the correlation coefficient depends upon the size of its probable error largely. Biometricians say that in order to be of much value, the coefficient must be from five to ten times as great as its probable error. But whether the coefficient shows a high, low, or intermediate degree of correlation between the two characters measured depends entirely upon its position with reference to its two limits, 0 and $+ 1$ or 0 and $- 1$. According to the size of *r* found *for the data used in our problem*, the correlation existing between the length of plant and its number of pods is not great.

EXERCISE 4

Statistical Study of Apples from Different Trees

Object. — To study the individuality of fruit trees.

Materials. — Apples representing the total product of different trees; scales; calipers.

Fill in the following form for each tree. Plot curves representing the entire population of trees.

NAME OF VARIETY.								
Tree no.								
Age of tree								
Condition of tree								
Total number of apples								
Number of marketable apples								
Total weight of apples								
Weight of marketable apples								
Average width of 50 apples								
Average length of 50 apples								
Color								
Any other noticeable differences								

EXERCISE 5

Statistical Study of Branches of Different Trees

Object. — To continue the study as outlined in Exercise 4, to test the individuality of trees.

Materials. — Fruit trees of different kinds, preferably dwarf trees; tapes.

Measure the new growth of various parts of each tree and of different trees. Plot curves of each tree and of all of the trees

F<small>IG</small>. 108. — A common form of ragweed.

Fig. 109. — Another form of ragweed.

as a population, to show graphically the extent of bud variation present.

Statistical Study of the Quantity of Grapes from Different Grape Vines

Use the same general method as in Exercise 4.

Study of Variation in Pressed Specimens of Ragweed or Some Plant showing Many Different Types

Object. — Careful study of the large and small variations among different biotypes of ragweed (*Ambrosia artemisiifolia*).

Materials. — Specimens of many different types of the above plant or any species of plant which is rich in biotypes. These specimens should be carefully pressed and mounted. (See Figs. 108 and 109.) Have each student make detail drawings to show minute differences.

Study of Bud Variations and Reversions in Ferns

Object. — To determine the nature and amount of reversion from the parental type, and if possible to find some cause for the same.

Material. — Obtain specimens of the sword fern (*Nephrolepis exaltata*) and Boston fern (*Nephrolepis bostoniensis*) and as many of the other ferns named below as possible.

Study the trueness to type of each variety and any reversions which they may contain. Draw typical specimens.

The following is the history, according to Cogswell, of some of the fern varieties. This is not a complete list but gives an idea of the origin of a few common horticultural varieties.

	INTRO-DUCED IN	SPORT OF
Nephrolepis bostoniensis	(about) 1880	nephrolepis exaltata (sword fern)
Nephrolepis Piersonii	1903	bostoniensis
Nephrolepis elegantissima	1904	Piersonii
Nephrolepis Scottii	1904	bostoniensis
Nephrolepis Barrowsii	1905	Piersonii
Nephrolepis Whitmanii	1906	Barrowsii
Nephrolepis todeaoides	1907	Whitmanii
Nephrolepis superbissima	1908	Scottii
Nephrolepis Scholzelii	1909	Scottii
Nephrolepis Pruessneri	1909	Whitmanii
Nephrolepis magnifica	1908	Whitmanii
Nephrolepis elegantissima compacta .	1909	elegantissima

EXERCISE 9

Study of the Morphology of Different Kinds of Flowers

Object. — To acquaint the student with floral parts and their functions. To determine the proper condition of the buds and flowers for emasculation, crossing, etc.

Material. — Buds and flowers of various kinds and in different stages of development; microscope or hand lens; set of dissecting instruments. The material should represent different natural families or orders.

Have the students make careful drawings of the floral organs, of various types of flowers. Take special care to distinguish the stamens and pistils.

The following outline by Dr. M. J. Dorsey may be found helpful in this exercise: —

STUDY OF FLOWERS (prerequisite to crossing)

Flower —
  Non-essential organs —
    Calyx — composed of sepals.
    Corolla —composed of petals.

Essential organs —
  Pistil —
    a, style; *b*, stigma; *c*, ovary $\left\{\begin{array}{l}\text{carpels.}\\\text{placenta.}\\\text{ovules.}\end{array}\right.$
  Stamens — composed of
    a, filament; *b*, anther $\left\{\begin{array}{l}\text{loculus or cell.}\\\text{pollen.}\end{array}\right.$

Degree of cross-relationship. —
  1. Self- or close-fertilization. (Occurring in perfect or hermaphrodite flowers.)
  2. Cross-fertilization. (Between individuals of same species or variety.)
  3. Hybridization. (Between species and sometimes between varieties which are very distinct.)

Causes of sterility. —
  1. Stamens and pistils maturing at different times. (Dichogamy.)
  2. Lack of affinity between pollen and stigma.
  3. Scanty or insufficient pollen.
  4. Lack of viability of pollen.

Relative position between stigma and anthers. —
  1. Stigma and anthers the same height.
  2. Stigma above anthers.
  3. Stigma below anthers.

Relative maturity of pistil and anthers. —

    1. Both maturing at same time.

    2. Stigma matures first — protogyny.

    3. Anthers mature first — protandry.

Methods of pollination. —

    1. Insects.

    2. Wind.

    3. Water.

    4. Self-pollination.

Types of plants in regard to sex. —

    1. Monœcious (both sexes on same plant).

    2. Diœcious (each sex on different individuals within the species or variety).

    3. Polygamous (perfect and imperfect flowers on the same plant).

Types of flowers in regard to sex. —

    1. Imperfect (1) Staminate — bearing only stamens.

                  (2) Pistillate — bearing only pistils.

    2. Perfect or hermaphroditic — bearing both stamens and pistils. Determine the following : —

    (*a*) Number of parts of flower. —

          a, sepals; *b*, petals; *c*, stamens; *d*, pistils.

    (*b*) Type of flower — perfect (hermaphrodite) or imperfect.

    (*c*) Relative position of stigma and anthers.

    (*d*) Relative maturity of pollen and stigma.

    (*e*) Is the flower pollinated by insects, wind, or selfed?

    (*f*) Draw the essential organs and label each part.

Exercise 10

Technique of the Cross-pollination of Plants

This exercise may be carried out in the winter in a greenhouse or conducted in the fall and spring out of doors, where additional expense is not involved in growing the plants under glass.

The following suggestive directions may be given to each student : —

Materials. — 1. Instruments: tweezers; scalpel; small, sharp-pointed scissors, hand lens, etc.

2. For covering flowers: Manila bags, waxed paper bags, cheese cloth, etc. Wire labels, stringed tags, fine copper wire or twine cut into short lengths may be used to fasten the bags.

Preliminary study of plant. —

Before attempting to cross plants, it is necessary to know the structure of the flower to be used. To do this (*A*) locate all parts — sepals, petals, anthers, filaments, stigma, style, ovary; (*B*) determine whether the flowers are perfect or imperfect; (*C*) learn to recognize the "ripe" or receptive condition of the stigma and pollen.

Technique. —

(*A*) Emasculation. (Unnecessary where stamens and pistils are borne on different flowers.) For crossing purposes select flowers in which the anthers have not opened. Remove the anthers with tweezers or scalpel, taking care not to injure the stigma. It may be necessary to remove part or all of the petals in some flowers in order to get at the anthers, but it is best to remove only the anthers, if possible.

(*B*) Bagging. After the anthers have been removed, the flower should then be covered with some material, as a manila or oil paper bag, to prevent the entrance of foreign pollen. When the stigma is receptive, remove the covering, pollinate with the desired pollen of known purity, and immediately cover again, leaving cover on until fertilization has taken place — as indicated by withered or brownish stigma. It is desirable to remove the covering when the cross has "set."

(*C*) The record. The record should include a description of each parent, giving particular attention to the contrasted characters. Colors may be recorded by comparing with a standard color chart. The female parent should always be mentioned first. The record on the label should include variety name or number of each parent, date of emasculation, and pollination. (Name of worker can also be placed on the label.) As far as possible reciprocal crosses should be made.

EXERCISE 11

Embryological Studies from Slides showing Cell Division at Different Stages, Chromosomes, Pollen Mother-cells, Development of the Embryo-sac, etc.

Provide each student with a high-power microscope and microscopic slides mentioned above. Careful drawings of each slide should be made.

EXERCISE 12

Study of Pollen Germination and Fecundation

Materials. — Fresh and preserved flowers showing structure of carpels in cross and long section; microscopic slides showing growth and penetration of pollen tubes into ovary, fecundation, etc. For study of germinating pollen, fresh pollen may be germinated in sugar solutions of various strengths mounted in the cells of hanging-drop slides. If this is done at the beginning of the practicum, the germinated pollen will be ready for examination before the end of the period.

Careful drawings of all stages observed should be made. The drawings should show all the differences in the length and size of the pollen tube in various degrees of concentration of the sugar solutions. Note also the effect of temperature and other external influences upon germination.

Exercise 13

Practice in the Cross-pollination of Apples, Pears, Peaches, Plums, etc.

To be carried on in the spring, when the trees are in bloom. For general methods of procedure, see Exercise 10.

Exercise 14

Purpose. — To teach the Laws of Probability; dominance and recessiveness; segregation and recombination; presence and absence hypothesis; inhibitory factors; complementary factors; inversed ratios, etc.

Materials. — Coins, wrinkled and smooth peas, both yellow and green in equal numbers for two character pairs; yellow and white kernels of both dent and flint corn; a pack of playing cards; and chemicals.

Program. — The instructor should take special care to make clear the significance of each step in the exercise and their concrete application to problems of plant-breeding and genetics.

1. The Law of Probability is taught by tossing coins. Each student should toss one coin for 2 or 3 minutes and record the number of times it falls head, and the number of times tail. Then the total for the whole class is summed up. It will be found that the latter count, including more tosses, approaches the theoretical ratio much more nearly. This should be explained by the instructor.

2. Then in the same way two coins may be tossed by each student. He now records heads; heads and tails; tails.

The application of this law in the formation of gametes should be made clear by the instructor.

3. Now the material may be changed by way of illustration. Peas or corn comprising two allelomorphs may be used for this exercise. They are mixed together in equal numbers in a bag

and each student draws blindly from the bag one seed at a time, recording his draw. This exercise illustrates segregation and the formation of gametic cells.

4. Now each student may remove simultaneously one pea from each of two bags, and lay them down side by side to illustrate the mating of gametes in an F_1 hybrid and the subsequent recombination of characters. He should record only the dominant characters present in each pair taken and his record will show the phenotypes of his F_2 hybrids.

5. The same principles can be illustrated by the use of a pack of playing cards. Draw at random two cards at a time. Record each combination observed. Two blacks coming simultaneously represent a homozygous black individual; a black and a red represent a heterozygous form appearing as black, two reds represent a pure recessive. For illustrating the combination of two character pairs, four cards may be drawn at a time.

6. Some simple chemical reactions [1] afford an excellent series of demonstrations illustrating the main features of Mendelism. The following apparatus and chemicals are required : —

4 500 cc. flasks
1 100 cc. flask
1 100 cc. graduate
4 50 cc. burettes
1 2 cc. pipette
500 cc. 10% cp. NH_4OH
500 cc. 25% cp. NH_4OH
500 cc. 10% cp. HCl

3 dozen test tubes
4 small funnels for burettes
1 iron stand and clamps
3 test tube racks
1 pipette dropper
500 cc. 5% cp. HCl
100 cc. 2% litmus powder
    solution
10 cc. phenolphthalein

While the burettes are not absolutely necessary, they will greatly facilitate the demonstrations. The solutions are to be made up beforehand by the instructor, who should try some pre-

[1] This portion of the exercise is based on an article by G. H. Shull, "A Simple Chemical Device for illustrating Mendelian Inheritance," *Plant World*, 12 : 145–153, 1909.

DEMONSTRATION OF ALLELLOMORPHISM
AND OF COMPLETE DOMINANCE

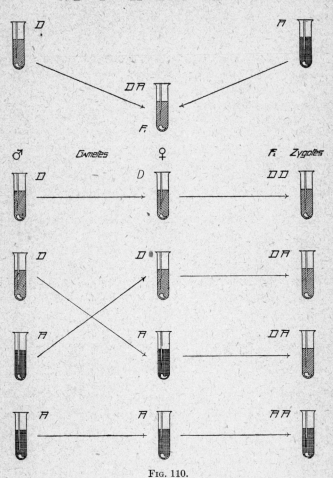

Fig. 110.

DEMONSTRATION OF PRESENCE AND ABSENCE HYPOTHESIS
AND OF INTERMEDIACY

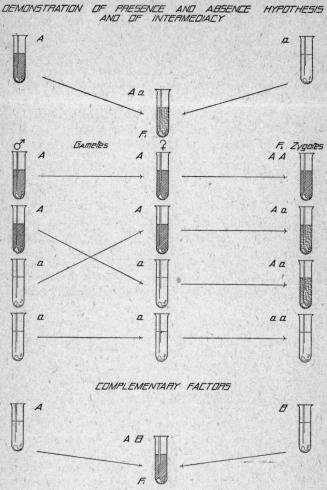

COMPLEMENTARY FACTORS

Fig. 111.

liminary experiments to see whether or not the strengths of the
solutions are correct. They may have to be varied slightly.
The contents of each test tube representing a gamete (labeled in
the accompanying figures) are given below. In order to secure
the simple $3:1$ or $1:3$ ratio in F_2, eight test tubes representing
the gametes of F_1 are necessary in each case. It is of course
impossible to represent the phenomenon of segregation in F_1
by using the test tube labeled F_1. The instructor will have to
explain that after segregation the gametes are exactly the same
in nature as those of the original parents of the cross, and that
the hybrid F_1 now forms gametes similar to those of both parents,
in equal numbers.

(*a*) Demonstration of Allelomorphism and of Complete
Dominance (Fig. 110).

> D contains 10 cc. $10\% \ HCl + 2$ cc. litmus solution.
> R contains 10 cc. $10\% \ NH_4OH + 2$ cc. litmus solution.

The dominance of blue over red can be shown by substituting
$5\% \ HCl$ for the 10%.

(*b*) Demonstration of the Presence and Absence Hypothesis
and of Intermediacy (Fig. 111a).

> A contains 10 cc. $10\% \ NH_4OH + 2$ drops Phenolphthalein.
> a contains 10 cc. $5\% \ HCl$.

(*c*) Demonstration of Complementary Factors (Fig. 111b).

> A contains 10 cc. $10\% \ NH_4OH$.
> B contains 10 cc. $H_2O + 2$ drops phenolphthalein.

Dominance of a character has usually been taken to be indicative of the presence of a positive factor determining that character. But in some cases the absence of a factor, *e.g.* cases of
awnlessness in wheat, or hornlessness in cattle, seems to be
dominant over its presence. To say that the *absence* of a thing,
in other words a purely negative condition, is dominant over its

2 F

DEMONSTRATION OF THE PRESENCE OF AN INHIBITOR FACTOR

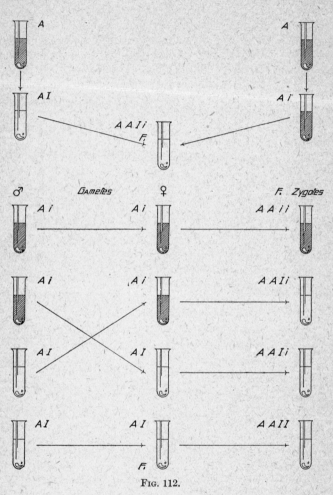

Fig. 112.

presence seems an absurdity. However, to make the facts consistent with the presence and absence hypothesis, two explanations are offered. One consists in assuming the presence of a positive inhibitory factor, which prevents the production of the character concerned. The other consists in assuming that one "dose" of the factor concerned is insufficient to produce the result, hence in its simplex or heterozygous condition, the character determined by the factor fails to appear, and it is only when the factor is in the duplex or positively homozygous condition that it does appear. The first of these explanations is embodied under demonstration (*d*). The last is embodied under the demonstration entitled "Explanation of So-called 'Dominance of Absence.'"

(*d*) Demonstration of the Presence of an Inhibitory Factor (Fig. 112).

> *A* contains 10 cc. 2.5% NH_4OH + 2 drops phenolphthalein.
> *Ai* equals *A* + 5 cc. 10% *HCl*.

(*e*) Explanation of So-called "Dominance of Absence" (Fig. 113).

> *A* contains 10 cc. 10% NH_4OH + 6 drops phenolphthalein.
> *a* contains 10 cc. 10% *HCl*.

After the zygotes of F_2 are obtained, in this last demonstration, the instructor should add 10 cc. − 10% NH_4OH to each *Aa* zygote of F_2 to show that another "dose" of factor *A* will now produce the result.

Exercise 15

A Study of Mendelian Characters in Timothy and Oats

Purpose. — To afford the student concrete illustrations of Mendel's laws; to find unit characters in plants and to see their segregation and recombination.

Materials. — Mature timothy plants of various strains, com-

EXPLANATION OF SO-CALLED "DOMINANCE OF ABSENCE"

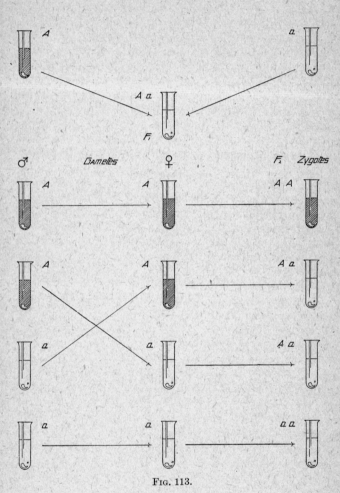

Fig. 113.

prising as great a variety of unit characters as possible. A small bundle of stems for each student containing samples from different plants. Photographs and mounted specimens. Varieties of oats comprising various unit characters that may be readily distinguished in hybrid plants, such as black and white grains, side and panicled types of inflorescence; also bearded and beardless varieties of wheat or barley. Specimen plants of parent types should be available for inspection, also specimens of the F_1 plants. A large number of F_2 plants resulting from each cross studied should be available for examination by the class.

Program. — 1. The instructor should first explain the purpose of the afternoon's exercise and outline the order of procedure. Unit characters are to be studied and illustrated with timothy and oats or barley. Dominance, recessiveness (or presence and absence), segregation, and recombination can be illustrated here.

2. At this occasion a talk may well be given on artificial crossing of small cereals for the purpose of creating new varieties. The instructor may describe the inflorescence of the oat plant, and the technique of making crosses in these plants. He should illustrate the talk with charts and with diagrams made on the blackboard.

3. Mounted specimens of oat types together with the F_1 and F_2 progeny resulting from their crossing may be handed around for examination by the class. If enough mounts are available, the specimens may be drawn and described by each student.

4. Composite samples of timothy should be handed to each student. He should study them to see what diversity of unit characters can be found there, in the nature of differentiating botanical characters. A list should be made of all the unit characters observed. Drawings of timothy heads may help to train his observation and fix the idea.

5. A large progeny of F_2 oat plants should be distributed among the class after the parent types have been shown and their differentiating characters discussed. The class may now examine

the plants given to them, and sort out the segregated characters. When sorting has been completed, the counts for the whole class may be ascertained. It should serve to illustrate the expected theoretical mendelian ratio.

Remarks. — Timothy affords very good material for this practicum, especially when bundled and mounted specimens, together with photographs, are available.

Oats exhibit excellently contrasted unit characters, but experience shows them rather poorly adapted for class study, except when mounted specimens are used. The reasons for this are : —

1. Side and panicled characters — the specimens are often pressed out of shape, due to drying and storing, and are, therefore, difficult to distinguish.

2. *Color.* — Black oats crossed with white give oats of intermediate color which are often difficult to distinguish from black. White and yellow are impossible of being distinguished by the inexperienced student. Moreover, color in oat hulls varies greatly with the seasonal conditions under which it was grown.

3. Plants are likely to become broken up in handling, thus spoiling the count when mendelian ratios are expected. The first two of these objections can be obviated by using mounted specimens. Other characters such as naked, hulled, awned, and awnless can be illustrated in this way. Probably a better exercise would be given by substituting corn for oats.

EXERCISE 16

Mendelian Problems

Purpose. — To enable students to become familiar with what might be called the mechanics of mendelism by working out mendelian problems by the method of squares.

Problem. — Given : Two pairs of contrasted characters — Tall vine (T), dwarf vine (t) ; Yellow seeds (Y), green seeds (y). Tallness and yellowness are completely dominant characters.

1. What gametes will be formed by an F_1 hybrid individual from the cross between tall, green and dwarf, yellow?

2. How many offspring will it be necessary to grow in order to allow every combination to appear in the second generation?

3. How many genotypes will there be?

4. How many phenotypes will appear?

5. In what ratio will the phenotypes appear?

6. How many pure dominant individuals?

7. How many pure recessive individuals?

8. If the combination $T \times t$ gave plants of medium height when a tall plant with yellow seeds is crossed with a dwarf plant with green seeds, how many genotypes will appear in F_2? How many phenotypes? In what ratio?

Illustrative problems. — The following problems may be studied by way of illustration. These are taken from actual cases with the tomato, but will apply in principle to other plants, by substituting other unit characters : —

Problem 1. —

Tall, homozygous (T) × dwarf, homozygous (t) = Tt; F_1

F_1 gametes = T; t

F_1 selfed =

	POLLEN-GRAINS	
	T	t
T	TT	tT
t	Tt	tt

EGG-CELLS

Phenotypes (visible types) (2^n) = 3 *TT* ; 1 *tt*.
Genotypes (actual types) (3^n) = 1 *TT* ; 2 *Tt* ; 1 *tt*.

Problem 2. —

Heterozygous Tall (*Tt*) × homozygous dwarf (*tt*).

Whenever a plant which is already heterozygous is used as a parent, its gametes will become segregated during their formation, and when the crossing takes place more than one kind of progeny will be produced. In this case the female parent will produce two kinds of egg cells, namely, tall and dwarf.

Graphically, this cross may be represented as follows : —

POLLEN GRAINS

	t	*t*
T	*Tt*	*Tt*
t	*tt*	*tt*

EGG CELLS

The male parent is pure dwarf, therefore all of the pollen grains will represent dwarfness only.

Phenotypes = 2 *Tt* ; 2 *tt*.
Genotypes = 2 *Tt* ; 2 *tt*.

If the female parent were crossed with a homozygous tall instead of a dwarf, the visible types the first year after crossing would all appear the same (tall) instead of two kinds as above. There would be

Phenotypes = 4 *TT*.
Genotypes = 2 *TT* ; 2 *Tt*.

Problem 3. —

The cases which have been considered hitherto show perfect dominance of one unit over another. This is not always the case. It frequently happens that the first generation hybrid is intermediate between the two parents, and in the second generation the heterozygote forms differ from either homozygous form. Thus when large, round tomatoes are crossed with small, plum-shaped ones, the F_1 hybrid is intermediate between the parents. If L represents largeness and (l) small, plum-shaped, then F_1 hybrids (Ll) will not be the same as (LL), but will be distinctly different. The formulæ previously given, 2^n, 3^n, etc., will not hold in cases of incomplete dominance. This will be more fully explained later. Large (L) $\times$ small, plum-shaped (l) = Ll, an intermediate type of fruit.

F_1 gametes = L, l.
F_1 selfed =

POLLEN GRAINS

	L	l
L	LL	Ll
l	Ll	ll

EGG CELLS

Phenotypes = 1 LL; 2 Ll; 1 ll
Genotypes = 1 LL; 2 Ll; 1 ll.

Problem 4. —

Intermediate (Ll) $\times$ Large, round (LL)

POLLEN GRAINS

	L	L
L	LL	LL
l	Ll	Ll

EGG CELLS

Phenotypes = 2 *LL*; 2 *Ll*.
Genotypes = 2 *LL*; 2 *Ll*.

Problem 5. —

Tall, smooth (*Th*) × dwarf, Hairy (*tH*) = Tall, Hairy (*TtHh*)

F_1 gametes = *TH*; *Th*; *tH*; *th*.

F_1 selfed =

POLLEN GRAINS

	TH	Th	tH	th
TH	TT HH	TT Hh	Tt HH	Tt Hh
Th	TT Hh	TT hh	Tt Hh	Tt hh
tH	Tt HH	Tt Hh	tt HH	tt Hh
th	Tt Hh	Tt hh	tt Hh	tt hh

EGG CELLS

Phenotypes (2^n) = 9 TH; 3 Th; 3 tH; 1 th.

Genotypes (3^n) = 1 $TTHH$, 1 $TThh$, 1 $ttHH$, 1 $tthh$, 2 $TTHh$, 2 $ttHh$, 2 $Tthh$, 2 $TtHH$, and 4 $TtHh$.

Problem 6. —

Tall (Heter)[1] smooth (Tth) × dwarf, Hairy (tH).

Female gametes = Th, th.

Male gametes = tH.

POLLEN GRAINS

tH

Th	$TtHh$
th	$ttHh$

EGG CELLS

It will be seen that two types are produced the first year after crossing instead of the one where pure parents are used. Segregation takes place immediately in the female parent because of its hybridity, and two kinds of gametes will be produced.

In order to get a comparison with the F_2 when pure parents are crossed, it is necessary to self both types as follows : —

(*a*) *TtHh* produces gametes as follows, *Th, Th, tH, th.* These are the same as in problem 5 and hence the resulting plants will be : —

Phenotypes = 9 TH, 3 Th, 3 tH, 1 th.

Genotypes = 1 $TTHH$, 1 $TThh$, 1 $ttHH$, 1 $tthh$, 2 $TTHh$, 2 $ttHh$, 2 $Tthh$, 2 $TtHH$, and 4 $TtHh$.

(*b*) *ttHh* produces the following gametes: *tH, th.*

[1] "Heter" is used for short in place of heterozygote, similarly "homo" is used for homozygote.

POLLEN GRAINS

	tH	*th*
tH	*tt* *HH*	*tt* *Hh*
th	*tt* *Hh*	*tt* ***hh***

EGG CELLS

Phenotypes = *ttHH*, *tthh*.
Genotypes = *ttHH*, 2 *ttHh*, 1 *tthh*.

Problem 7. —

Tall, large-round (*TL*) × dwarf, small plum-shaped (*tl*) = Tall intermediate (*TtLl*).

F_1 gametes = *TL*; *Tl*; *tL*; *tl*.

POLLEN GRAINS

	TL	*Tl*	*tL*	*tl*
TL	*TTLL*	*TTLl*	*TtLL*	*TtLl*
Tl	*TTLl*	*TTll*	*TtLl*	*Ttll*
tL	*TtLL*	*TtLl*	*ttLL*	*ttLl*
tl	*TtLl*	*Ttll*	*ttLl*	*ttll*

EGG CELLS

It must be remembered in this problem that we have incomplete dominance in one allelomorphic pair, therefore the number of visible types is different than in cases where both units exhibit dominance.

Phenotypes = 3 *TTLL*, 6 *TTLl*, 3 *TTll*, 1 *ttLL*, 2 *ttLl*, 1 *ttll*.

Genotypes = 1 *TTLL*, 1 *TTll*, 1 *ttLL*, 1 *ttll*, 2 *TTLl*, 2 *Ttll*, 2 *Ttll*, 2 *ttLl*, and 4 *TtLl*.

What visible types would be produced if incomplete dominance occurred in both characters?

Problem 8. —

Self-fertilize-Tall, intermediate (*TTLl*). This is a pure tall, hence all of its progeny will be tall.

POLLEN GRAINS

EGG CELLS		*TL*	*Tl*
	TL	*TTLL*	*TTLl*
	Tl	*TTLl*	*TTll*

Phenotypes = 1 *TTLL*, 2 *TTLl*, 1 *TTll*.
Genotypes = 1 *TTll*, 2 *TTLl*, 1 *TTll*.

EXERCISE 17

Ear-to-Row Test with Corn

Field Practicum

Purpose. — To demonstrate to the student the method of testing out the transmitting power of individual plants; to show him how a breeding plot should be arranged for corn; to teach him how to harvest the corn and make notes on which to base his selections. A practical demonstration of the method of pure line selection.

Materials. — For each student a sack for holding ears, wired tags and strings for tying sacks, and sheets for taking data. A wooden rack with spikes for drying ears of corn. Grocery scales for weighing the ears from each row.

Data Sheet for Corn Selection

(Ear-to-Row Method)

Mark Dent (+); mark Flint (V).

No. of row				
Total no. of hills				
Total no. of stalks				
No. barren stalks				
Total no. of ears				
Total wt. of ears				
No. mature ears				
Wt. mature ears				
No. immature ears				
Wt. immature ears				
Percentage mature ears				
Percentage immature ears				

Choose 10 of the best-looking ears from one row on which to take the following data:—

Wt. of ears						
Length of ears						
Circumference [1] of ears						
No. of rows per ear						
Wt. of shelled corn						
Wt. of cob						

A field plot planted by the ear-to-row method, saving unused half of each ear for comparison with its progeny. It should contain two or more rows, as space permits, for each student. Each row should contain 50 hills. The rows should be planted

---

[1] Circumference should be measured at a point about $\frac{1}{3}$ of the distance from the butt toward the tip.

and cultivated under regular field conditions. Two buffer rows should be planted completely around the plot. These should be cut and discarded before the interior rows of the plot are studied. Their purpose and use should be explained to the class.

Program. — After the instructor has explained the purpose of the practicum, and the manner of procedure for the afternoon, the class may be taken to the field. Each student should have one or two rows for himself. Students may be permitted to work in pairs, if desirable. Careful and detailed notes should be made on each row and recorded on data sheets provided for that purpose. The corn may be taken back to the laboratory for weighing. Statistics for the whole plot should then be compiled, so that the individuality of different rows can be compared. The student should select 10 of the best ears from each of his rows and put them on the drying rack provided. These ears are to be used later for a study in the laboratory.

EXERCISE 18

Corn-judging

Students of plant-breeding should be trained to have a critical judgment of agricultural and horticultural plants. Exercises in comparative judging are the best way to attain this end. Utility should be kept constantly in mind.

Details of corn judging will not be given here; they are too well known to need emphasis. For the East, both dent and flint varieties should be used. The ears which are judged in this exercise may be the ones the student himself has previously harvested from the ear-to-row plot. The best ten ears should be used for Exercise 19, which should always accompany exercise 18.

Object. — To encourage critical judgment of corn and, by the same means, of other crops.

Materials. — Ten ears of different races and types of corn to each student; tape, scales, charts, etc.

Each student should score a sample of flint corn according to the following score card : —

New England Flint

	POINTS
Maturity and seed condition	20
Uniformity (or regularity of single ears)	15
Kernels	15
Weight of ear	10
Length and proportion	10
Tips	5
Butts	10
Sulci (space between rows)	10
Color	5
Total	100

EXERCISE 19

Statistical Study of Ears of Corn

This should accompany or follow Exercise 18.

Object. — (*a*) To study critically and statistically the various parts of ears of corn. (*b*) To work up these data by biometrical methods, drawing curves, and ascertaining mean, standard deviation, coefficient of variability, etc., for the various parts of the ear. (*c*) To illustrate testing for germination.

Materials. — Each student should be given the same ears of corn which he had for Exercise 18; tapes, scales, etc.

The following form should be filled in by each student : —

NOTE. — This should not be merely a mechanical process, but the student should give each step very careful thought. These tables are given to assist in organizing the student's method and his thinking, but not to replace them. Do not study the method but the plants. Consider carefully the significance of each step.

Variety: Dent, flint, sweet, pop. (Underline.)

Where grown				
(a) Length of ear in cm.				
(b) Circumference of ear in cm. ($\frac{1}{3}$ butt to tip)				
(c) Weight of ear				
(d) Number of rows				
(e) Circumference of cob ($\frac{1}{3}$ butt to tip)				
(f) Weight of shelled corn				
(g) Weight of cob				
(h) Percentage of shelled corn				
(i) Total number of kernels				
(j) Average weight of kernel				
(k) Width of kernels in cm. (taken at random)				
(l) Compute average width				
(m) Length of 50 kernels in cm. (taken at random)				
(n) Compute average length				

Exercise 20

Study of Correlations of Characters in Corn

Use the same data as employed in Exercises 17 and 19. Make correlation tables by accepted biometrical methods of such characters as length and circumference; length and number of grains; weight and number of grains; length and weight; etc. Work out correlation coefficients.

Object. — To find out if certain characters are associated so that a measurement of one will give an indication of the other.

Materials. — Data from Exercises 17 and 19; cross-section paper.

Corn Selection — Laboratory Study

Purpose. — To give the student an understanding of the qualities that constitute a good ear of corn; to teach the benefits and dangers of cross-pollination.

Material. — For each student: 1 tape measure; 1 scalpel; 1 hand lens; 10 ears of corn selected from a row in breeding plot; samples of various types and colors of corn. These should have been shelled and soaked in water for 24 hours previous to this laboratory period in order to render them easy to dissect. Cobs of corn bearing mixed kernels to illustrate zenia; scales; data sheets; germinator.

Program. — The instructor should first explain the purpose of the practicum and outline the afternoon's work. He should explain the structure of a kernel of corn, calling attention to the difference between the various types of corn and the advantage of certain shaped kernels. Fecundation should be thoroughly discussed, and its effect in causing zenia. Illustrate with diagrams, charts, and specimens.

Discuss the dangers of mixing varieties by close planting. The danger of close fertilization and the stimulus resulting from cross-fertilization should also be discussed.

The advantage and manner of making germination tests should be explained.

The student should remove 6 kernels from each ear and place them in the germinator to be examined later, at which time he should record the percentage of germination.

Questions and problems concerning zenia printed on the outline sheet should be answered in a written report.

Laboratory Directions for Corn Study

1. Complete taking data on 10 ears of corn. Compare with remnant half of parent ear. From your data select the best 3 ears for breeding purposes.

2. Remove 6 kernels from each ear for germination test, along a spiral line from 1 inch of butt to near the top, revolving the ear twice.

3. Draw a typical kernel.
    (*a*) Face aspect.
    (*b*) Side aspect.

4. Make and draw longisections through the middle line both ways of the kernel, showing the following structures: —
    (*a*) Mass of starch or endosperm.
    (*b*) Crescent-shaped body, the germ or scutellum near the smaller end of the grain.
    (*c*) Remaining portion of embryo lying in the depression between scutellum and seed-coat.
    (*d*) In sample kernels where does color lie, in the pericarp, aleurone layer, or endosperm?
     (*e*) Note relative amount and position of starchy and horny endosperm in
        1. flint kernel,
        2. dent kernel,
        3. pop-corn kernel,
        4. sweet-corn kernel.

5. How would an F_1 kernel of corn appear in a cross between

♀	♂
white sugar	× yellow flint?
yellow flint	× white sugar?
white flint	× purple flint?
purple flint	× white flint?
red sweet	× purple flint?
purple sweet	× red flint?

Dominant Characters. —

Colored over white.
Yellow over non-yellow.

Red pericarps may conceal purple aleurone.
Purple in aleurone over red in aleurone.
Starchy over non-starchy.

EXERCISE 22

A Study in Potato Selection

Purpose. — 1. To teach the essential characteristics of a good tuber and a good tuber-line.

2. To teach the principles of selection by a study of variability in pure tuber-lines.

3. To demonstrate the tuber-unit method of potato selection.

4. To study variability by means of biometrical data, and the interpretation of constants and curves derived therefrom.

5. To fix in mind how the hills of different weights look.

6. To calculate the theoretical weights per acre when given certain weights per hill.

First Exercise

Materials. — Printed directions and sheets for recording data. Manila paper bags, size 12, for containing product of each hill. Cloth bags for carrying a number of these small bags when filled.

A breeding plot planted by the 4-hill tuber-unit method, that is, each four hills having the same progeny-number should come from the same mother tuber, and they should be planted and staked so that the progeny of each hill and unit can be distinguished.

This plot should be planted in good soil and given excellent care throughout the season as its usefulness to the class will depend entirely on the condition of the crop at harvest time. The rows and tuber-units should be labeled carefully and accurately in a convenient way, so that they may be made an object lesson in record-keeping.

DATA SHEET FOR POTATO STUDY

	Unit No.	Hill No. 1	Hill No. 2	Hill No. 3	Hill No. 4	Unit Total	Unit No.	Hill No. 1	Hill No. 2	Hill No. 3	Hill No. 4	Unit Total
PLANT												
Plant size												
Plant erect and compact												
Plant vigorous												
Plant healthy												
TUBERS												
No. per hill												
Wt. per hill												
No. of marketable tubers per hill												
Wt. of marketable tubers per hill												
Size												
Shape												
Shape all uniform in hill												
Shape all regular in hill												
Condition — healthy												
Flesh — firm												
Flesh — color ( )												
Grain — fine												
SKIN — color ( )												
Skin — texture ( )												
Eye — shallow												
Eye — small												
Eyebrow inconspicuous												
TOTAL POINTS												

Enough hills should be provided so that each student may have for himself several tuber-units. Five to ten units to each student will be enough if the student is required to observe and compare a large number as they lie in the field. The complete data for the whole field should be compiled by the class as a whole, and distributed to each student for a comparative study.

Program. — Just prior to the exercise, each hill should be dug carefully and the tubers replaced where they grew, but exposed to sight, especial care being taken that no labels be misplaced nor lost. The class may then be taken to the field. The instructor should explain the purpose of the exercise, the principles of pure-line selection as illustrated here, and the method of planting a potato-breeding plot by the tuber-unit method. He should give careful instructions for the afternoon's work. The class may then examine and compare the units as they lie exposed in the rows. The instructor should point out such differences as occur. A certain number of tuber-units should then be assigned to each student, and he should be required to take data from these units, as directed on the printed sheets provided. Such data-taking as involves the use of apparatus will necessarily have to be postponed until the following period, when it can be done in the laboratory.

Each student should carefully preserve his tubers properly labeled for the next laboratory exercise.

Second Exercise

Materials. — Data taken in Exercise 1; the tubers collected in Exercise 1; scales; paper plates (6 for each student).

Program. — The instructor should first outline the afternoon's work. He should explain the qualities that constitute a good tuber; also how that ideal form, size, and color differ in various varieties. He should explain a score-card.

The students may now proceed to finish taking the data on the tubers that they collected at the previous laboratory period.

When the data are complete, they can all be summed up for each tuber-unit and the units compared.

Each student should next make out a score-card embodying the points of his ideal unit, and score his units by it. The instructor may now give out a score-card by which the whole class may score their units alike.

Make up hills weighing $\frac{1}{2}$, 1, $1\frac{1}{2}$, 2, 3, and 4 pounds, and draw them natural size.

Compute the yield per acre from the above weights per hill, assuming the hills to be planted in rows 3 feet apart and 18 inches apart in the rows. One bushel weighs 60 pounds.

Directions for Report on Potato Selection

1. Distribute the data for the number of tubers per hill into classes.

2. Determine the mode, modal coefficient, mean, standard deviation, coefficient of variability, and their probable errors for the number of tubers per hill.

3. Determine the mode, mean, standard deviation, and co-efficient of variability for the number of marketable tubers per hill, weight of tubers per hill, and weight of marketable tubers per hill.

4. Draw Quetelet curve, showing frequency distributions for number of tubers per hill, number of marketable tubers per hill, weight of tubers per hill, and weight of marketable tubers per hill.

5. Distribute into classes the data for the number of tubers per four-hill-unit, number of marketable tubers per four-hill-unit, weight of tubers per four-hill-unit, and weight of marketable tubers per four-hill-unit.

6. Draw Quetelet curves, showing frequency distributions for number of tubers per four-hill-unit, number of marketable tubers per four-hill-unit, weight of tubers per four-hill-unit, and weight of marketable tubers per four-hill-unit.

7. Make a transmission curve from the data on the accompanying sheet. Which progeny units would you select for breeding purposes? How do you account for the apparent discrepancies which occur, such as the cases where the offspring give a very different yield from their parents?

8. Taking into account the number of tubers per hill, weight of tubers per hill, number of marketable tubers per hill, and weight of marketable tubers per hill, select the best 25 four-hill-units. Tabulate these, giving their progeny number and data for number of tubers per four-hill-unit, number of marketable tubers per four-hill-unit, weight of tubers per four-hill-unit, and weight of marketable tubers per four-hill-unit.

9. Give briefly your reasons for selecting the above four-hill-units. Draw Galton curves for these 25 four-hill-units, showing variation in the number of marketable tubers per four-hill-unit and weight of marketable tubers per four-hill-unit.

10. Determine the possible yield of marketable tubers from an acre of the highest and lowest yielding of the 150 four-hill-units, also for the highest and lowest and for the average of the 25 selected units.

11. Give a short summary of results as shown by the constants and curves and their bearing on your final selection.

12. Give direction for starting a potato breeding-plot.[1]

Potato Data for making a Transmission Curve

The following data have been obtained by the method outlined above. They represent the weights in grams of parent hills and the average weight of their corresponding progeny. The parent hills have been listed in the order of their weight from lowest to highest (forming a Galton curve).

[1] Reference: H. J. Webber, "Plant Breeding for Farmers." New York Agr. Exp. Sta., Cornell University, Ithaca, N. Y., Bull. 251: 162–171, 1908.

Nos.	Parents	Progeny	Nos.	Parents	Progeny
1	1077	1463	26	1588	1454
2	1106	1080	27	1588	1615
3	1106	1240	28	1616	1175
4	1361	1881	29	1616	1575
5	1361	837	30	1644	1775
6	1361	1136	31	1644	1807
7	1361	1536	32	1644	1917
8	1361	1605	33	1758	2250
9	1361	1660	34	1814	1660
10	1361	1800	35	1871	1275
11	1361	1895	36	1871	1280
12	1389	1972	37	1871	1665
13	1418	1696	38	1871	1688
14	1418	1904	39	1871	1750
15	1471	1440	40	1874	1555
16	1474	1086	41	1874	1861
17	1474	1215	42	1874	1889
18	1474	1480	43	1928	1440
19	1531	711	44	1928	1481
20	1531	1294	45	1928	1620
21	1531	1574	46	1928	1982
22	1531	1725	47	1984	1575
23	1531	1755	48	2041	1236
24	1588	1320	49	2041	1880
25	1588	1365	50	2098	2365

Exercise 23

Study of Citrus Hybrids

Object. — (*a*) To study the possibility of obtaining valuable kinds of citrus fruits by means of hybridization. (*b*) To study the structure of citrus hybrids as compared with their parents. (*c*) To study the economic value of these hybrids.

Materials. — Obtain from some of the extreme southern experiment stations, or from nurserymen or growers, samples of citrus hybrids, such as citranges, tangelos, and the like, and samples of *Citrus trifoliata.* Purchase oranges, lemons, grape-fruits, and tangerines from the fruit stores. Provide also for each student, or group of students, a glass, spoon, sugar, and water.

Compare the hybrids with their parents, with special reference to the following points : —

(*a*) Fruit — size, shape, color, amount of juice, quality of juice, condition of segments, etc.

(*b*) Trees (if branches or photos are available) — size, shape, branching, kind of leaves, etc.

(*c*) General — length of season, resistance to cold, etc.

Squeeze out the juice from several fruits, add sugar and water, and test the adaptability for beverage and other economic purposes.

EXERCISE 24

Study of the Results of the Plant-to-Row Tests of Wheat, Oats, Cabbage, Onions, or any Crop where Data are Available

EXERCISE 25

Studies of Origin of Varieties — Corn, Wheat, Apples, Plums, Grapes, Etc.

Literature study of the history of varieties. Methods employed to originate varieties should be carefully noted.

EXERCISE 26

Field Trip to Experimental Grounds

Most experiment stations have plant-breeding experiments under way, and if a fall inspection of the plats would be instructive to students, they should be taken on such a trip early in the fall and required to make careful notes, to be written up later in the form of a report.

EXERCISE 27

Working Plans for Practical Breeding Experiments

Object. — To familiarize the student with field methods of breeding plants.

Outline for Timothy Breeding

First Year. — Select 10 heads of timothy and grow 50 plants from each.

100 ft.

40 ft.

10 rows.
500 plants in 10 rows 100 ft. long. Plants 2 ft. apart in the rows.

Second Year. — Cultivate.

Third Year. — Choose several of the best plants from the best two rows, and the one best plant from each of the other rows — 14 or 15 in all. With the seed from these, plant a "test plat," and plow up the original seedling plat.

60 ft.

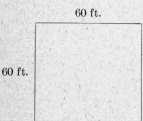

60 ft.

15 rows.
Rows 4 ft. apart — plants 2 ft. apart in the rows.

Fourth Year. — Cultivate the test plat.

Fifth Year. — Choose 2 or 3 or more of the best rows and save separately the seed from each. Plow up the remainder of the rows and plant to vegetables.

60 ft.

60 ft.

4 selected rows. Plant $\frac{1}{8}$ acre multiplication plat from each select row. Seed them broadcast at the rate of 16 pounds per acre. Remainder of the plat utilized for vegetables.

Sixth Year. — Use seed from multiplication plats to plant a fairly large-sized field. Continue selection of seedlings, if desired, from select rows according to above scheme.

Outline for Selective Breeding of Timothy

First Year. 1. *Manner of procuring seed from starting a selection.* — When timothy is ripening, go over a field and choose a number of good ripe seed-heads from tall, robust culms which appear to come from good plants. Also look for exceptionally good plants from along the roadsides and fences, and whenever they are found, preserve good heads for seed. Choose good seed-heads from at least 10 or 12 of these good plants. Thresh the seed from these heads, keeping the seeds from each plant separate, and sow them immediately. No time should be lost.

2. *Planting the seed.* — The seed should be planted early in August. Take small boxes about 2 feet long by 1½ feet wide and 4 inches deep; fill them with good soil from some locality where there has been no timothy and thus where there is little likelihood of timothy seed being in the soil. Pack the soil down slightly in the box and smooth off the top, removing all lumps. Plant the seed in the boxes in short rows, placing the rows about 2 to 2½ inches apart. In planting the seed open shallow furrows in the soil and sow the seed by hand, arranging so that the seed will be only very lightly covered. Sow the seed as thinly as possible in the rows and thin out later so that the plants will

stand about 1 inch apart. Sow enough seed in rows of sufficient length, so that when properly thinned there will remain about 300 plants. If thinned to 1 inch apart, this will require rows aggregating 25 feet long. Be careful to keep the seeds from each head or plant separate from one another and plainly labeled.

After the seed is sown, water the seed boxes carefully, using a fine spray, in order to prevent washing the seed out. A good method is to cover the soil with an open mesh cloth, such as cheese cloth, and sprinkle the water on this until the soil is thoroughly wet. Then place the seed box in the shade in a moist place, such as the north side of the house. It is a good practice to keep the boxes covered with paper or glass, until the young plants begin to appear. It is important to keep them moist at all times. When the young plants are well up, thin them to about one inch apart in the rows, leaving the strongest plants.

The plants should be kept in boxes until about the 20th of September, when they should be planted in the field. About a week before transplanting they should be gradually exposed to the full sunlight in order to harden them up. At this time each plant should have 2 or 3 leaves, 3 or 4 inches long.

3. *Transplanting into the field.* — Choose a place in the field where the plants may remain for at least two years without being disturbed. Set the plants two feet apart in rows that are four feet apart. By this method the greater part of the cultivation can be done with a horse cultivator. In transplanting the seedlings from the boxes, a time must be chosen shortly after a rain, when the soil is well moistened. The plants should be set out about the 20th of September, if possible, so that they may become well rooted before winter comes on. It may be necessary to hoe them before winter, but this is not likely if the land is well prepared before planting.

If 10 heads were originally chosen and 50 plants are grown from each head, there should be 10 rows 100 feet long, which would occupy a piece of land 40 × 100 feet.

4. *Second Year. Cultivating the seedlings.* — In the spring the seedlings must be cleaned out very early before they are hidden by other grasses. The cultivation and hoeing must be done at sufficient intervals to keep the ground free from weeds and in good condition. These plants will produce a few culms each the first summer, which should be cut as soon as they have bloomed, in order that the strength shall go into the general growth. Do not attempt to select the best plants the first season. A safe judgment cannot be rendered until the second season.

5. *Third Year. Selecting the best plants.* — When the plants reach the stage for cutting in the second summer, that is, when they are in full bloom, the final selection of the best individuals can be made. Examine each row critically in order to determine which head or heads have given the best progeny as a whole. If any one or two rows are markedly superior to the others, choose several of the best plants in each of these rows. Also, choose the one best plant in each of the other rows.

6. *Testing the selected plants as clonal varieties.* — In order to make a further test of the 14 or 15 best plants, choose another uniform plat of fairly good soil between the 5th and 20th of September and prepare for planting an area of slightly over 60 feet square. This plat should be located at some distance from any other timothy, preferably 200 to 300 feet. Dig up each selected plant; divide it into slips or clons and plant this new plat with them as before, in rows 4 feet apart. Plant one row with slips from each selected plant, placing the plants 2 feet apart in the rows. Transplant about 30 slips from each of the selected plants, so there will be a single row from each about 60 feet long. This plat may be designated as "the clonal test plat."

As soon as this clonal test plat is planted from the selected plants, the seedling test plat may be plowed up and used for other purposes.

7. *Fourth Year. Cultivation of "clonal test plat."* — The

clonal test plat should be cultivated and hoed sufficiently to keep the weeds down and to allow the full development of the plants.

8. *Fifth Year. Selecting the best clonal rows.* — When the plants are well headed and are about to begin blooming, the final examination can be made. Go over each row carefully, and examine it with reference to yield and desirability of type, and select the superior row or rows. It will be best to retain at least 2 or 3 of the best rows; or more, if there is but little difference in them. Good early-maturing and late-maturing rows should be retained if both are present in the test plat. When this selection has been made, cut the crop on the discarded rows immediately so that the pollen from these discarded rows will not contaminate, by cross-fertilization, the seed which is being developed in the selected rows. At any convenient time these discarded rows may be dug up and the space filled with new plants grown from cuttings of the chosen plants. By a little care and cultivation these select rows can be retained 5 or 6 years as a source of supply of seed of a superior kind. As the rows of selected types begin to run out, or become impure by ordinary timothy plants around them, or by other grasses growing in the clumps, other or more extended clonal rows could be planted from them.

9. *The multiplication plat.* — The seed from the select rows of the clonal test plat should be sown in the early fall, sometimes before the 15th of September in broadcast plats, as large as the amount of seed obtained will permit. Sow these plats, at the rate of about 16 pounds to the acre. There should be enough seed from each row to plant about $\frac{1}{8}$ acre.

Sixth Year. — The seed from these broadcast multiplication plats can be utilized the next year to plant a fairly large field which, if desired, may be harvested for seed to plant still larger areas. These plats may be utilized for seed for several years before they run out.

10. *Continuation of the selection.* — If the farmer has in mind the continuous selection of his seed, with the view of selling his seed as improved seed, he should plant small samples of seed from each of the selected rows in the clonal test plat. Their treatment and subsequent selection should be a repetition of the original scheme outlined above.[1]

General Directions and Questions for Report on Corn Breeding

Suppose you buy a farm of 200 acres on which are growing the following crops: potatoes, corn, timothy, and one of the three cereals, wheat, oats, or barley. There are 50 acres of pasture and woodland. You wish to continue growing these same crops, and at the same time to improve them by a scheme of selective breeding. Plan the arrangement of fields and breeding plots for the first 6 years, using the following directions. Timothy breeding plots should be 200 to 300 feet from any other timothy. Corn plots 1200 feet from any other corn. (Why?) Each year should be planned separately, using maps and diagrams, but should be included in a definite six-year scheme. Observe proper rotations for crops where desirable.

1. In selecting plants for breeding purposes, why do we choose individual plants?

2. In breeding work, why do we test out the selected individuals by breeding each one separately?

3. Why is it most satisfactory for the breeder to work with plants that are self-fertilized?

4. Why do we plant border rows around breeding plots?

5. Why do we detassel alternate halves of adjacent rows in corn breeding plots?

---

[1] For more detailed directions for timothy breeding, see Webber, H. J., "Production of New and Improved Varieties of Timothy." Cornell University Agr. Exp. Sta. Bull. 313, 1912.

6. Why should corn breeding plots be isolated? What is a safe distance?

7. Why should timothy breeding plots be isolated? What is a safe distance?

8. Is it necessary to isolate breeding plots of the small cereals?

9. In selection work, what three rules should the breeder follow who understands the principles of pure-line breeding?

Scheme for Potato Breeding Plots [1]

First Year. — Choose 500 good tubers. Plant them in a breeding plot by the tuber-unit method. Rows should be 3 feet apart, hills $1\frac{1}{2}$ feet apart in the rows. At harvest time choose the best 50 units. Save the best 10 from each of these units for planting a breeding plot the next year.

Second Year. — Plant the selected tubers in a breeding plot as in the first year. At harvest time discard all poor units. Select the best 50 units. Save 10 of the best tubers from each of these units for planting the third year's breeding plot. Use the rest for planting a field crop the next year.

Third Year. — Use these 500 tubers to plant a breeding plot. Plant your field crop with the remaining choice tubers. How

---

[1] For details of the following schemes read Cornell University Exp. Sta. Bull. 251, "Plant Breeding for Farmers," 1908; also Bull. 313, "The Production and Improvement of New Varieties of Timothy."

For cotton breeding, see Webber, H. J., "Improvement of Cotton by Seed Selection," U. S. Department of Agr. Yearbook, 1902, pp. 365–386.

16.5 ft. = 1 rod; 160.0 sq. rd. = 1 acre.

Plant: Corn, 8–12 qt. per acre; Oats, 2–3 bu. per acre; Wheat, 2–3 bu. per acre; Barley, 2–3 bu. per acre; Potatoes, 12–15 bu. per acre; Timothy, 6–8 qt. or 16 lb. per acre.

Standard weights: Corn, 1 bu. = 70 lb. shelled, or 56 lb. on cob; Oats, 1 bu. = 32 lb.; Wheat, 1 bu. = 60 lb.; Barley, 1 bu. = 48 lb.; Potatoes, 1 bu. = 60 lb.; Timothy, 1 bu. = 45 lb.

Average yield per acre in United States for 1902: Corn, 20.2 bu.; Wheat, 15.9 bu.; Oats, 37.4 bu.; Barley, 50.4 bu.; Potatoes, 113.4 bu.

2 н

large a field can be planted if the yield has been at the rate of 200 bushels per acre?

Fourth and Subsequent Years. — Continue this same scheme, constantly discarding the poor units and selecting the best for breeding.

Estimate how large your breeding plot should be in order to supply a 5-acre field with seed in the third year, supposing the yield from your selected units to be the same as the average yield given by the 25 best selected units in your former report, *i.e.* about 370 bu. per acre.

Scheme for Corn Breeding Plots

All corn breeding and increase plots should be at least 1200 feet from any other corn. Why?

First Year. — Select from the field 100 ears. From these choose the best 50 for planting a breeding plot the next year.

Second Year. — From these 50 ears, plant a breeding plot by the ear-to-row method. Rows should be 4 feet apart, hills 3 feet apart in the row, each row to contain 100 hills. Surround the breeding plot with 2 or more border rows planted with seed from the unused select ears. Why? Detassel alternate halves of adjacent rows. Why? Select from the best 10 or 12 rows 50 to 100 of the best ears, choosing the best 50 for the next year's breeding plot. Save the seed from the other best-yielding rows for an increase plot, or the general field.

Third Year. — Plant your breeding plot as before, with the best selected 50 ears. With the other selected ears plant an increase plot or general field. Select as before the best 50 ears from the breeding plot for the next year's breeding plot, saving the remainder for a new increase plot. Save ears from this year's increase plot for planting next year's field.

Fourth and Subsequent Years. — As before, plant your breeding plot, increase plot, and field, using a continuous and progressive scheme of selection.

Scheme for Wheat Breeding Plots

First Year. — Choose 100 fine heads for starting your improvement work.

Second Year. — Plant seed from these select plants in short rows by the plant-to-row method. Space the rows 1 foot apart. Select a few rows, say twenty, to furnish seed for a breeding plot in the third year.

Third Year. — Plant seed from each of these select rows in a breeding plot. Do not mix the seed from different rows. Plant as many 17 foot rows in each plot as the amount of seed saved will permit. This is at the rate of 1½ bushels per acre. The rows should be 1 foot apart.

Fourth Year. — Find average yield of progeny rows that came from the selected rows of the third year. Select several of the best strains which may yield about 24 bu. per acre. With this seed plant increase plots from each kind of seed. Save seed from 2 or 3 of the best yielding plots for more extensive trials in the 5th year. The rest of the seed can be used for planting a field. Make new selections of heads in the fields and repeat the whole program as before. There may be many more valuable types in the fields that can thus be isolated.

Fifth Year. — Test out your select strains and choose one or two of the best for increase plots and for planting your field. Plant the field this year with seed from last year's increase plot and from the test rows.

Scheme for Oat or Barley Breeding Plots

The principles of selection and methods of breeding these cereals are the same as for wheat.

INDEX

*The following pages
contain advertisements of books by the same
author or on kindred subjects*

CYCLOPEDIA OF
AMERICAN AGRICULTURE

Edited by L. H. BAILEY

With 100 *full-page plates and more than* 2,000 *illustrations in the text; four volumes; the set,* $20.00   *half morocco,* $32.00

Vol. I—Farms   Vol. III—Animals
Vol. II—Crops   Vol. IV—The Farm and the Community

This is unquestionably the most important agricultural cyclopedic work published in this country. The leading experts in the United States and Canada, both investigators and practical farmers, contribute to its chapters, which are arranged not alphabetically, but topically, each subject being treated in its various aspects by men especially familiar with it. It contains advice for the city man who is seeking a home in the country, as well as for the professional farmer. The book is strictly new and up-to-date in its methods and advice, thoroughly readable, and a standard work of reference. It is profusely illustrated, about one-third of the total space being assigned to illustrations—all original.

"Indispensable to public and reference libraries . . . readily comprehensible to any person of average education."—*The Nation.*

"The completest existing thesaurus of up-to-date facts and opinions on modern agricultural methods. It is safe to say that many years must pass before it can be surpassed in comprehensiveness, accuracy, practical value, and mechanical excellence. It ought to be in every library in the country."—*Record-Herald, Chicago.*

THE MACMILLAN COMPANY
PUBLISHERS   64-66 Fifth Avenue   NEW YORK

The Standard
Cyclopedia of Horticulture

Edited by L. H. BAILEY
With the assistance of over 500 collaborators

New edition, entirely rewritten and enlarged with many features, with 24 plates
in color, 96 full-page half-tones and over 4,000 text illustrations.
To be complete in six volumes.

Each volume: Cloth, $6.00; *Leather* $10.00.
Sold only in sets by subscription.

———

Two opinions of Volume I of the new Cyclopedia:

"No one who knows anything at all about the literature of gardening needs to be told that the Cyclopedia is unique. It is the Bible
and Britannica of the garden-folk, amateur and professional alike.
And the remarkable thing is that, while it is fundamentaly a work
of reference, it also contains limitless quantities of good reading of
the sort dear to the heart of the garden enthusiast."—*The Nation.*

"It is no exaggeration to state that Bailey's new work is the best
cyclopedia obtainable for all who are connected, either remotely or
intimately, as amateurs or professionals, with horticultural pursuits.
It is the best for the student of botany who is investigating the subject
in a purely scientific way; best for the commercial grower who likes
to be well informed on matters in general and his own trade in particular, and best for the other sort of commercial grower, who does
not bother himself particularly about hunting for any information
except such as will give him immediate help in producing a better
crop."—*The Florist's Review.*

———

THE MACMILLAN COMPANY

PUBLISHERS   64-66 Fifth Avenue   NEW YORK

RURAL TEXT-BOOK SERIES

Edited by L. H. BAILEY

Each volume illustrated. Cloth, 12mo.

While the RURAL SCIENCE SERIES is designed primarily for popular reading and for general use, this related new series is designed for classroom work and for special use in consultation and reference. The RURAL TEXT-BOOK SERIES is planned to cover eventually the entire range of public school and college texts.

THE MACMILLAN COMPANY

Publishers   64-66 Fifth Avenue   New York

RURAL SCIENCE SERIES

Edited by L. H. BAILEY

Each volume illustrated. Cloth, 12mo.

A series of practical books for farmers and gardeners, sold as a set or separately. Each one is the work of a competent specialist, and is suitable for consultation alike by the amateur or professional tiller of the soil, the scientist or the student. Illustrations of marked beauty are freely used, and the books are clearly printed and well bound.

ON SELECTION OF LAND, ETC.
Isaac P. Roberts' The Farmstead	$1 50
T. F. Hunt's How to Choose a Farm	1 75
E. S. Cheyney and J. P. Wentling's The Farm Woodlot	1 50
Glenn W. Herrick's Insects Injurious to the Household	1 75

ON TILLAGE, ETC.
F. H. King's The Soil	1 50
Isaac P. Roberts' The Fertility of the Land	1 50
F. H. King's Irrigation and Drainage	1 50
Edward B. Voorhees' Fertilizers	1 25
Edward B. Voorhees' Forage Crops	1 50
J. A. Widtsoe's Dry Farming	1 50
L. H. Bailey's Principles of Agriculture	1 25
S. M. Tracy's Forage Crops for the South	1 50

ON PLANT DISEASES, ETC.
E. C. Lodeman's The Spraying of Plants	1 25

ON GARDEN-MAKING
L. H. Bailey's Garden-Making	1 50
L. H. Bailey's Vegetable-Gardening	1 50
L. H. Bailey's Forcing Book	1 25
L. H. Bailey's Plant Breeding	2 00
P. H. Rolfs' Subtropical Vegetable-gardening	0 00

ON FRUIT–GROWING, ETC.
L. H. Bailey's Nursery Book	1 50
L. H. Bailey's Fruit-Growing (New Edition)	1 75
L. H. Bailey's The Pruning Book	1 50
F. W. Card's Bush Fruits	1 50
W. Paddock & O. B. Whipple's Fruit-Growing in Arid Regions	1 50
J. E. Coit's Citrus Fruits	2 00
S. W. Fletcher's The Strawberry in North America. *Preparing*	

ON THE CARE OF LIVE STOCK
Nelson S. Mayo's The Diseases of Animals	1 50
W. H. Jordan's The Feeding of Animals	1 50
I. P. Roberts' The Horse	1 25
M. W. Harper's Breaking and Training of Horses	1 75
George C. Watson's Farm Poultry. New edition	1 50
John A. Craig's Sheep Farming	1 50
E. F. Phillips' Beekeeping	2 00

ON DAIRY WORK, FARM CHEMISTRY, ETC.
Henry H. Wing's Milk and Its Products. New edition	1 50
J. G. Lipman's Bacteria and Country Life	1 50

ON ECONOMICS AND ORGANIZATION
William A. McKeever's Farm Boys and Girls	1 50
I. P. Roberts' The Farmer's Business Handbook	1 25
George T. Fairchild's Rural Wealth and Welfare	1 25
H. N. Ogden's Rural Hygiene	1 50
J. Green's Law for the American Farmer	1 50
G. H. Powell's Coöperation in Agriculture	1 50
J. B. Morman's Principles of Rural Credits	1 25

THE MACMILLAN COMPANY

Publishers   64–66 Fifth Avenue   New York